Brush border membranes

Ciba Foundation symposium 95

1983

Pitman

London

© Ciba Foundation 1983

ISBN 0 272 79659 x

Published in March 1983 by Pitman Books Ltd, London. Distributed in North America by CIBA Pharmaceutical Company (Medical Education Administration), Summit, NJ 07006, USA.

Suggested series entry for library catalogues:
Ciba Foundation symposia.

Ciba Foundation symposium 95
x + 340 pages, 104 figures, 17 tables

British Library Cataloguing in publication data:

Brush border membranes.—(Ciba Foundation symposium;
  95)
  1. Cell membranes—Congresses
  2. Cell physiology—Congresses
  I. Porter, Ruth   II. Collins, Geralyn
  III. Series
  611'.0781   QH601

Text set in 10/12 pt Linotron 202 Times, printed and bound
in Great Britain at The Pitman Press, Bath

Brush border membranes

The Ciba Foundation is an international scientific and educational charity. It was established in 1947 by the Swiss chemical and pharmaceutical company of CIBA Limited—now CIBA-GEIGY Limited. The Foundation operates independently in London under English trust law.

The Ciba Foundation exists to promote international cooperation in biological, medical and chemical research. It organizes international multidisciplinary meetings on topics that seem ready for discussion by a small group of research workers. The papers and discussions are published in the Ciba Foundation symposia series. Every year about eight symposia are organized, together with many shorter meetings. The staff always welcome suggestions for future meetings.

The Foundation's house at 41 Portland Place, London, provides facilities for all the meetings. It also contains a library which is open to graduates in science or medicine who are visiting or working in London, whilst an information service provides details of international scientific meetings and answers enquiries. Accommodation is also provided in the house for scientists from any part of the world passing through London on working visits.

Contents

Symposium on Brush border membranes held at the Ciba Foundation, London, 8–10 June 1982

Editors: Ruth Porter (Organizer) and Geralyn M. Collins

Participants

D. H. ALPERS Division of Gastroenterology, Department of Internal Medicine, 722 Wohl Clinic Building, Box 8124, Washington University School of Medicine, 660 South Euclid Avenue, St Louis, Missouri 63110, USA

A. G. BOOTH Department of Biochemistry, University of Leeds, Leeds LS2 9JT, UK

C. A. R. BOYD Department of Human Anatomy, University of Oxford, South Parks Road, Oxford OX1 3QX, UK

A. BRETSCHER Section of Biochemistry, Molecular and Cellular Biology, Cornell University, Wing Hall, Ithaca, New York 14853, USA

N. P. CURTHOYS Department of Biochemistry, University of Pittsburgh School of Medicine, Pittsburgh, Pennsylvania 15261, USA

P. DESNUELLE CNRS–CBM, Centre de Biochimie et de Biologie Moleculaire, 31 Chemin Joseph-Aiguier, B.P. 71, 13277 Marseille Cedex 9, France

H. P. HAURI Division of Clinical Pharmacology, University Hospital, Rämistrasse 100, CH-8091 Zurich, Switzerland

J. HERMON-TAYLOR Department of Surgery, St George's Hospital Medical School, Cranmer Terrace, London SW17 0RE, UK

M. INOUE Department of Biochemistry, Kumamoto University Medical School, 2–2–1, Honjō, Kumamoto 860, Japan

P. L. JØRGENSEN Institute of Physiology, University of Aarhus, Universitetsparken, DK–8000 Aarhus C, Denmark

A. J. KENNY (*Chairman*) Department of Biochemistry, University of Leeds, Leeds LS2 9JT, UK

D. LOUVARD   EMBL, Postfach 10.2209, Meyerhofstrasse 1, 6900 Heidelberg, Federal Republic of Germany

S. MAROUX   CNRS–CBM, Centre de Biochimie et de Biologie Moleculaire, 31 Chemin Joseph-Aiguier, B.P. 71, 13277 Marseille Cedex 9, France

P. T. MATSUDAIRA   MRC Laboratory of Molecular Biology, Hills Road, Cambridge CB2 2QH, UK

M. S. MOOSEKER   Department of Biology, Kline Biology Tower, P.O. Box 6666, Yale University, New Haven, Connecticut 06511, USA

O. NORÉN   Department of Biochemistry C, University of Copenhagen, Panum Institute, Blegdamsvej 3C, DK–2200 Copenhagen, Denmark

D. S. PARSONS*   Department of Biochemistry, University of Oxford, South Parks Road, Oxford OX1 3QU, UK

A. QUARONI   Gastroenterology Unit, Massachusetts General Hospital, Boston, Massachusetts 02114, USA, *now at* Department of Biological Sciences, Section of Physiology, 820 Veterinary Research Tower Building, Cornell University, Ithaca, NY 14853, USA

A. R. REES   Laboratory of Molecular Biophysics, Department of Zoology, University of Oxford, South Parks Road, Oxford OX1 3PS, UK

R. RODEWALD   Department of Biology, Gilmer Hall, University of Virginia, Charlottesville, Virginia 22901, USA

A. RUBINO   Cattedra di Puericultura, Università di Napoli, 2ª Facoltà di Medicina e Chirurgia, Via S. Pansini 5, 80131 Napoli, Italy

J. SCHMITZ   Departement de Pediatrie, Necker Enfants Malades, 149 Rue de Sevres, 75730 Paris, Cedex 15, France

G. SEMENZA   Laboratorium für Biochemie, ETH-Zentrum, CH–8092 Zurich, Switzerland

---

* Unable to chair the symposium because of illness

H. SJÖSTRÖM Department of Biochemistry C, University of Copenhagen, Panum Institute, Blegdamsvej 3C, DK–2200 Copenhagen, Denmark

M. SMITH ARC Institute of Animal Physiology, Babraham, Cambridge CB2 4AT, UK

H. WACKER Laboratorium für Biochemie, ETH-Zentrum, CH–8092 Zurich, Switzerland

Chairman's introduction

A.J. KENNY

Department of Biochemistry, University of Leeds, Leeds LS2 9JT, UK

Several of the participants at this symposium were also present at Ciba Foundation symposium 50 (Peptide transport and hydrolysis). On that occasion the
emphasis was on functional questions such as whether peptides were hydrolysed at the cell surface, in the lumen or inside the cell, and whether hydrolysis
preceded transport. Consequently only a minority of the papers were concerned with structure and topology. In the six years that followed that symposium our attitudes and understanding have developed in such a way that we can
now concentrate with profit on the molecular aspects of this topic. I believe this
is an important development. Major progress in the biological sciences has
usually depended on clarifying molecular interactions that were formerly considered to be very mysterious events.

Among the group of people assembled here, some, like me, are mainly
concerned with the group of hydrolases in the brush border membrane that face
towards the lumen, anchored to the lipids by only a very small portion of the
polypeptide chain. During the symposium this group of participants should also
try to look below the membrane, into the cytoplasm, and ask what interactions
may take place with the cytoskeleton. Others, whom I may refer to as cyto-
osteologists, and who have for different reasons become enamoured of the
brush border, have recently made remarkable progress in defining the proteins
of the cytoskeleton. But possibly they may know little about the membrane
proteins and may, therefore, be inspired to look outwards towards the cytoplasmic domains of these membrane proteins to ask if any of them interacts
with the cytoskeleton, and what this means functionally. I would guess that the
raison d'être of the microvillus relates to the function of the membrane proteins—the hydrolases, the transport proteins, receptors and so on. Yet microvilli become shapeless vesicles once the cytoskeleton is disorganized. So we do
need to ask why the cytoskeleton exists in the form it does, and how its
components interact with each other and with the membrane.

*1983 Brush border membranes. Pitman Books Ltd, London (Ciba Foundation symposium 95)
p 1-2*

Others here are currently concerned with activities deeper in the cell, in particular the molecular events in the biosynthesis of the brush border enzymes. There is a need to define the primary translation product of the membrane proteins, and to understand how the polypeptide chain becomes associated with a membrane, as well as the details of the post-translational processing and the membrane pathway in the cell through which the precursor forms move. Much has been done in this area in the last few years, and I have no doubt that it is one of the fast moving topics at present.

One topic that some may think is missing from the symposium is a molecular description of the systems concerned with transport of small solutes such as amino acids, sugars and anions. It seems to me that this subject has not really broken out from the confines of its 'black box', and hence it is difficult for us to describe the events in precise molecular terms. Our compromise has been to include in our discussions one well defined transport protein, Na^+,K^+-ATPase (see p 253–272). We must overlook the fact that it is not in the brush border membrane but situated at the opposite pole of the cell. However, it will serve to focus our thoughts on the architecture of a well researched transport protein.

Macromolecules cross the membrane by the process of receptor-mediated endocytosis. We are beginning to learn something about the nature of the molecules involved in, say, the uptake of immunoglobulin across a brush border. Receptors are involved, the cytoskeleton is implicated and questions also arise about the pathway of the coated vesicles through the cell. Again we are concerned with events that are analogous to those concerned with the assembly of newly synthesized or recycled membrane proteins.

I am optimistic that as each section of the symposium develops, it will be the hitherto uncharted border areas between the different approaches that may provide the greatest interest. I hope we shall all try to see where our own area of research links with that of the next person. The apparent differences between the various organs that contain brush borders—the kidney, the intestine and the placenta—will, I hope, become unimportant in these discussions. All microvilli have the same basic architecture in common, and all share some functions, though there are important specializations, too. At this stage in our understanding it may be more profitable to concentrate on the similarities before we try to explain the differences.

Introductory remarks on the brush border

D. S. PARSONS*

Department of Biochemistry, University of Oxford, South Parks Road, Oxford OX1 3QU, UK

Abstract The specialized surface of the luminal border of small intestinal epithelial cells was first described by J. Henle in 1837 and for many years controversy raged about the nature of this region. Was it a plate rendered porous by perforating canals or was it composed of an array of rods with their long axes normal to the surface? Because the diameter of the microvilli was below the limits of resolution by optical microscopy, the arguments could not be settled until the region had been observed under the electron microscope in 1950. In 1961, the brush border membrane (also known as the free border or microvillus membrane) was separated for biochemical study and results on transport using vesicles were first described in 1973. The increase in surface area due to the microvilli is about 40 times and the surface : volume 'ratio' for a single microvillus is $4 \times 10^5 \, \mathrm{cm^{-1}}$, about 20 times that for an erythrocyte. An important but unresolved question concerns the relationships between transporter proteins in the membrane and proteins that have digestive functions; the physiological role of the glycocalyx is not yet resolved.

1983 Brush border membranes. Pitman Books Ltd, London (Ciba Foundation symposium 95) p 3–11

> *Cock up your beaver, and cock it fu' sprush;*
> *We'll over the border and gie them a brush.*
> from *Cock up your beaver* (James Hogg 1821)

Some history of the intestinal brush border

The presence of a specialized surface at the luminal border of intestinal epithelial cells has been recognized for nearly 150 years. Henle (he of the loop) described how the free border of intestinal epithelial cells consisted of a refractile lamella, 0.0012–0.0015 lines (3–4 μm) thick, containing fine striations. He demonstrated that the structure disappears on exposure to acetic

---

* Unable to attend the symposium. Paper read by Dr C. A. R. Boyd.

3

acid, thereby distinguishing these cells from those of squamous epithelia which are scarcely changed by acetic acid (Henle 1837, 1841), (Fig. 1). The presence of a fibrillar structure at the surface of dog intestinal cells was mentioned by Gruby & Delafond in 1843. Funke (1855a,b) described histological observations on fat absorption and provided illustrations of the epithelial cells which depicted a striated structure of the luminal surface. In the same year an excellent description, with illustrations, of the brush border

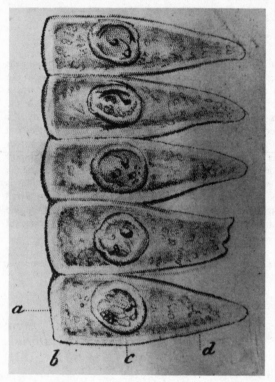

FIG. 1. Epithelial cell of rabbit intestine. (a) the *Freie oberfläche*. From Henle (1841, plate 1, figure 8).

of the cylindrical epithelial cells of mammals, birds and amphibia was provided by Kölliker (1855). He stated that with a good microscope it was possible to recognize a clear striation in the luminal border of the cells, which when viewed from above presented a very fine stippled appearance. Kölliker recognized that when working at the limits of optical resolution of a good microscope it was not possible to decide whether the striations (which he estimated to be equivalent to 0.25–0.45 µm in width) were solid structures or

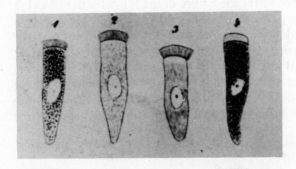

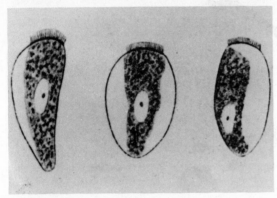

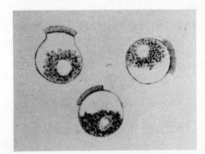

FIG. 2. Intestinal epithelial cell brush border as depicted by Kölliker (1855, plate IV). Upper panel: fresh cells. Centre and lower panels: cells in water, showing separation of the brush border.

little canals. Particularly interesting were his observations on the effects of immersing the epithelial cells in various solutions. In water and in hypotonic solutions the *streifige Zellenwand* becomes swollen and detached from the cell contents (Fig. 2).

Until 1950 controversy raged over the nature of the brush border. Was it a plate rendered porous by perforating canals (Baker 1942a,b) or was it composed of an array of rods with their long axes normal to the surface? The early published work and that on the controversy was reviewed by Baker (1942a) who also reported studies of his own which, alas, convinced him that what he called the 'free border' was composed of a continuous substance traversed by canals perpendicular to the plane of its surface (Fig. 3). At this time Baker also described the 'intercellular band' (terminal bar) and the

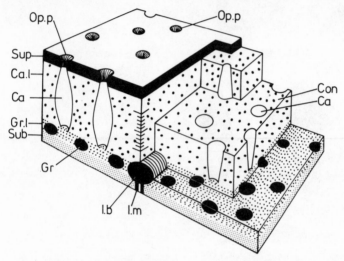

FIG. 3. Diagram from Baker (1942a) representing his views on the structure of the 'free border' of the intestinal epithelial cell of vertebrates. The central vertical scale represents 1 μm divided into tenths. The dimensions are those for newts (*Triturus vulgaris*). *Abbreviations*: Ca, canal; Ca.l, canal layer; Con, continuous substance of canal layer; Gr, granule; Gr.l, granular layer; I.b, intercellular band; I.m, intercellular membrane; Op.p, open pore; Sub, sub-granular layer; Sup, superficial layer.

'intercellular membranes' (basolateral membranes) that terminate at this 'band' (Baker 1942a).

The limit of resolution of a microscope, as first shown by Abbé (see Carpenter & Dallinger 1901, Beck 1938) is given by $R = 0.6\lambda/N.A.$, where R is the distance resolved, λ the wavelength of incident radiation and $N.A.$ the numerical aperture of the objective. Thus, with visible light of, say, 500 nm and with an objective of $N.A. = 1.30$ perfectly illuminated, the theoretical resolution should be 230 nm (0.23 μm). In fact, various practical problems prevent this limit being achieved, and the early arguments between microscopists were concerned with the structure of what proved to be an array of objects 1 μm or more in length and about 100 nm in diameter, that is, well below the limit of resolution of the optical microscope in the visible spectrum. It was not until 1950 that B. Granger & R. F. Baker produced the first electron microscope pictures that revealed the true structure of the refractile *streifige Zellenwand* of Kölliker.

In the second half of the nineteenth century microscope objectives with numerical apertures of 1.30–1.50 were available from manufacturers such as Zeiss (in Germany) and Powell and Lealand (in England); from 1883 onwards, superbly corrected apochromatic objectives of high *N.A.* were produced by the same makers, those from Zeiss being designed by Abbé (see Bradbury 1967). With the increasing use of such high-quality objectives appropriately illuminated, it is not surprising that some details of cellular ultrastructure became revealed even if that of the 'free border' did not. Thus, the T-system of striated muscle was clearly described in the 1880s, but was then forgotten, to be rediscovered much later by electron microscopists (see Huxley 1977).

Nomenclature

The specialized border that we now call 'brush border'—Baker (1942a) hyphenates the two words—has been given many names. In addition to Kölliker's term mentioned above it has been called *bürsten*, cuticle, *cuticula*, free border, *freie Oberfläche*, microvillus membrane, *Stäbchensaum*, *Stäbchenorgan* and *Stäbchen cuticula* (Baker 1942a). According to the Oxford English Dictionary the use of the word 'brush' in a biological connection to mean a brush-like bunch or comb goes back to 1581—the tail of a fox—while in 1828 a brush-like organ was described 'on the legs of bees etc'.

Recent interest in the brush border

A search of the published work (MEDLARS; Medical Literature Analysis and Retrieval System) for papers in which the term 'brush border' appears in the title shows a great increase in such publications after 1976 (Table 1). The

TABLE 1 Citations in MEDLARS (Medical Literature Analysis and Retrieval System) of articles that contain in the title the term 'brush border'

Period	Titles per month
1969–1971	1.25
1972–1974	2.58
1975–1976	3.40
1977–1978	18.5
1979	20.2
1980	32.5
Jan.1.1981–Oct.1.1981	31.0

paper of Miller & Crane, which first described the separation of brush border membranes for biochemical study, was published in 1961, and accounts of the preparation of vesicles of brush border membrane and their use for studies of transport began to appear from 1973 onwards (Hopfer et al 1973, Murer & Hopfer 1977).

Increase in area due to microvilli

In mammals microvilli are about 1μm long although in lower animals, including amphibia, they may be longer; Baker depicts the 'free border' of the newt intestinal cell to be about 2μm in length (Fig. 2). For a mammalian microvillus considered as a right cylinder 1μm high and with an external diameter (excluding the glycocalyx structure) of 100 nm, the external surface is 3.3×10^{-9} cm^2, while the area of the base is only 8×10^{-11} cm^2. Thus, for a structure of these dimensions the microvillar structure increases the external surface by about 40 times. This can be a useful increase in area at a surface where digestive enzymes are deployed. But what are the effects of such an increase on transport? Clearly, more membrane is available for the insertion of copies of transporter proteins, but all the traffic traversing the microvillus membrane nevertheless has to enter the main body of the cell by passing through the *base* of the microvillus. With a membrane thickness of, say, 5 nm the internal diameter in the above example is 90 nm, across a base area of 6×10^{-11} cm^2, ie, only one fiftieth of the external surface. This area may be further reduced by the presence of longitudinal fibrils passing into the cell from the microvillus for attachment to the terminal web.

An important consideration here is the very large surface : volume 'ratio' of microvilli. For the example given above it is about 4×10^5 cm^{-1} compared with about 4.4×10^3 cm^{-1} for a cylindrical cell of radius 5μm and depth 25μm (the approximate size of an intestinal epithelial cell) and 1.6×10^4 cm^{-1} for an erythrocyte. The effect of the large surface : volume 'ratio' will be to increase the concentration of the transported substrate on the *trans*-side of the membrane, although the extent to which this occurs will depend on the density (number of proteins per unit area of brush border membrane) and turnover number of the transporter proteins inserted in the microvillus membrane, the 'leakiness' of the membrane and the permeability of the exit pathway from the microvillus into the cell. The relevant transport processes described in the brush border membrane include those for monosaccharides, amino acids, peptides, sodium chloride, short-chain fatty acids, purines and pyrimidines. The entry of micelles of long-chain fatty acids and triglycerides also has to be considered. It is interesting to speculate whether the large surface : volume 'ratio' of brush border membranes is related to the alleged ability of the microvilli to contract longitudinally (see Mooseker et al, this volume, p 195–215).

How are products of hydrolysis by brush border enzymes captured for transport?

The monosaccharides released by the action of hydrolytic proteins in the brush border membrane on disaccharides have two fates: they are either captured by the monosaccharide transport systems and then move into the cell, or they appear in the bulk phase in the intestinal lumen. At low concentrations of disaccharide the efficiency of capture for transport can be

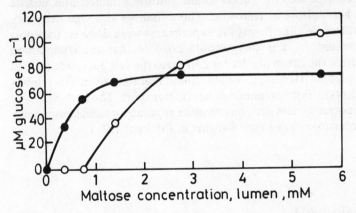

FIG. 4. Rate of transport of glucose into portal venous vasculature (solid circles) and rate of backflux of glucose into bulk phase of intestinal lumen (open circles) measured simultaneously during absorption of maltose at different concentrations by small intestine of *Rana pipiens*. Redrawn from Parsons & Prichard (1968).

remarkably high; for frog intestine at luminal concentrations of maltose up to 1 mM none of the liberated glucose appears in the lumen; only at maltose concentrations above 3 mM does free glucose appear in the lumen at rates in excess of its transport rate into the mesenteric blood (Parsons & Prichard 1968), (Fig. 4). Although these findings were made on amphibian intestine, the small intestinal epithelium of such animals is remarkably similar to that of mammals in both structure and functions (Parsons & Prichard 1968; see also Boyd in General Discussion III, p 318).

Two sorts of explanations have been proposed for such a high efficiency of capture. The membrane-bound oligosaccharidases may form part of the sugar transporter system in the brush border membrane. If this is so, then in mammals not more than about 10% of hexose derived from disaccharides could be transported in this way; Semenza (1977) has discussed this point and the possible ways in which the sucrase–isomaltase complex may be involved in the transport.

Our own experiments on amphibian small intestine favour the alternative supposition that the hexose molecules derived from disaccharides are liberated into a pool immediately adjacent to the hexose transport system, the pool being also accessible to any free hexose units present in the lumen. We find no evidence for a competition for hydrolysis between maltose and trehalose, yet competition for transport does take place between the hexose units derived from these two disaccharides. Competition for transport is also observed between free hexose added to the intestinal lumen and hexose derived from either maltose or trehalose. These findings although necessary are not sufficient to prove the point; the experiments were done on transport across the epithelium so it is theoretically possible that the competition occurred not outside the brush border for entry into the cell but inside the cell for exit into the plasma. However, we also found that the cation Tris inhibits disaccharide hydrolysis but not monosaccharide transport. The hydrolase and the hexose-transporter system can thus be quite separate protein components of the brush border membrane (see Parsons & Prichard 1971).

Possible roles of glycocalyx

Models based on the existence of a pool external to the transporter systems in the brush border can be devised, which predict the relationships between the disaccharide concentration in the bulk phase of the lumen and the ultimate fate of the products of hydrolysis, as depicted in Fig. 4. Such models require the presence of a diffusive resistance superficial to the site of membrane transport (Hamilton & McMichael 1968) and also require that this region of diffusive resistance has the capacity to adsorb monosaccharides in such a fashion that they are eventually available for transport into the microvillus core (Prichard 1969). The glycoproteins of the brush border membrane that constitute the *glycocalyx* (polysaccharide cell coat) are obvious candidates for the physical basis of the barrier postulated in such models.

As well as acting as a barrier as described above, the glycocalyx may play an indirect role in digestion as a surface on which digestive enzymes of exogenous origin (e.g. from the pancreas) are adsorbed and act on substrates moving inwards from the lumen towards the brush border.

REFERENCES

Baker JR 1942a The free border of the intestinal epithelial cell of vertebrates. Q J Microsc Sci
84:73-103

Baker JR 1942b Some aspects of cytological technique. In: Bourne GH (ed) Cytology and cell
physiology. Clarendon Press, Oxford, p 1-27

Beck C 1938 The microscope, theory and practice. R & J Beck Ltd, London

Bradbury S 1967 The evolution of the microscope. Pergamon Press, Oxford

Carpenter WB, Dallinger WH 1901 The microscope and its revelations. 8th edn, J & A Churchill,
London

Funke O 1855a Beiträge zur Physiologie der Verdauung. I: Die Resorptionswege des Fettes. Z
Wiss Zool 6:307-320

Funke O 1855b Beiträge zur Physiologie der Verdauung. II: Durchgung des Fettes durch das
Darmepithel. Z Wiss Zool 7:315-327

Granger B, Baker RF 1950 Electron microscope investigation of the striated border of intestinal
epithelium. Anat Rec 107:423-441

Gruby, Delafond 1843 Résultats des recherches faites sur l'anatomie et les fonctions des villosités
intestinales, l'absorption, la préparation et la composition organique du chyle dans les
animaux. C R Hebd Séances Acad Sci 16:1194-1211

Hamilton JD, McMichael HB 1968 Role of the microvillus in the absorption of disaccharides.
Lancet 2:154-157

Henle J 1837 Symbolae ad anatomia villorum intestinaticum imprimis eorum epithelii et vasorum
lacteorum Berolini. MD thesis, University of Berlin

Henle J 1841 Allgemeine anatomie. Verlag von Leopold Voss, Leipzig

Hogg J (ed) 1821 The Jacobite relics of Scotland; being the songs, airs, and legends, of the
adherents to the House of Stuart. Second series, Blackwood, Edinburgh, p 127-128

Hopfer U, Nelson K, Perrotto J, Isselbacher KJ 1973 Glucose transport in isolated brush border
membranes from rat small intestine. J Biol Chem 248:25-32

Huxley AF 1977 Looking back on muscle. In: Hodgkin AL et al, The pursuit of nature. Informal
essays on the history of physiology. Cambridge University Press, Cambridge, p 23–64

Kölliker A 1855 Nachweiss eines besonderen Baues der Cylinderzellen des Dünndarms, der zur
Fettresorption in Bezug zu stehen scheint. Verh Phys-Med Ges Würzburg 6:253-273

Miller D, Crane RK 1961 The digestive function of the epithelium of the small intestine.
II: Localisation of disaccharide hydrolysis in the isolated brush border portion of intestinal
epithelial cells. Biochim Biophys Acta 52:293-298

Murer H, Hopfer U 1977 The functional polarity of the intestinal epithelial cell: studies with
isolated plasma membrane vesicles. In: Kramer M, Lauterbach F (eds) Intestinal permeation.
Excerpta Medica, Amsterdam, p 294-311

Parsons DS, Prichard JS 1968 A preparation of perfused small intestine for the study of
absorption in amphibia. J Physiol (Lond) 198:405-434

Parsons DS, Prichard JS 1971 Relationships between disaccharide hydrolysis and sugar transport
in amphibian small intestine. J Physiol (Lond) 212:299-319

Prichard JS 1969 Role of the intestinal microvilli and glycocalyx in the absorption of disaccharides. Nature (Lond) 221:369-371

Semenza G 1977 Intestinal membrane-bound carbohydrases as sugar translocators. In: Kramer
M, Lauterbach F (eds) Intestinal permeation. Excerpta Medica, Amsterdam, p 273-280

Microvillar endopeptidase, an enzyme with special topological features and a wide distribution

A. JOHN KENNY and IAN S. FULCHER

Department of Biochemistry, University of Leeds, Leeds LS2 9JT, UK

Abstract The endopeptidase present in the kidney microvillar membrane (EC 3.4.24.11) has been purified by immunoadsorbent chromatography from the pig. Three physically different forms have been obtained. The toluene–trypsin solubilized form has hydrophilic properties. The detergent and detergent–trypsin forms are amphipathic. Only a small change in apparent relative molecular mass of the subunit is produced by trypsin, indicating that little of the polypeptide is removed by the proteinase. Although apparently immunologically identical, the intestinal form has slightly different molecular properties, possibly attributable to differences in glycosylation. In spite of the failure of papain and other proteinases to release the endopeptidase from the membrane, reconstitution of the purified enzyme in liposomes has shown that it is a stalked dimeric protein, thus resembling other hydrolases in this membrane. In addition to its main locations in kidney and intestinal microvilli, there is clear evidence from inhibitor and immunological studies that the enzyme has a wide distribution including membrane fractions prepared from spleen, lung aorta and myocardium.

1983 Brush border membranes. Pitman Books Ltd, London (Ciba Foundation symposium 95) p 12–33

Kidney microvilli contain an endopeptidase that hydrolyses peptides, such as insulin B chain (George & Kenny 1973). The rabbit kidney enzyme was the first example to be purified and fully characterized (Kerr & Kenny 1974a,b), and it hydrolyses peptide bonds involving the amino groups of hydrophobic amino acids. An interesting feature of this Zn^{2+}-metalloenzyme (EC 3.4.24.11) is that it resembles the microbial group of chelator-sensitive endopeptidases in its mode of attack and, in particular, in its sensitivity to inhibition by phosphoramidon (Kenny 1977), a reagent that is specific for this group of peptidases. For several years the kidney endopeptidase was the only mammalian example of this type of enzyme. Recently endopeptidases with similar characteristics have been shown to be present in intestinal brush

12

borders (Danielsen et al 1980), spermatozoa (McRorie et al 1976) pituitary (Orlowski & Wilk 1981), pancreas (Mumford et al 1980) and in brain (Almenoff et al 1981, Fulcher et al 1982). In this paper we wish to describe some recent molecular and topological studies on the purified endopeptidase from pig kidney and intestine and to report the presence of a similar enzyme in a variety of other pig tissues.

Purification of endopeptidase from pig kidney

The rabbit kidney enzyme was solubilized by treatment of the membrane pellet with toluene, followed by incubation with trypsin (Kerr & Kenny 1974a). This method yielded a hydrophilic form of the enzyme in which the polypeptide chain had been subjected to limited proteolysis, thus cleaving the hydrophilic protein from its hydrophobic anchor (see e.g. Kenny & Maroux 1982). The detergent form, representing the intact amphipathic protein, has only recently been purified (Kenny et al 1981, Mumford et al 1981). Column chromatography of detergent forms of membrane proteins is often associated with poor resolution, compared with resolution of the corresponding proteinase forms. Hence an affinity step was sought. In this case it depended on the production of a specific antiserum, achieved in a step-wise fashion, as outlined in the scheme shown in Fig. 1. A partially purified form was first obtained and electrophoresed into an agarose gel containing antibodies raised to the whole membrane. The immunoprecipitate corresponding to the endopeptidase was excised and the electrophoresis was repeated until a sufficient quantity of the immune precipitate had been accumulated for use as an antigen for injecting into a rabbit. The antiserum thus obtained was used to prepare an immunoadsorbent column. The column could bind endopeptidase from relatively crude extracts of either kidney or intestine and the activity could be eluted in an almost pure form. Some traces of other microvillar hydrolases could be removed by a second immunoadsorbent column, prepared from an antiserum raised to the whole membrane. The final product was homogeneous in sodium dodecyl sulphate (SDS)/polyacrylamide gel electrophoresis (Fig. 2). The kidney enzyme is seen as a single band, stained with Coomassie blue, (lane 2) and corresponding to the faster moving band in the 90 000–95 000 relative molecular mass (M_r) region of kidney microvilli (lane 1). The intestinal form has a slightly lower mobility (lane 3) and appears to correspond to a minor band in intestinal microvilli (lane 4).

Immunoelectrophoresis is a more rigorous criterion of purity. The endopeptidase is less immunogenic than many other microvillar enzymes. Hence, minor contaminants in the preparation are readily revealed by crossed

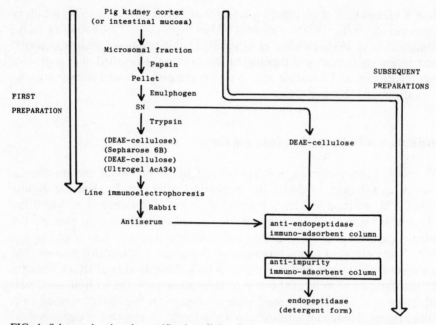

FIG. 1. Scheme showing the purification of the detergent form of the endopeptidase from pig kidney and intestine. The first purification, employing conventional steps, produced only a partially pure preparation. Immunoelectrophoresis against an antiserum to the whole membrane was successful in resolving the endopeptidase from most of its contaminants. This immunoprecipitate was used as an antigen to raise a specific antiserum. Subsequent preparations exploited the immunoadsorbent column prepared from this antibody. Traces of other microvillar hydrolases were removed by a small second immunoadsorbent column which contained antibodies to the whole membrane. SN, supernatant.

immunoelectrophoresis of the purified enzyme into an antiserum raised to the whole membrane. This has consistently revealed only one precipitate attributable to the endopeptidase. The positive identification of the antigen has been achieved by a novel histochemical stain (Kenny et al 1981), using glutaryl-glycylglycylphenylalanyl-2-naphthylamide as substrate. It is hydrolysed by the endopeptidase thus: Glutaryl–Gly–Gly–Phe–2-NNap → Glutaryl–Gly–Gly + Phe–2-NNap. The addition of aminopeptidase N (EC 3.4.2.11) to the staining mixture releases free 2-naphthylamine (2-NNap) which can be visualized by a diazo reaction. A control, containing phosphoramidon, can be used to confirm the identity of the enzyme that hydrolyses the Gly–Phe bond (results not shown).

Our standard assay uses [^{125}I]iodo-insulin B chain as substrate. The apparent activity in crude samples is markedly affected by the presence of aminopeptidases, since they can rapidly generate some smaller trichloroacetic

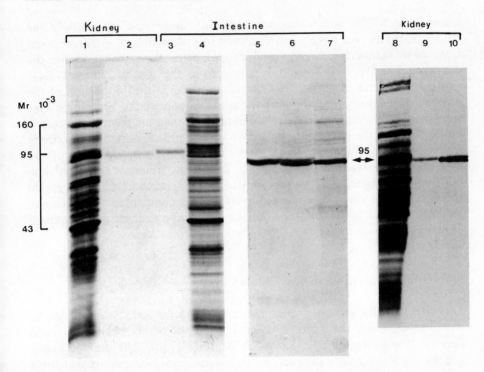

FIG. 2. Sodium dodecyl sulphate/polyacrylamide gel electrophoresis of microvilli and purified endopeptidase. 7–17% acrylamide gradient gels were used and the polypeptides were revealed by Coomassie blue. Lanes: 1, kidney microvilli; 2, kidney d-form (detergent-solubilized); 3, intestine d-form; 4, intestine microvilli; 5, intestine d-form; 6, intestine d-form + dt-form (d-form, trypsin-treated); 7, intestine dt-form; 8, kidney microvilli; 9, kidney dt-form; 10, kidney d-form.

acid (TCA)-soluble fragments from the initial cleavage products of the endopeptidase. The pure enzyme releases only half the substrate radioactivity in a TCA-soluble form. Crude extracts containing exopeptidases can achieve total conversion. This limitation of the assay affects the calculation of the enrichment factor in the purification. The rabbit kidney enzyme was purified 250-fold over the homogenate. The purification of the pig kidney enzyme has given a value of 135, which, if corrected for the effect of aminopeptidases in the homogenate, should be 1.5–2.0 times higher, i.e. a value in the range 200–270. Our results contrast sharply with the purification factor of 4200 obtained by Mumford et al (1981). Their assay substrate was a fluorogenic compound, the succinyl–Ala–Ala–Phe derivative of 7-amino-4-methyl-coumarin (a compound that is comparable to the peptide naphthyl-amide that we have used for histochemical purposes). They also reported a recovery of 870%, which they attributed to unspecified inhibitors in the cruder fractions. We have never observed this phenomenon in any purification (now numbering twelve) and cannot offer an explanation for the discrepancy, except to suggest it arises from the use of different assay methods. A more important consideration concerns the proportion of the proteins of the microvillus membrane that the endopeptidase represents. Our view is that the endopeptidase is a significant membrane component contributing 3–5% of the microvillus protein, a view that is supported by the strong staining of the 93 000 M_r band seen in SDS-polyacrylamide gels of the membrane. Extraction by non-ionic detergents removes most of the polypeptides migrating in this region, leaving only a cytoskeletal polypeptide (presumed to be villin). Such an observation is not compatible with a genuine enrichment value of 4000 which would be observed only if the endopeptidase were a very minor component.

Species differences in microvillar endopeptidases

Several microvillar enzymes so far purified from rabbit have been found to be monomeric, while the corresponding enzyme in other species has been dimeric (for examples, see Kenny & Maroux 1982). The endopeptidase follows the same rule. However, a more significant difference is that some species possess a second endopeptidase. In rat microvilli, only half the endopeptidase activity (towards [125I]insulin B chain) can be inhibited by phosphoramidon (Kenny et al 1981). This contrasts with microvilli from the kidneys of pig, rabbit and human. Mouse kidney microvilli also contain a phosphoramidon-insensitive endopeptidase (Kenny et al 1981). Indeed, the metalloendopeptidase purified from mouse kidneys (Beynon et al 1981) is

TABLE 1 Enrichment values of peptidases in microvillus preparations from rat and mouse kidneys

Enzyme	Rat	Mouse
Aminopeptidase N (EC 3.4.11.2)	12.9	15.8
Dipeptidyl peptidase IV (EC 3.4.14.5)	12.3	13.3
Endopeptidase I (EC 3.4.24.11, phosphoramidon-sensitive)	11.2	18.5
Endopeptidase II (phosphoramidon-insensitive)	9.2	15.4

The microvillus fraction was prepared and the peptidases were assayed as previously described (Booth & Kenny 1974). For endopeptidase II the assays were done in the presence of 1 μM-phosphoramidon.

most likely to be of microvillar origin. Both endopeptidases I and II have enrichment values comparable to other microvillar enzymes found in preparations of microvilli from rat and mouse kidneys (Table 1). The phosphoramidon-insensitive enzyme (endopeptidase II) is readily released from rat kidney microvilli by a papain treatment, and we have achieved a partial purification (100 times) of the enzyme after solubilization by this means. We found that at each chromatographic step, the hydrolysis of azocasein followed that of the [^{125}I]insulin B chain assay. At present we are in the process of obtaining a specific antiserum, by the same approach that we have used for the pig endopeptidase.

Molecular properties of the endopeptidase from pig kidney and intestine

In all species examined the endopeptidase is unusual, although not unique, in resisting release from the microvillus membrane by treatment with proteinases. The rabbit enzyme was obtained in a hydrophilic form only after prolonged stirring with toluene followed by a lengthy incubation with trypsin, and it was a monomeric glycoprotein, of M_r 93 000, which showed no amphipathic properties. Now that we have purified the pig kidney enzyme after detergent solubilization it is possible to define the differences between it and the proteinase-treated forms. We have now studied three structurally distinct forms of the active enzyme from kidney: (1) the detergent-solubilized form (d-form); (2) the detergent form also treated with trypsin (dt-form); and (3) a form that was solubilized by the use of toluene and trypsin (tt-form). The d- and dt-forms have many physical properties in common. Both require the presence of detergent to prevent aggregation, both show hydrophobic binding to octyl-Sepharose (Table 2) and phenyl-Sepharose (not shown) and both have generally similar M_r values by gel filtration (Fig. 3) and SDS-polyacrylamide gel electrophoresis (Fig. 2). The d- and dt-forms of the kidney enzyme yielded mean M_r values of 330 000 on Ultrogel AcA 34, but there was

TABLE 2 Hydrophobic chromatography of different forms of pig kidney endopeptidase

Form of the enzyme	Binding to octyl-Sepharose 4B	
	Bound and eluted (%)	Unbound (%)
Detergent-solubilized (d)	85	15
Detergent–trypsin-solubilized (dt)	74	26
Toluene–trypsin-solubilized (tt)	10	90

Enzyme samples were loaded in 150 mM-NaCl, 10 mM-sodium phosphate buffer at pH 7.4, with 0.1% (w/v) Triton X-100 and washed with the same medium without detergent. Elution medium was 1 mM-sodium phosphate at pH 7.4, with 2.5% (w/v) Triton X-100.

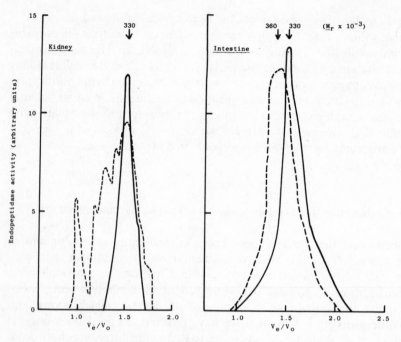

FIG. 3. Gel filtration on Ultrogel AcA 34 of endopeptidase from kidney and intestine. Dotted line, d-form; solid line, dt-form. V_e, elution volume; V_o, void volume.

a marked change in peak width after trypsin treatment. The d-form was polydisperse in its behaviour; the dt-form seemed to be monodisperse. We have observed this effect of trypsin repeatedly with different batches. Yet trypsin has little effect on the mobility in SDS-polyacrylamide gel electrophoresis (Fig. 2, lanes 9, 10). Thus, if there is a reduction in size as a result of trypsin treatment, it is not easily quantifiable, nor is it possible to resolve the two forms when they are run in the same track (not shown). Trypsin may cleave a small fragment from one end of the polypeptide chain. This fragment is presumably strongly hydrophobic and is capable of binding variable amounts of detergent. The estimated M_r of 330 000 is consistent with a dimeric protein that binds Triton X-100, thereby contributing about 150 000 to the M_r—a value which is higher than necessary for a simple micelle (Helenius & Simons 1975).

The intestinal form of the enzyme has a slightly different response to trypsin treatment (Fig. 3). The d-form has an M_r of 360 000 and the dt-form is significantly smaller (330 000). More surprisingly, the apparent M_r on SDS-polyacrylamide gel electrophoresis is demonstrably changed by trypsin and, with careful loading, the d- and dt-forms can just be resolved (Fig. 2, lanes 5, 6, 7).

Toluene–trypsin treatment is effective in solubilizing pig kidney endopeptidase (though yields were often disappointing compared to the rabbit form). In contrast to the d- and dt-forms, the tt-form from the pig behaves as a simple hydrophilic protein, does not aggregate in the absence of detergent and does not bind to octyl-Sepharose (Table 2). Chromatography on Ultrogel AcA 22 gave an M_r of 210 000, which is consistent with a dimeric structure.

Comparison of the microvillar endopeptidases from pig kidney and intestine

The d- and dt-forms have been purified from both tissues using the same immunoadsorbent column prepared from IgG raised to the kidney enzyme. The binding capacity and efficiency of elution were also the same for kidney and intestine enzymes. When we used the double diffusion method of Ouchterlony, complete identity was observed. Immunologically, therefore, the two enzymes are indistinguishable. Yet structural differences exist. Fig. 2 shows a small but clear difference in apparent M_r on SDS gel electrophoresis (lanes 2, 3), the intestinal form being the larger. There is also a detectable difference in size of the d-forms revealed by gel filtration (Fig. 3). It may be that the primary translation products are not quite identical. Alternatively, or in addition, there may be differences in glycosylation, but our data on this aspect are not yet complete.

Topology of endopeptidase in the kidney microvillar membrane

Until recently we had not been able to draw conclusions about the relationship of the enzyme molecules to the lipid bilayer. We know that the enzyme is a transmembrane protein (Booth & Kenny 1980) but, because of the failure of proteinases to release it from the membrane, there has been doubt about whether it is more deeply embedded in the membrane than, for example, aminopeptidase N, dipeptidyl peptidase IV or sucrase–isomaltase, all of which are 'stalked' proteins (for review, see Kenny & Maroux 1982). However, the observation that the toluene–trypsin form is truly hydrophilic and of comparable subunit size to the d- and dt-forms suggests that the bulk of the protein is exposed at the luminal surface. Further proof of the dimeric state of the enzyme (presumed from the behaviour on gel filtration) and evidence for its also being a stalked protein have come from electron microscopic studies. Negative staining of the dt-form has revealed a marked tendency for it to form aggregates of 4–10 subunits on the grid, but at some

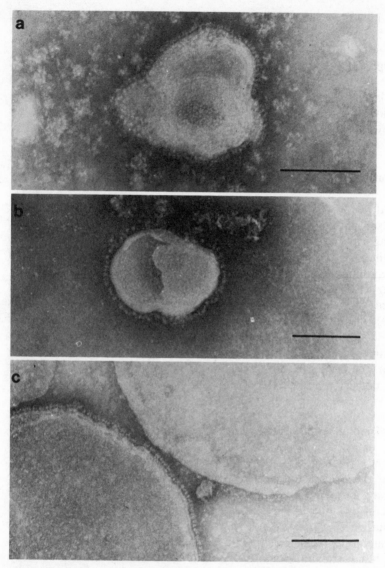

FIG. 4. Electron micrographs of microvilli and reconstituted liposomes. (a) Liposome reconstituted with the dt-form of kidney endopeptidase. Some enzyme molecules can be seen as dimers. Note the closeness of the knobs to the surface. (b) Liposome reconstituted with an unfractionated Triton X-100-extract of kidney microvilli. Compared with (a), the knobs are further from the liposome surface. (c) Kidney microvilli. The vesicle fraction had been treated with papain; parts of two vesicles are seen. One is smooth, presumably as a result of papain treatment. The other shows a coating of knobs that are relatively close to the surface, perhaps explaining their resistance to papain. All micrographs were negatively stained with potassium phosphotungstate. The bars represent 100 nm. Reconstitution was done by n-octyl β-D-glucopyranoside treatment, using extracted microvillar lipids.

dilutions dimers have been seen to predominate (not shown). Reconstitution of the dt-form in liposomes supports the view that the endopeptidase resembles other stalked microvillar proteins (Fig. 4a). The liposome is seen to be coated with knobs, some of which are clearly dimeric in appearance. A significant point is that the knobs are located rather close to the surface of the liposome. This is different from the proteins visualized in Fig. 4b, which shows liposomes reconstituted with a crude Triton X-100 extract of kidney microvilli. In this preparation there is a gap of about 5 nm between the knobs and the membrane, and for the endopeptidase the gap is 1–2 nm. Fig. 4c shows kidney microvilli that have been treated with papain. One microvillus is smooth, and was presumably stripped of stalked proteins by papain. The other is well coated with knobs, which in their disposition resemble those in Fig. 4a rather than those in Fig. 4b. They may therefore represent stalked proteins like the endopeptidase, which are not released by papain. It is tempting to extend the argument to suggest that different populations of microvilli exist, some bearing papain-sensitive and others bearing papain-resistant stalks, but this has yet to be investigated.

Thus, we can propose a simple structural explanation for the inability of proteinases to release the endopeptidase from the membrane. It is not because the endopeptidase is deeply imbedded in the membrane but, rather, because it belongs to another class of stalked protein in which the stalk is shorter than most, thereby hindering access to the stalk by trypsin or papain. Hussain et al (1981) have reconstituted aminopeptidase N, purified from pig intestine, into liposomes. Examination of their micrographs shows that this enzyme, which is among the most sensitive to papain, has globular heads that are well separated from the membrane surface by a gap of 4–5 nm.

The role of toluene in enabling trypsin to generate a truly hydrophilic form of the protein is not clear. The gross effect of toluene, when used in the purification procedure, is to produce a white emulsion that on centrifugation resolves into a soft white solid mass which floats to the surface and contains the membrane hydrolases. In this form the hydrolases are all apparently susceptible to attack by trypsin. Presumably an alteration in the organization of the lipids takes place such that trypsin then has access to the stalk polypeptide. This interpretation is the basis of the model shown in Fig. 5. Here the endopeptidase is drawn for simplicity as a monomer, although in reality the pig enzyme is dimeric. The model also attempts to explain the inability of trypsin to convert the detergent form into a truly hydrophilic molecule. We suggest that the Triton X-100 micelle also obstructs access by trypsin to the stalk polypeptide chain, yet allowing access to a loop of the cytoplasmic domain. Limited proteolysis at this site could reduce the amount of bound detergent by removal of one or more hydrophobic regions that also contribute to the anchor. In this model three hydrophobic anchors are shown

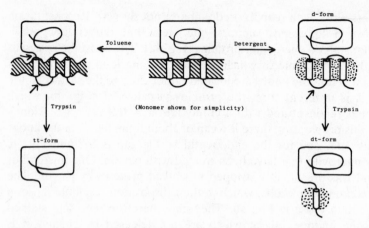

FIG. 5. Models of the different forms of the endopeptidase. The endopeptidase is shown throughout as a monomer, purely for simplicity. The central form is that in the microvillar membrane. It is shown with three hydrophobic sequences anchoring it to the membrane, though two such anchors would suffice if the chain termination were at the luminal surface. Detergents produce a large micelle which, like the membrane lipids, prevents the access of trypsin to the stalk, but does permit limited proteolysis so as to trim the size of the anchor, thus generating the dt-form. Toluene is shown to be perturbing the lipids of the membrane in such a way that the stalk becomes accessible to trypsin, thus enabling the tt-form to be generated. The short arrows indicate sites accessible to trypsin.

such that the polypeptide chain terminates at the cytoplasmic side. But the existence of only two anchors with the termination at the luminal surface would also suffice for the explanation. We have no information on this point, nor do we yet know if the anchor is, as for other microvillar hydrolases, adjacent to the N-terminus.

Endopeptidase (EC 3.4.24.11) in other pig tissues

Synaptic membranes from brain attack enkephalins (e.g. Tyr–Gly–Gly–Phe–Leu) at two principal sites. Attack by an aminopeptidase liberates tyrosine. The second site is at the Gly–Phe bond and is consistent with either an endopeptidase or a peptidyldipeptidase attack. There has been much discussion about the identity of this enzyme. We have shown that thiorphan, considered to be a specific inhibitor of the brain peptidyldipeptidase (Roques et al 1980), inhibits kidney endopeptidase just as efficiently as phosphoramidon. Both inhibitors are also effective on synaptic membrane preparations (Fulcher et al 1982). We have recently confirmed that the enzyme is identical to the kidney endopeptidase by immunological means. A rabbit antiserum to the pig kidney endopeptidase strongly inhibited enkephalin hydrolysis by synaptic membranes, while preimmune serum was without effect.

Other tissues contain endopeptidase activity that is detectable by the [125I]insulin B chain assay. In most of the tissues surveyed part of the activity was susceptible to phosphoramidon. Some of the tissues are shown in Fig. 6. The first point to note is that the specific activities in crude microsomal fractions are two or three orders of magnitude lower than those in microvilli purified from kidney or intestine. Liver contained no detectable phosphoramidon-sensitive activity, while spleen, aortic endothelium, myocardium and

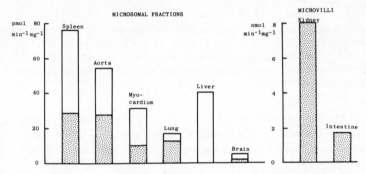

FIG. 6. Endopeptidases in pig tissues. Specific activities are shown in either nmol or pmol units. For kidney and intestine, microvillar fractions were prepared and assayed by using [125I]insulin B chain as substrate. For the other tissues microsomal pellets were prepared, solubilized with Triton X-100 and assayed similarly. In each case the stippled portion is the phosphoramidon-sensitive component.

lung all contained significant levels of phosphoramidon-sensitive endopeptidase activity. The activity was low in brain and the sensitivity to phosphoramidon was somewhat variable unless a synaptic membrane fraction was isolated.

The susceptibility of endopeptidase to this inhibitor suggests that the microvillar enzyme is more widely distributed than in the two locations— kidney and intestine—from which it has been purified. We have now obtained further evidence that at least in some tissues the phosphoramidon-sensitive activity is the same enzyme. The antibody to the kidney enzyme is strongly inhibitory to the endopeptidase activity in each of the tissues so far tested— lung, heart and spleen (Fig. 7). The phosphoramidon-insensitive component was unaffected by the antiserum. Preimmune serum had no effect on lung and heart but partially inhibited the activity in spleen. On the basis of this preliminary survey we propose that the endopeptidase is widely distributed in the membranes of different cell types. Its broad specificity (towards the

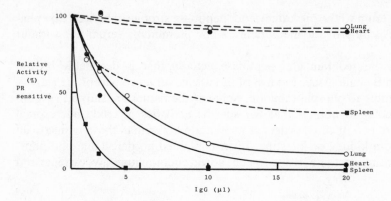

FIG. 7. Inhibition of phosphoramidon (PR)-sensitive endopeptidase activity in lung, heart and spleen by an antiserum to the kidney enzyme. The dashed lines show control experiments using preimmune serum. The continuous lines show the effect of the anti-endopeptidase serum. Not shown is the effect of the antiserum on the phosphoramidon-insensitive activity—no inhibition was observed in any of the three tissues.

peptide bonds of hydrophobic residues) makes it generally useful in degrading many different biologically active peptides. Its roles in limiting the activity of various peptide hormones or neurotransmitters may depend on its precise cellular location rather than on its specificity for a particular substrate.

Acknowledgements

We thank Douglas Kershaw for the electron micrographs, Jean Ingram for technical assistance and Anne Turner for preparing the typescript. The work was supported by the Medical Research Council.

REFERENCES

Almenoff J, Silk S, Orlowski M 1981 Membrane-bound pituitary metalloendopeptidase: apparent identity to enkephalinase. Biochem Biophys Res Commun 102:206-214

Beynon RJ, Shannon JD, Bond JS 1981 Purification and characterization of a metalloendopeptidase from mouse kidney. Biochem J 199:591-598

Booth AG, Kenny AJ 1974 A rapid method for the preparation of microvilli from rabbit kidney. Biochem J 142:575-581

Booth AG, Kenny AJ 1980 Proteins of the kidney microvillar membrane. Asymmetric labelling of the membrane by lactoperoxidase-catalysed radioiodination and by photolysis of 3,5-di[^{125}I]iodo-4-azidobenzenesulphonate. Biochem J 187:31-44

Danielsen EM, Vyas JP, Kenny AJ 1980 A neutral endopeptidase in the microvillar membrane of pig intestine. Biochem J 191:645-648

Fulcher IS, Matsas R, Turner AJ, Kenny AJ 1982 Effect of inhibitors on kidney neutral endopeptidase and enkephalin hydrolysis by synaptic membranes. Biochem J 203:519-522

George SG, Kenny AJ 1973 Studies on the enzymology of purified preparations of brush border from rabbit kidney. Biochem J 134:43-57

Helenius A, Simons K 1975 Solubilization of membranes by detergents. Biochim Biophys Acta 415:29-79

Hussain MM, Tranum-Jensen J, Norén O, Sjöström H, Christiansen K 1981 Reconstitution of purified amphiphilic pig intestinal microvillus aminopeptidase. Mode of membrane insertion and morphology. Biochem J 199:179-186

Kenny AJ 1977 Endopeptidases in the brush border of the kidney proximal tubule. In: Peptide transport and hydrolysis. Elsevier, Amsterdam (Ciba Found Symp 50) p 209-219

Kenny AJ, Fulcher IS, Ridgwell K, Ingram J 1981 Microvillar membrane neutral endopeptidase. Acta Biol Med Ger 40:1465-1471

Kenny AJ, Maroux S 1982 Topology of microvillar membrane hydrolases of kidney and intestine. Physiol Rev 62:91-128

Kerr MA, Kenny AJ 1974a The purification and specificity of a neutral endopeptidase from rabbit kidney brush border. Biochem J 137:477-488

Kerr MA, Kenny AJ 1974b The molecular weight and properties of a neutral metallo-endopeptidase from rabbit kidney brush border. Biochem J 137:489-495

McRorie RA, Turner RB, Bradford MM, Williams WL 1976 Acrolysin, the aminoproteinase catalysing the initial conversion of proacrosin to acrosin in mammalian fertilization. Biochem Biophys Res Commun 71:492-498

Mumford RA, Strauss AW, Powers JC, Pierzchala PA, Nishino N, Zimmerman M 1980 A zinc metalloendopeptidase associated with dog pancreatic membranes. J Biol Chem 255:2227-2230

Mumford RA, Pierzchala PA, Strauss AW, Zimmerman M 1981 Purification of a membrane-bound metalloendopeptidase from porcine kidney that degrades peptide hormones. Proc Natl Acad Sci USA 78:6623-6627

Orlowski M, Wilk S 1981 Purification and specificity of a membrane-bound metalloendopeptidase from bovine pituitaries. Biochemistry 20:4942-4950

Roques BP, Fournié-Zaluski MC, Soroca E et al 1980 The enkephalinase inhibitor thiorphan shows antinociceptive activity in mice. Nature (Lond) 288:286-288

DISCUSSION

Norén: What is the argument for the detergent–trypsin-solubilized (dt) form of endopeptidase being amphipathic?

Kenny: Both the dt- and detergent (d)-forms showed the phenomenon of charge-shift when electrophoresed with anionic or cationic detergents. However, these two amphipathic forms differ in that the d-form aggregates readily in low concentrations of detergents—(part of the activity elutes in the void volume when run on AcA 34 columns)—and this is not observed with the dt-form.

Curthoys: Have you examined the behaviour of the toluene–trypsin (tt) form on sodium dodecyl sulphate (SDS) gels, and is this form significantly smaller than the dt-form?

Kenny: Although we have not obtained a completely homogeneous preparation of the tt-form, the major band has the same mobility as the other forms of the kidney enzyme when run in SDS-denaturing conditions.

Alpers: Do you use protease inhibitors at all points except for the trypsin treatment, or do endogenous proteases act on the preparations throughout the purification?

Kenny: We use a cocktail of diisopropylphosphorofluoridate (Dip-F), phenylmethanesulphonyl fluoride (Pms-F), elastinal, antipain, chymostatin and leupeptin for all purifications from the intestine and for most of those from the kidney.

Alpers: That might be important in the intestine, depending on the species, because relatively large amounts of pancreatic enzymes bind to the brush border (Goldberg et al 1969).

Jørgensen: I am concerned with your arguments that this is a dimeric molecule in the detergent-solubilized (d)-form. Presumably the relative molecular mass (M_r) of 330 000 was obtained from a standard curve for proteins run on the gel exclusion column?

Kenny: Yes.

Jørgensen: So that would obviously include the detergent, and it gives you a determination of the Stokes radius of the protein–detergent complex. Did you do any ultracentrifugation, and what is the sedimentation coefficient of that complex?

Kenny: We do not have any ultracentrifugation data. The argument that the d-form contains two subunits is as follows: (1) the subunit M_r is 95 000; (2) the hydrophilic tt-form is dimeric (M_r 210 000); (3) the additional mass for the amphipathic forms is roughly that expected for the bound detergent; and (4) electron microscopy has shown dimers, in addition to larger aggregation states.

Jørgensen: A membrane protein with an M_r of 140 000 could, after binding of detergent, elute from the gel exclusion column with an apparent M_r of 200 000–300 000, without being a true dimer.

Kenny: The M_r of a symmetrical (spherical) Triton micelle is about 100 000. The difference in M_r between the tt- and d- or dt-forms is about 130 000. It does seem to be a rather larger micelle than has been observed for other hydrolases from this membrane. It may therefore *not* be spherical but somewhat deformed and ovoid. Are you implying that we have a monomer with detergent which contributes more than 200 000 to the M_r?

Jørgensen: Yes. But the aggregation could also be unspecific. Was your detergent Triton?

Kenny: We now always use Triton X-100, but the earlier preparations were solubilized with Emulphogene BC 720.

Jørgensen: You would expect to see unspecific aggregation when the hydrophobic parts of the molecule are present, as after cleavage with trypsin, when you would still see an aggregation of the stalk–detergent complexes.

Kenny: The dt-form may be slightly less hydrophobic than the d-form: there is a small difference in the binding to octyl-Sepharose and the dt-form is less prone to aggregate at low detergent concentrations. Our model proposes additional hydrophobic anchor sequences in the d-form, but this is only speculation.

Bretscher: Your data for the tt-form in solution are obtained in the absence of detergent, where you have an effective M_r of 200 000. If you had a sedimentation coefficient for that form (without detergent) it would tell you immediately whether it was a rod-shaped molecule or a globular dimer.

Kenny: We should do this. Nevertheless the electron micrographs show that the molecule is globular.

Semenza: The enzyme complex that we have studied most—sucrase–isomaltase—is in the detergent form and is water-soluble even in the absence of detergent (Sigrist et al 1975). That is, when the detergent is removed as far as possible, what is left in solution is a rather homogeneous population of aggregates of about 1.2 million. You can make gel filtrations of the detergent form of sucrase–isomaltase even without the detergent being present, just because these aggregates are highly water-soluble.

Kenny: We have also observed a soluble aggregate (with M_r greater than 500 000) in the absence of detergent. Presumably it is a protein micelle, with all the hydrophobic domains in the centre. Simons et al (1978) have described such a structure for the Semliki Forest virus spike glycoprotein and other membrane proteins.

Louvard: Can you prove at the end of such an experiment, Dr Semenza, that you still have the hydrophobic domain?

Semenza: Yes; the enzyme can still form proteoliposomes. Furthermore, papain-solubilized sucrase–isomaltase, which has no hydrophobic 'anchor', does not form aggregates any more.

Curthoys: We have observed similar results with γ-glutamyltransferase (EC 2.3.2.2). When one removes detergent, the transpeptidase initially forms an aggregate of a defined size that elutes as a single peak from a Sepharose 4B column. With time it aggregates into larger forms. The enzyme is still amphipathic, because it can be reconstituted into lecithin vesicles.

Semenza: The hydrophobic domain accounts for only some 3% of the whole protein, so it is not unreasonable that this 3% may club together and that all the hydrophilic surface is on the outside.

Alpers: It is difficult, as you point out, to know that you have removed all the detergent.

Semenza: Yes. My point was only that one can do gel filtration in the absence of *further* addition of detergent.

Alpers: I was interested, Dr Kenny, that you initially expected much of the enzyme to be in the membrane. About 90% or more of every protein that we have studied from the brush border is external to the membrane. The receptor for intrinsic factor–cobalamin (which one might have expected to be more in the membrane) has almost all the molecule in the water-soluble phase, and external to the membrane (Seetharam et al 1982).

Kenny: Is that papain-sensitive?

Alpers: Yes.

Kenny: In our case, here was an enzyme that remained firmly attached to the membrane, no matter how long the microvillus was incubated with papain, trypsin or elastase. In this property, it is similar to kidney alkaline phosphatase (EC 3.1.3.1) (George & Kenny 1973). We had to consider that a substantial proportion of the enzyme was involved in interactions with the membrane. In the event, we found that the endopeptidase is a stalked protein like the others.

Alpers: Yes, but some intestinal alkaline phosphatase comes off with papain treatment. The soluble form of alkaline phosphatase, which is not a product of the membrane form, seems to be synthetically separate, yet it is immunologically identical to the membrane form (Young et al 1981). In cell-free systems we find a single product of the gene, at least in the enterocyte. There, by analogy, one can estimate that most of the molecule is not membrane-bound. The difference between the liposome-incorporated form and the non-liposome-incorporated form is only about 5% of the molecule (Yedlin et al 1981). So most of the proteins in each of these enzymes is likely to be at the surface.

Kenny: I don't disagree with that. My problem was to explain this particular protein with its rather unusual properties. The answer is that it is a stalked protein, but a *short* stalked protein.

Mooseker: Do you retain insensitivity to protease when you reconstitute the enzyme in liposomes?

Kenny: We have not treated the reconstituted liposomes with proteinases.

Sjöström: This endopeptidase enzyme is not solubilized by proteinases *in vitro*, unlike most of the so-called stalked enzymes. Do you think that this resistance is functionally important? Could endopeptidase take part in the metabolism of the stalked enzymes by splitting the main part of these enzymes from the anchor? Have you tried *in vitro* solubilization of the stalked enzymes with your endopeptidase?

Kenny: No; I would be surprised if it were any good. In addition to its side-chain specificity for bonds involving hydrophobic residues, it also seems to have a size-specificity: it is quite happy with simple peptides like glucagon and the A or B chains of insulin, but it is rather weak at attacking insulin itself. If there is any degree of structure in the substrate molecule, the enzyme doesn't seem to have access to the susceptible bonds, so proteins above a certain size are resistant to attack. So I would be surprised if it could solubilize essentially native structures in the membrane. Perhaps you are suggesting that the stalk peptide contains a rather floppy loop.

Sjöström: Yes; the junctional part of the anchor may well resemble a 'floppy' simple peptide substrate. Furthermore, the localization of endopeptidase near to the membrane makes sense because it perhaps can diffuse in the membrane, beneath the main part of the stalked enzyme, and split.

Wacker: Does your tt-form charge-shift?

Kenny: No; it behaves as a simple hydrophilic molecule.

Semenza: We are beginning to collect some data about the length of the stalk of sucrase–isomaltase (M. Spiess et al, unpublished). It is interesting that trypsin cannot chop off native sucrase–isomaltase but, if the enzyme is partially denatured, the stalk becomes accessible to trypsin. I should imagine that in your enzyme the length of the stalk is determined partially by the secondary and tertiary structure in the 'body' of the protein. The polypeptide chain may fold up sooner in your enzyme than in others, and so the stalk remains short.

Kenny: Have you reconstituted the sucrase–isomaltase and measured the spacing between the 'knob' and the surface?

Semenza: Yes. It was greater than 1 nm (Brunner et al 1978).

Kenny: Is it likely, as I speculated, that different populations of renal microvilli, derived from different cells, have different enzymic compositions?

Curthoys: From the S1 to S2 to S3 regions of the proximal tubule there are differences in the amounts of various enzymes contained in the brush border membrane. Thus, it is likely that there are differences in structure of the brush border membrane in different regions of the kidney.

Kenny: One report showed that centrifugation of kidney membrane preparations in Percol gradients produced three resolved peaks of activity corresponding to γ-glutamyltransferase, alkaline phosphatase and Na^+,K^+-ATPase (EC 3.2.1.96) (Mamelok et al 1980). This suggests that there are two populations of microvillous vesicles.

Curthoys: I and others have attempted to reproduce those results, but without success.

Alpers: Your evidence for that suggestion, Dr Kenny, was based on your negative-staining experiments where you saw the knobs in some vesicles but not in others. I am confused about whether those knobs really indicate the protein in which you are interested, or *some other* membrane component.

Kenny: I wouldn't dignify it with the term 'evidence'. In electron micrographs of a papain-treated membrane we have seen smooth vesicles as well as others coated with knobs which had the same spacial organization that we saw when the endopeptidase was reconstituted in liposomes.

Alpers: Have you seen dimers on those knobs?

Kenny: Yes, but not consistently. It depends which way they are oriented in the membrane. If the subunits happen to be side by side you would expect to see a dimer; if they are superimposed you would not.

Alpers: Has anyone produced evidence for an enzyme that has been removed but where the knobs remain?

Schmitz: Yes; Benson et al (1971) did that 11 years ago.

Alpers: So are these knobs related to what we would like to think they are related?

Kenny: All I am saying is that if we treat with papain we don't remove all knobs. Nor do we remove all the hydrolase activity. Are you now saying that the knobs are not the hydrolases?

Alpers: I don't know. Could they be other proteins?

Kenny: The Copenhagen group have shown that aminopeptidase N appears as knobs when reconstituted in liposomes that look very much like those seen on microvilli (Hussain et al 1981).

Jørgensen: Clearly, only one protein is present and the knobs on the reconstituted liposomes are likely to be formed by this protein. However, to prove this, one would have to find a significant correlation between the protein:lipid ratio in the reconstitution medium and the density of knobs in the liposomes. Apparently, the protein concentration in the medium is very high, corresponding to the high density of knobs on the surface. But if you varied the protein: lipid ratio in the range of 1–700 μg protein per mg phospholipid (Skriver et al 1980) you would perhaps see a significant relationship between the density of the knobs and the protein:lipid ratio.

Kenny: Yes. Working at low protein:lipid ratios, it was difficult to get an answer, partly because of spreading problems of the liposomes, but when we used much higher ratios it became clearer.

Jørgensen: How does the stalk behave in freeze-fracture?

Kenny: We have not looked at freeze fracture of reconstituted liposomes.

Matsudaira: If you have the antibody, can't you just add it to the liposomes, or even to the membranes, and make observations after negative staining?

Kenny: Yes; we have done that, and have used protein A–gold, but our results are preliminary at present.

Matsudaira: But you don't even need the protein A–gold. The antibody should be big enough for visualization.

Kenny: Yes, I agree. One can see antibody bound to the knobbly surface of the membrane. So far we have not obtained good micrographs with the anti-endopeptidase antibody.

Schmitz: Some of your electron micrographs showed vesicles of natural brush border with only the endopeptidase on it, and another micrograph showed vesicles completely free of protein because of the papain treatment. When you study such natural membranes, are you not able to see those proteins as two ranges of knobs, one very near the membrane, which would correspond to endopeptidase, and another one further away?

Kenny: The ones further away tend to be the dominant ones.

Schmitz: It is surprising that when you add papain everything disappears and no endopeptidase is found.

Kenny: Yes; but several times we have seen micrographs containing both smooth vesicles and knobbly ones after papain.

Quaroni: How do you prepare the liposomes; did you try to vary their lipid composition?

Kenny: We use extracts of microvillous membrane lipid rather than lecithin. We either exchange detergents by binding the enzymes onto DEAE–cellulose, replacing with β-octylglucoside before elution, or we solubilize the membrane directly with β-octylglucoside.

Quaroni: So they were not sonicated?

Kenny: Not in these experiments.

Rees: The model that you mentioned was obviously designed to fit the various sensitive sites for trypsin degradation. What is the probability of a single polypeptide chain folding in the membrane to form three isolated hydrophobic domains in the way that you proposed? I am interested in the implications for assembly of such a protein, and in why there should not be aggregation of those hydrophobic domains, which would be, thermodynamically, a much more favourable orientation.

Kenny: Multiple hydrophobic domains are well recognized, and we shall hear more from Dr Sjöström about that later (p 50-72). Whether they aggregate or whether they each bind their own lipids in an annular structure, I don't know.

Desnuelle: Do you not think that after reconstitution the assembly of a protein within the membrane bilayer may differ from that *in vivo*?

Kenny: Why should it?

Desnuelle: Because *in vivo*, the protein is synthesized inside the cell. Then, it crosses the bilayer and remains bound in a way that is not yet fully understood. The possibility that, during reconstitution, the lipid spontaneously rearranges with the protein anchor as it does in the native state has not been checked in all cases.

Kenny: I don't see why it should not assemble with essentially the original topology, but you may be right. We know that they assemble the right way round; we never observe any latency; if one assays the enzyme before and after detergent treatment of the liposomes there is no increase in activity. They are all the right way round, which might suggest that they are assembling in the native form.

Desnuelle: The segments that link adjacent domains in ordinary and membrane proteins (the 'interdomain junctions') have often been described as extremely sensitive to proteolytic attack. This is especially true for the junctions between hydrophobic anchors and catalytic heads in several brush border hydrolases. However, it is not a general rule. In your case, perhaps the junction is relatively 'resistant' and is cleaved only after treatment with toluene, which may alter the lipid arrangment near the protein and the conformation of the protein.

Kenny: Yes, I agree, but it is a question of access, rather than a lack of sensitive bonds. Once access is possible, as a result of toluene treatment, release is possible. I would guess that other proteins of this kind, which are not released by papain, e.g. alkaline phosphatase, may have a similar topology.

Jørgensen: I am concerned with the question raised earlier by Dr Rees about the number of trans-membrane segments in the anchor. You have achieved cleavage by trypsin from the cytoplasmic surface of the membrane, but what is the evidence that there are three trans-membrane segments rather than one or two?

Kenny: As I said, this is speculation. There could be other numbers of transmembrane segments.

Jørgensen: When you tried hydrophobic labelling did you see specific activities of label in the anchor, which would correspond to more than one transmembrane segment?

Kenny: No; we are actually looking for that in our current work.

Rodewald: Other people commented that this endopeptidase was not the only brush border enzyme that was built on a stalk. What is the possible significance of this? Is it merely a way of stacking more material on the membrane?

Kenny: This is among several enzymes that are either not released by proteinase or are released rather slowly. I imagine that there is a whole gradation of stalk lengths, but their function is still obscure.

REFERENCES

Benson RL, Sacktor B, Greenawalt JW 1971 Studies on the ultrastructural localization of intestinal disaccharidases. J Cell Biol 48:711-716

Brunner J, Hauser H, Semenza G 1978 Single bilayer lipid– protein vesicles formed from phosphatidylcholine and small intestinal sucrase–isomaltase. J Biol Chem 253:7538-7546

George SG, Kenny AJ 1973 Studies on the enzymology of purified preparations of brush border from rabbit kidney. Biochem J 134:43-57

Goldberg DM, Campbell R, Roy AD 1969 Studies on the binding of trypsin and chymotrypsin by human intestinal mucosa. Scand J Gastroenterol 4:217-226

Hussain MM, Tranum-Jensen J, Norén O, Sjöström H, Christiansen K 1981 Reconstitution of purified amphiphilic pig intestinal microvillus aminopeptidase. Mode of membrane insertion and morphology. Biochem J 199:179-186

Mamelok RD, Groth DF, Prusiner SE 1980 Separation of membrane-bound γ-glutamyl transpeptidase from brush border transport and enzyme activities. Biochemistry 19:2367-2373

Seetharam B, Bagur SS, Alpers DH 1982 Isolation and characterization of proteolytically derived ileal receptor for intrinsic factor–cobalamin. J Biol Chem 257:185-189

Sigrist H, Ronner P, Semenza G 1975 A hydrophobic form of the small intestinal sucrase–isomaltase complex. Biochim Biophys Acta 406:433-446

Simons K, Helenius A, Leonard K, Sarvas M, Gething MJ 1978 Formation of protein micelles from amphiphilic membrane proteins. Proc Natl Acad Sci USA 75:5306-5310

Skriver E, Maunsbach AB, Jørgensen PL 1980 Ultrastructure of Na,K-transport vesicles reconstituted with purified renal Na,K-ATPase. J Cell Biol 86:746-754

Yedlin ST, Young GP, Seetharam B, Seetharam SS, Alpers DH 1981 Characterization and comparison of soluble and membranous forms of intestinal alkaline phosphate from the suckling rat. J Biol Chem 256:5620-5626

Young GP, Yedlin ST, Alpers DH 1981 Independent biosynthesis of soluble and membrane bound alkaline phosphatases in the suckling rat. Biochem J 200:645-654

Aminopeptidases and proteolipids of intestinal brush border

S. MAROUX, H. FERACCI, J. P. GORVEL and A. BENAJIBA

Centre de Biochimie et de Biologie Moléculaire, Centre National de la Recherche Scientifique, 31 Chemin Joseph-Aiguier, B.P. 71, 13277 Marseille Cedex 9, France

Abstract The presence of human blood group A determinants has been shown on the A^+ rabbit intestinal brush border glycoproteins, particularly hydrolases. Sugar compositions of aminopeptidases N from A^+ and A^- rabbits were compatible with the presence in these molecules of eight N-linked glycans and of two O-linked glycans bearing the A determinants in A^+ animals. The exact relative molecular masses of hydrophobic domain(s) of aminopeptidases N and A from pig and rabbit intestinal brush border have been determined by an isotopic dilution technique. The values obtained were compatible with the anchorage in the membrane of the monomeric rabbit enzymes, or of each subunit of the dimeric pig enzymes, by their N-terminal sequences, composed of 20–25 hydrophobic amino acids. This N-terminal hydrophobic sequence (14 residues) has been determined for rabbit aminopeptidase N. Short peptides containing approximately 60% hydrophobic amino acids have been extracted by chloroform–methanol from purified brush border and basolateral membranes of pig enterocytes. Their molecular properties were very similar to those of the aminopeptidase anchors released by trypsin treatment of detergent-extracted enzymes. However, several lines of evidence failed to support the assumption that these free hydrophobic peptides can be identified with anchors left inside the bilayer after proteolytic cleavage of surface hydrolases.

1983 Brush border membranes. Pitman Books Ltd, London (Ciba Foundation symposium 95) p 34-49

The brush border hydrolases are highly glycosylated glycoproteins. However, little information is available on their sugar moieties. Difficulty in obtaining specific anti-aminopeptidase antibodies that were suitable for intracellular localization led us to study the human blood group antigenicity of brush border hydrolases. The eventual involvement of hydrolases in the transport of their own degradation products held our attention. Further characterization of the hydrophobic domains of aminopeptidases showed that they cannot, alone, form channels for amino acid transport. However, we have demonstrated the presence of short hydrophobic peptides that, as for ATPases, can be associated with the hydrophobic domain of hydrolases.

Presence of human blood group antigenicity on the enterocyte plasma membrane

The presence of human blood group-like substances in animal secretions is well documented. The presence or absence of human blood group A type in the intestinal mucus of the rabbit has been particularly well studied and has permitted the respective classification into A^+ or A^- animals (Zweibaum & Bouhou 1973, Oriol & Dalix 1977).

Immunofluorescence labelling of ultra-thin frozen jejunal sections (150 nm) from A^+ rabbit or A^- rabbit with anti-human blood group A antibody showed that in A^+ rabbits the surface of intestinal absorbing cells also bears the A antigenicity (Feracci et al 1982a).

Identification of enterocyte plasma membrane that bears human blood group A-like determinants has been possible by using crossed immuno-electrophoresis. Precipitating antibodies of the major membranous proteins were obtained from guinea-pig sera raised against detergent extracts of brush border or basolateral membranes that were prepared (Colas & Maroux 1980) from exclusively A^- rabbits. To these precipitating antibodies ^{125}I-iodinated rabbit anti-human blood group A antibody was added to label the A-like determinants (Gorvel et al 1982). Fig. 1b shows that protein immunoprecipitates that have an A-type antigenicity can be specifically revealed by autoradiography. If the antigens were proteins from A^- rabbit membranes, no immunoprecipitate could be revealed by autoradiography. By contrast, for A^+ rabbit membrane proteins, all the peaks revealed by Coomassie blue (Fig. 1a) were also revealed by autoradiography (Fig. 1b). Almost all the peaks can be identified with hydrolases. Consequently, when the brush border hydrolases were purified from non-typed animals, antibodies raised against these enzyme preparations cross-reacted with all the other hydrolases and mucus components. Nevertheless, specific antibodies can easily be obtained by depletion of serum on human blood A erythrocytes or on mucus (Feracci et al 1982a). Peak 1 of Fig.1 cannot be identified with any hydrolases. It was more heavily labelled by anti-A than were the hydrolases and it was undetectable in A^- rabbit membranes. The quantity of A-determinants in peak 1 antigen was sufficient for it to be precipitated by anti-A alone, as shown in Fig. 1c. We have tentatively identified this antigen, named 'enterocyte surface antigen', with a constituent of the glycocalyx that remains in the membrane preparation. Indeed, as shown in Fig. 2, the glycocalyx is particularly rich in A determinants. Ugolev et al (1979) showed that the particularly long fibrillar glycoconjugates at least, from the summit of the microvilli, were very sensitive to mechanical cleavages. A portion of this material may thus be lost during subcellular fractionation. Thus, only smaller fibres and a residual basal portion of broken long filaments may remain in membrane preparations. Consequently these

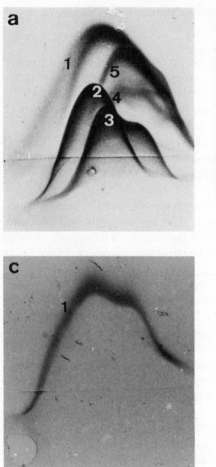
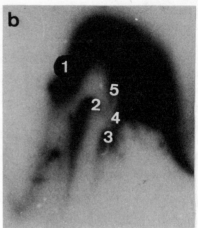

FIG. 1. Crossed immunoelectrophoresis of Emulphogene-extracted protein from brush border. The gel used in the second dimension (from bottom to top) contained 100 μg/ml of immunoglobulins from guinea-pig sera raised against an Emulphogene extract of brush border membrane from A⁻ rabbits, plus 60 μg/ml of [125I]immunoglobulins from rabbit sera raised against human blood group A erythrocytes (in a and b) and only anti-A immunoglobulins (200 μg/ml) in c. Applied samples : 6 μg of proteins from brush border membrane from A⁺ rabbit. The precipitates were revealed by staining with Coomassie blue in a and c. In b, autoradiography of a plate is shown.

membrane glycoconjugates may be expected to have a heterogeneous size distribution. Fig. 1c shows that both the shape and the width of the immunoprecipitate corresponding to enterocyte surface antigen express a large heterogeneity. This observation also argues in favour of the identity of this antigen and the glycocalyx remaining in the membrane preparations.

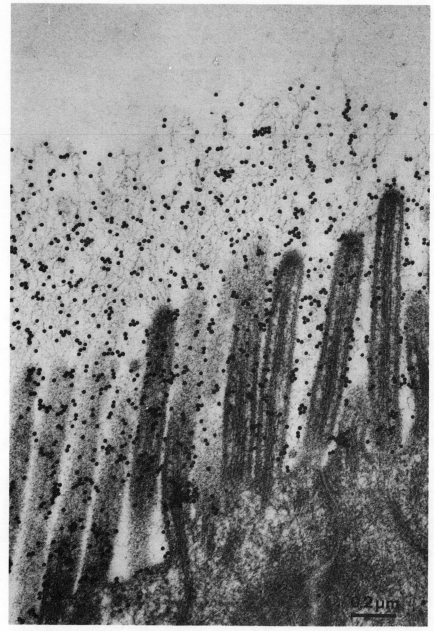

FIG. 2. Electron micrograph of glycocalyx and microvilli of rabbit absorbing cell after immunocolloidal gold labelling (sandwich technique) of 50 nm section of jejunum embedded in Epon, with rabbit anti-human blood group A antibody.

Sugar composition of rabbit aminopeptidase N

Aminopeptidase N has been purified (Feracci & Maroux 1980) from exclusively A^+ and A^- rabbits and the sugar composition of the two types of enzyme has been determined by J. Montreuil and colleagues. Table 1 shows the results obtained.

TABLE 1. Sugar composition (residues/mole) of aminopeptidase N from A^+ and A^- rabbits

	A^+ rabbit	A^- rabbit
Galactose	23	22
Glucose	4	4
Mannose	25	25
Fucose	16	21
N-acetyl glucosamine	38	38
N-acetyl galactosamine	4	2
Amino-acid[a]	988	988

[a]From Feracci & Maroux (1980)

The A antigenicity is due to the presence on the antigens of the trisaccharide α-GalNAc-[α-Fuc-(1– 2)]β-Gal-, in which the terminal N-acetylgalactosamine is the characteristic sugar of the A antigenicity. Until now, this antigenic determinant has always been found on O-linked oligosaccharides (Slomiany et al 1980). This type of glycan is almost always bound to serine or threonine of the polypeptide chain by an N-acetylgalactosamine residue (Montreuil 1980). Comparison of the N-acetylgalactosamine content of aminopeptidase from A^+ and from A^- rabbits strongly suggests that the enzyme contains two O-linked oligosaccharide chains that bear the A antigenicity in A^+ rabbit.

In glycoproteins, all the mannose residues are found in N-linked oligosaccharides. When they are not sensitive to Endoglycosidase H (Kobata 1979), as for aminopeptidase N, only three mannose residues per chain remain from the high mannose precursor of this oligosaccharide type (Montreuil 1980). Consequently, considering the mannose content of the enzyme, we tentatively proposed the presence of eight N-linked glycans on the monomeric rabbit aminopeptidase N molecule (Feracci & Maroux 1980).

The anchor domain of aminopeptidases

Among aminopeptidases, the monomeric structure of rabbit aminopeptidase is exceptional and has been suitable for the precise determination of the relative molecular mass of the hydrophobic anchor peptide by an isotopic dilution technique (Feracci & Maroux 1980). Radioactive anchor peptide Pep* was first purified from trypsin hydrolysis of an ^{125}I-iodinated detergent form (Maroux & Louvard 1976). Only a small amount (b counts per min and x nanomole) of this peptide was added to the unlabelled detergent form of aminopeptidase (d-aminopeptidase) before limited trypsin hydrolysis generated y nanomole of unlabelled peptide (Pep), thus diluting the radioactive peptide.

The dilution factor: (Pep* + Pep)/Pep = $(x + y)/x$ can be determined from the amino acid composition of both Pep* and (Pep* + Pep). If, in each case, a given amino acid is expressed as moles per b counts per minute (c.p.m), the resulting ratio is therefore equal to the dilution factor $(x + y)/x$.

In the case of a monomeric enzyme, hydrolysis of d-aminopeptidase simultaneously liberates y nanomole of Pep and y nanomole of the protease form of the enzyme. This value can be measured precisely by chromatography on a phenyl-Sepharose column from which the hydrophilic protease form (p-aminopeptidase) is excluded. This gives a yield of 100% for this p-aminopeptidase whereas the detergent form and peptide are bound. Thus, x can be calculated. This value enables the amino acid analysis to be interpreted in terms of the number of residues per mole and, hence, the relative molecular mass of the peptide can be computed. For a dimeric enzyme, $2 \times y$ moles of peptide can be liberated per mole of aminopeptidase, thus leading to a dilution factor of $(x + 2y)/x$.

This is true for pig aminopeptidases N and A, assuming that the anchor peptides of these enzymes have the same relative molecular masses as the anchor peptide of rabbit aminopeptidase, which is strongly suggested by analysis on polyacrylamide gel electrophoresis in the presence of sodium dodecyl sulphate (SDS) (Benajiba & Maroux 1980, 1981).

The anchor peptides released from the detergent form of rabbit aminopeptidase N and pig aminopeptidases N and A contain 35–40 amino acids, of which 60% are hydrophobic. This small size means, as shown in Fig. 3, that the hydrophobic part(s) of these molecules spans the membrane only once.

The position of a hydrophobic anchorage peptide in the N-terminal region of each subunit of aminopeptidases has been suggested by determination of the N-terminal residues. Indeed, the isolated hydrophobic part always has the same N-terminal residue as the detergent subunits. This residue is different from the N-terminal residue of the protease form. In addition the N-terminal sequences of the detergent and the protease forms of rabbit enzyme have been determined (Feracci et al 1982b). Fig. 3 shows that they are different.

The first 14 amino acids of the detergent form are hydrophobic, except for the third and fourth ones. It is supposed in Fig. 3 that non-sequenced hydrophobic residues remaining in the anchor peptide that is released by trypsin could complete this hydrophobic sequence by crossing the lipid bilayer. The hydrophilic residues could be located, on the other hand, in a region following this hydrophobic core, and could emerge from the membrane on the luminal side. The presence, in positions 3 and 4, of the hydrophilic peptide Ser-Lys could suggest that the first four residues are located on the cytoplasmic face of

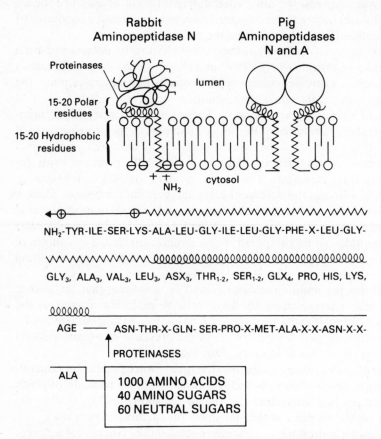

NH₂-TYR-ILE-SER-LYS-ALA-LEU-GLY-ILE-LEU-GLY-PHE-X-LEU-GLY-

GLY₃, ALA₃, VAL₃, LEU₃, ASX₃, THR₁₋₂, SER₁₋₂, GLX₄, PRO, HIS, LYS,

AGE —— ASN-THR-X-GLN- SER-PRO-X-MET-ALA-X-X-ASN-X-X-

PROTEINASES

ALA

1000 AMINO ACIDS
40 AMINO SUGARS
60 NEUTRAL SUGARS

FIG. 3. Schematic representation of the integration of aminopeptidases in the lipid matrix by their N-terminal sequence. The residues given in brackets are contained in anchor peptide released by trypsin from detergent form of rabbit enzyme, minus the 14 first residues of the N-terminal sequence of the detergent form, indicated on the first line. The protease form begins on the right of the arrow which indicates the cleavage that releases the anchor peptide from the detergent form. Zig-zag line indicates hydrophobic sequence and looped line indicates hydrophilic sequence in anchor peptide; straight line indicates polypeptide chain of protease form; angled (bent) line indicates saccharide chain.

the membrane, especially if it is assumed that the anchor peptide could play the role of a signal peptide during its biosynthesis (Feracci et al 1982b and p 47–48).

Presence of free hydrophobic peptides in the brush border and basolateral membranes of pig enterocytes

The hydrophobic domain of aminopeptidases, as described above, is too small, even in the dimer, to form channels. Svenson (1979) has shown that pig enzyme does not seem to form higher polymers in membrane. For the participation of aminopeptidases in the transport of digested amino acids, we must imagine that, as for several ATPases (Schlesinger 1981, Forbush et al 1978, Mac Lennan 1974), the hydrophobic domain of aminopeptidases could be associated with low relative molecular mass amphiphilic protein, generally named proteolipid. We have searched for such molecules in the brush border and basolateral membranes of pig enterocytes and found them in large amounts (Benajiba et al 1982).

Anchor peptides of aminopeptidases had been found, as for proteolipids, to be extractable by the chloroform–methanol mixture of Folch. We have there-fore used radioactive-purified anchor peptides as markers to follow the puri-fication of similar free molecules from the membrane. The main steps of the purification procedure are summarized in Fig. 4.

When tested by analytical high-performance thin-layer chromatography or electrophoresis on polyacrylamide gel in the presence of SDS, purified peptide extracted from the brush border membrane seemed to be homogeneous and to behave exactly as the purified aminopeptidase anchor peptide. If, before chloroform–methanol extraction, the membrane is treated with papain, the peptide material extracted always seems to be homogeneous. In this case, we know that the generated anchor peptides of hydrolases were heterogeneous, and so the analytical techniques used must apparently be unable to reveal this heterogeneity. Nevertheless, they show that all the anchor peptides of hydrolases and free hydrophobic peptide(s) have a similar molecular character.

The heterogeneity of anchor peptides released by papain from hydrolases is revealed by analysis of the N-terminal amino acid residues; alanine and leucine, known to be the N-terminal residues of aminopeptidases and maltases, were the most abundant. Isoleucine, phenylalanine, valine, glycine and aspar-tic acid were also found. By contrast, no N-terminal residues were found in peptides derived from non-papain-treated membrane.

Free hydrophobic peptides were also found in the basolateral membrane. The amount of peptide in this membrane, determined by amino acid composi-tion calculated on a protein basis (residues per mg of membrane proteins) was approximately twice the peptide in the brush border membrane. However, since the protein density is lower in the basolateral region, the two types of membranes may be assumed to contain about the same quantity of hydropho-bic peptides compared to the lipid phase. The amount of peptides was approximately doubled after papain treatment of brush border membrane, suggesting that the molar amount of free peptides in the brush border is nearly equal to that of the hydrolases. Amino acid analysis shows that free peptides and hydrolase anchors do not have widely different composition and that each contains about 60% hydrophobic amino acids.

It may be asked whether these free hydrophobic peptides are synthesized as an independent population of molecules or whether they are degradation products of membrane proteins in particular hydrolases. It is difficult to answer

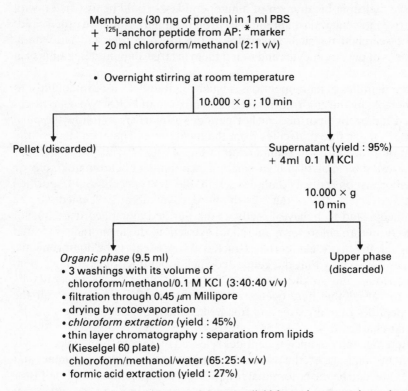

Membrane (30 mg of protein) in 1 ml PBS
+ ^{125}I-anchor peptide from AP: *marker
+ 20 ml chloroform/methanol (2:1 v/v)

• Overnight stirring at room temperature

10.000 × g ; 10 min

Pellet (discarded)

Supernatant (yield : 95%)
+ 4ml 0.1 M KCl

10.000 × g
10 min

Organic phase (9.5 ml)
• 3 washings with its volume of
  chloroform/methanol/0.1 M KCl (3:40:40 v/v)
• filtration through 0.45 μm Millipore
• drying by rotoevaporation
• chloroform extraction (yield : 45%)
• thin layer chromatography : separation from lipids
  (Kieselgel 60 plate)
  chloroform/methanol/water (65:25:4 v/v)
• formic acid extraction (yield : 27%)

Upper phase
(discarded)

FIG. 4. Flow-sheet of the purification of the proteolipid from plasma membrane fractions.

this question definitely, but the hypothesis that they really differ from anchors is supported by the following observations:

(1) No N-terminal residues were found in the free peptides whereas, after papain treatment of membrane vesicles, several were found in generated hydrolase anchor peptides.

(2) Substantial amounts of hydrophobic peptides are also present in the baso-lateral membrane.

(3) The activities found in the content of the intestinal lumen of the animals at death are not soluble in the aqueous phase but are attached to membrane fragments, suggesting that, *in vivo*, extensive cleavage of surface hydrolases is unlikely (Louvard et al 1973).

(4) In canine renal tubular epithelial cells as well as in rat liver (Arias & Kyte 1979) the hydrophobic and hydrophilic moieties of plasma membrane proteins were found to be degraded at approximately the same rate.

A function for these small amphiphilic molecules remains to be found. However, the brush border and basolateral membranes of enterocytes are crossed by a considerable flux of molecules during intestinal absorption. This process requires the participation of very efficient transport systems which are still poorly understood. It is tempting to speculate that the free peptides characterized in the course of the present work are involved in the transport function either alone or, at least for the brush border, in association with the hydrophobic domains of the hydrolases. This role would be comparable to that played by the proteolipid of ATPases in translocation of cations.

REFERENCES

Arias IM, Kyte J 1979 Examination of intramolecular heterogeneity of plasma membrane protein degradation in canine renal tubular epithelial cells and in rat liver. Biochim Biophys Acta 557:170-178

Benajiba A, Desnuelle P, Maroux S 1982 Presence of free hydrophobic peptides in the brush-border and basolateral membranes of pig enterocytes. Biochim Biophys Acta 687:167

Benajiba A, Maroux S 1980 Purification and characterization of an aminopeptidase A from hog intestinal brush border membrane. Eur J Biochem 107:381-388

Benajiba A, Maroux S 1981 Subunit structure of pig small-intestinal brush border aminopeptidase N. Biochem J 197:573-580

Colas B, Maroux S 1980 Simultaneous isolation of brush border and basolateral membranes from rabbit enterocytes. Presence of brush border hydrolases. Biochim Biophys Acta 600:406-420

Feracci H, Maroux S 1980 Rabbit intestinal aminopeptidase N. Purification and molecular properties. Biochim Biophys Acta 599:448-463

Feracci H, Bernadac A, Gorvel JP, Maroux S 1982a Localization by immunofluorescence and histochemical labeling of aminopeptidase N in relation to its biosynthesis in rabbit and pig enterocytes. Gastroenterology 82:317-324

Feracci H, Maroux S, Bonicel J, Desnuelle P 1982b The amino acid sequence of the hydrophobic anchor of rabbit intestinal brush border aminopeptidase N. Biochim Biophys Acta 684:133-136

Forbush B, Kaplan JH, Hoffman JF 1978 Characterization of a new photoaffinity derivative of ouabain: labeling of the large polypeptide and a proteolipid component of Na,K-ATPase. Biochemistry 17:3667-3676

Gorvel JP, Wisner-Provost A, Maroux S 1982 Identification of glycoproteins bearing human blood group A determinants in rabbit enterocyte plasma membrane. FEBS (Fed Eur Biochem Soc) Lett 143:17-20

Kobata A 1979 Use of Endo- and Exoglycosidases for structural studies of glycoconjugates. Anal Biochem 100:1-14

Louvard D, Maroux S, Baratti J, Desnuelle P 1973 On the distribution of enterokinase in porcine intestine and on its subcellular localization. Biochim Biophys Acta 309:127-137

Mac Lennan DH 1974 Isolation of proteins of the sarcoplasmic reticulum. Methods Enzymol 32:291-302

Maroux S, Louvard D 1976 On the hydrophobic part of aminopeptidase and maltases which bind the enzyme to the intestinal brush border membrane. Biochim Biophys Acta 419:189-195

Montreuil J 1980 Primary structure of glycoprotein glycans. Basis for the molecular biology of glycoproteins. Adv Carbohydr Chem Biochem 37:157-223

Oriol R, Dalix AM 1977 Differences in the maturation of the immune response of A^- and A^+ rabbits; good and poor responders respectively for the A antigen. Immunology 33:19-99

Schlesinger MJ 1981 Proteolipids. Annu Rev Biochem 50:193-206

Slomiany BL, Murty VLN, Slomiany A 1980 Isolation and characterization of oligosaccharides from rat colonic mucus glycoprotein. J Biol Chem 255:9719-9723

Svensson BM 1979 Covalent cross-linking of porcine small intestine microvillar aminopeptidase. Subunit structure of the membrane-bound and the solubilized enzyme. Carlsberg Res Commun 44:417-430

Ugolev AM, Smirnova LF, Iezuitova NN et al 1979 Distribution of some adsorbed and intrinsic enzymes between the mucosa cells of the rat small intestine and the apical glycocalyx separated from them. FEBS (Fed Eur Biochem Soc) Lett 104:35-38

Zweibaum A, Bouhou E 1973 Studies on digestive groups. I: The A allo antigen-allo antibody system in rabbits. Transplantation (Baltimore) 15:191-293

DISCUSSION

Norén: Does the evidence for O-linked glycans on the aminopeptidase come from alkaline treatment of the enzyme? This method cannot differentiate between O-linked and N-linked glycans (Ogata & Lloyd 1982).

Maroux: We have no direct evidence yet, but in all cases human blood group antigenicity was found on the O-linked chain and never on the N-linked oligosaccharide chain. So we suppose that it is the same for this protein.

Hauri: I have a question concerning the topology of the hydrophobic anchor of aminopeptidase. What is the evidence that the N-terminus is indeed on the cytoplasmic side, as you proposed?

Maroux: We have found that pig aminopeptidase is a transmembrane protein. By labelling it from the cytoplasmic face we can show that the anchor peptide crosses the membrane.

Hauri: But can you label the actual N-terminus?

Maroux: No; but the short size of the hydrophobic chain of this peptide is not compatible with its crossing the bilayer twice.

Hauri: So this would be different from sucrase–isomaltase (see Semenza et al, this volume).

Maroux: Yes, I believe so.

Sjöström: In the aminopeptidase sequence that you showed there is, at position 12, an unidentified amino acid. In sucrase–isomaltase, at position 11, there is a threonine which is probably glycosylated. Assuming that position 12 in aminopeptidase N corresponds to position 11 in sucrase–isomaltase (see Table 3 in Sjöström et al, this volume) two leucines and basic amino acids at position 3 or 4 coincide. Do you know whether the unidentified amino acid in aminopeptidase N is glycosylated? Such information would be interesting in connection with the localization of the N-terminal amino acid in relation to the membrane.

Maroux: It is possible, but we have no evidence for glycosylation.

Wacker: Determination of the size of the hydrophobic anchoring piece is based on the amino acid composition of the isolated peptide. Some error may be introduced because, in our experience, a peptide as hydrophobic as the one you isolated is difficult to hydrolyse. Perhaps you do have a peptide of a size sufficient to span the membrane twice. If your size determination is at odds by only a few amino acid residues, it might increase the size of the anchoring piece sufficiently for it to span the membrane twice. If the unidentified amino acid at position 12 were glycosylated, it could hardly be located on the cytosolic side. Your data would then actually fit with ours on sucrase–isomaltase (Frank et al 1978), where the amino acid at position 11 is a glycosylated threonine.

Louvard: But the size determination, as far as I understood, was not done by hydrolysis but by the isotopic dilution method, which does not rely on amino acid composition but on another technique.

Wacker: But even in the method that uses the iodinated peptide, acid hydrolysis of the isolated hydrophobic anchor is done. Dr Maroux's interpretation of the membrane anchoring of the peptidase would be more convincing if it did not rely solely on the size of the anchor peptide but provided some independent evidence, say, for the actual location of the N-terminus.

Maroux: Are you saying that after acidic hydrolysis it is impossible to do a correct amino acid composition of these peptides?

Wacker: It may not be impossible but it may be difficult. You might easily lose, say, dipeptides during the hydrolysis and the consequent compositional analysis.

Maroux: During the amino acid analysis, if peptide hydrolysis was not complete, the resulting peptides did not elute at the same positions at which the amino acids were recovered on the column.

Smith: You speculated, Dr Maroux, that the free peptides associated or unassociated with aminopeptidase may be concerned with amino acid movement across the brush border membrane. But in the intestine the expression of aminopeptidase becomes complete before transport function starts. This time-course is difficult to reconcile with your speculation.

Maroux: But we think that free proteolipids in association with anchor peptides could be involved only in the transport of amino acids released by aminopeptidase hydrolysis of peptides.

Smith: Yes; it is the amino acid transport that I am talking about, which takes place at a late stage in enterocyte differentiation.

Kenny: Dr Maroux could argue that these other small proteolipids are expressed later than the hydrolases, so that if they subserve a transport function it is dissociated from the hydrolases in development.

Hermon-Taylor: I have a point in relation to Dr Maroux's work on the immunological determinants of the carbohydrate moiety of aminopeptidase N. Rabbit antisera to human enteropeptidase, purified to apparent homogeneity (Grant & Hermon-Taylor 1976), had a high titre of anti-A activity, specifically agglutinating human A erythrocytes and staining goblet cells in human intestinal mucosal biopsies of subjects of blood group A but not of B or O (Hermon-Taylor et al 1977). We wished to know whether blood group activity could be a consistent feature of the heavily glycosylated enteropeptidase in individual subjects and whether the enzyme could exist as catalytically active immune complexes with immunoglobulin directed against the carbohydrate moiety, if displaced from the intestine into the circulation. A further batch of human enteropeptidase, prepared from accumulated duodenal fluid by a procedure that included 'negative' as well as 'positive' low M_r ligand affinity chromatography (Grant et al 1978), was examined for lectin specificity, carbohydrate composition and blood group determinants (Magee et al 1981). Three populations of human enteropeptidase were identified by their affinities for Helix pomatia (α-D-GalNAc), Lotus tetragonolobus (α-L Fuc) or neither of these lectins. On this occasion none of the rabbit antisera raised to these enteropeptidase subpopulations demonstrated blood group A reactivity; rabbit antibody to purified human blood group A substance, however, complexed with the Helix pomatia binding enzyme, suggesting an 'A-like' determinant. The immunological determinants expressed in the carbohydrate moiety of human enteropeptidase are complex and apparently heterogeneous. There is no apparent correlation between a person's blood group and the antigenic determinants on their enteropeptidase.

Alpers: Not all the enzymes have blood-group reactivity. Alkaline phosphatase in our hands does not, but sucrase does. Another possible explanation of your data is that blood-group substance itself, which will be contained in fragments of mucus, is highly antigenic. Could one of your preparations have allowed some contamination with tiny amounts of another substance that had blood-group reactivity while the other preparation did not?

Hermon-Taylor: The carbohydrate content of 140 μg (enzyme protein) of the first preparation of human enterokinase that we purified (Grant & Hermon-Taylor 1976) was kindly analysed by Professor R.D. Marshall using gas–liquid chromatography. Neither N-acetylgalactosamine nor glucose was detected in the assay, whose sensitivity was about 1 mol per mol of highly purified enzyme. In both this and later enteropeptidase preparations (Grant et al 1978), after affinity chromatography on low M_r ligand gels, purification was itself completed by immunological means, subtracting residual co-purifying contaminants. For these reasons, contamination with other components that bear blood group A determinants seems highly unlikely.

Hauri: Is anything known about the biosynthesis of enteropeptidase? It is a heterodimer, but do you have any indication that it is synthesized as a single-chain precursor?

Hermon-Taylor: We don't yet know. The structure of enteropeptidase differs between species; in humans the enzyme appears to be a heterotrimer (Magee et al 1981). We don't know much about biosynthetic precursor forms but we hope to soon. However, biosynthesis of the enzyme in the high enteropeptidase-secreting proximal small intestine appears to be triggered in response to mediated sodium transport (Bett et al 1981).

Desnuelle: Some aspects of Dr Maroux's presentation may help to give us a clearer understanding of how brush border enzymes are assembled within the bilayer. My first comment is about the extraordinarily high number of unidentified amino acids in the N-terminal sequence of the protease form of aminopeptidase N. We have recently been able to determine the complete sequence of porcine pancreatic lipase, with 449 amino acids, and we were not obliged to put a single unknown in the formula. Therefore, something—we don't know what—must happen in this region of the chain. Secondly, the N-terminal sequence of the detergent and protease forms of the enzyme are quite different. This finding, and the accumulation of hydrophobic amino acids at the beginning of the detergent form, confirm earlier observations that the protein is bound to the membrane by the N-terminus (Maroux & Louvard 1976).

Next, the N-terminal sequence of the detergent form can be broken down into two parts: (a) a 'pre-piece' of four amino acids which contains two positive charges, one on the N-terminal residue and the other on the lysine at position 4; this 'pre-piece' may be formed by more than four residues in the native protein if proteolytic cleavages are taking place during purification of the enzyme; and (b) an uninterrupted stretch of hydrophobic residues which starts just after the lysine; this structure is very similar to those observed in a number of prokaryotic and eukaryotic leader sequences.

Finally, the relative molecular mass of the anchoring peptides of aminopeptidases N and A, as found by isotope dilution, does not exceed 3500–4000. From this value and the known amino acid composition of the peptides, the number of hydrophobic residues in the peptides must be about 20, a number just sufficient for the peptides to cross the membrane once.

Smith: In some of the hydrophobic regions you have described there is quite a high concentration of glycine, which is not at all hydrophobic, and in some of the hydrophilic regions were found tyrosine and isoleucine, which are two of the most hydrophobic amino acids that one can find. So what is the definition of hydrophobicity or hydrophilicity?

Desnuelle: I am not an expert in this problem, but hydrophobicity may be defined as the free energy which must be spent to bring a compound from a lipid phase to water. The importance of a free charge to induce strong hydrophilicity is demonstrated by the fact that zwitterionic tyrosine, with an OH group, is hardly soluble in water while tyrosine hydrochloride and sodium tyrosinate are soluble. For membrane proteins, the electrostatic interactions (attraction or repulsion) between charged amino acids and the negative (or sometimes positive) charges of the phospholipid polar heads must also be taken into account. These interactions may represent electrostatic 'bolts' which stabilize the nascent protein with respect to the membrane.

Smith: So are we really talking about a *charge* as being a stopping signal rather than hydrophilicity?

Desnuelle: Yes. Uncharged hydrophilic amino acids such as serine and threonine are sometimes found in leader sequences which penetrate into the bilayer.

Inoue: Since anchoring domains of membrane proteins have similar hydrophobic amino acid residues, some structural homology may exist in this portion between different membrane proteins. Are there any examples in which the specific antibody to the anchoring portion of one membrane protein also reacts with that of another protein?

Maroux: We don't know, because a specific antibody against this region is not available.

Semenza: There is no real homology among the 'pre-pieces' described although they are analogous in that they are all hydrophobic.

Alpers: The intestine may be a special case, so I would like to modify that a little. We have now sequenced the pre-pieces of apolipoprotein AI (Gordon et al 1982a) and AIV (Gordon et al 1982b) from the intestine, and we found that 60% of the amino acids are identical. We don't yet know whether other pre-pieces in the intestine are similar or whether this is special for apolipoproteins as a group. Furthermore, the human pre-piece is identical to the rat pre-piece. Incidentally, the terminology can become confusing here. The term *pre-piece* has a special meaning for people who work with cell-free synthesis, but general biochemists sometimes use the term differently.

Desnuelle: The number of different hydrophobic amino acids present in hydrophobic sequences is relatively low, so the probability of finding any homology in these sequences is higher than for ordinary proteins. However, a 60% homology is significant.

Alpers: I think more pre-pieces need to be sequenced, and functional differentiations need to be sought. For instance, apolipoprotein AI has a pro-piece as well as a pre-piece, and AI and IV apolipoproteins end up differently when they leave the cell: AI is associated with the nascent high density lipoprotein and AIV is not. I don't know whether the pro-piece is responsible for the difference, and more structural information is needed before one can usefully discuss function.

REFERENCES

Bett NJ, Grant DAW, Magee AI, Hermon-Taylor J 1981 Induction and maintenance of mucosal enterokinase activity in proximal small intestine by a genetically determined response to mediated sodium transport. Gut 22: 804-811

Frank G, Brunner J, Hauser H, Wacker H, Semenza G, Zuber H 1978 The hydrophobic anchor of small-intestinal sucrase–isomaltase. N-terminal sequence of the isomaltase subunit. FEBS (Fed Eur Biochem Soc) Lett 96: 183-188

Gordon JI, Smith DP, Andy R, Alpers DH, Schonfeld G, Strauss AW 1982a The primary translation product of rat intestinal apolipoprotein A-I mRNA is an unusual preproprotein. J Biol Chem 257: 971-978

Gordon JI, Smith DP, Alpers DH, Strauss AW 1982b Proteolytic processing of the primary translation product of rat intestinal apolipoprotein AIVmRNA: comparison with preproapolipoprotein AI processing. J Biol Chem 257:8418-8423

Grant DAW, Hermon-Taylor J 1976 The purification of human enterokinase by affinity chromatography and immunoadsorption. Biochem J 155: 243-254

Grant DAW, Magee AI, Hermon-Taylor J 1978 Optimisation of conditions for the affinity chromatography of human enterokinase on immobilised p-aminobenzamidine. Eur J Biochem 88: 183-189

Hermon-Taylor J, Perrin J, Grant DAW, Appleyard A, Bubel M, Magee AI 1977 Immunofluorescent localisation of enterokinase in human small intestine. Gut 18: 259-265

Magee AI, Grant DAW, Hermon-Taylor J 1981 Further studies on the subunit structure and oligosaccharide moiety of human enterokinase. Clin Chim Acta 115: 241-254

Maroux S, Louvard D 1976 On the hydrophobic part of aminopeptidase and maltases which bind the enzyme to the intestinal brush-border membrane. Biochim Biophys Acta 419: 189-195

Ogata S-I, Lloyd KO 1982 Mild alkaline borohydride treatment of glycoproteins—a method for liberating both N- and O-linked carbohydrate chains. Anal Biochem 119: 351-359

Structure of microvillar enzymes in different phases of their life cycles

HANS SJÖSTRÖM, OVE NORÉN, E. MICHAEL DANIELSEN and HANNE SKOVBJERG*

*Department of Biochemistry C, The Panum Institute, and *Medical-Gastroenterological Department C, Herlev University Hospital, University of Copenhagen, Copenhagen, Denmark*

Abstract Structural changes have been studied during the life cycles of three glycosidases: sucrase–isomaltase (EC 3.2.48-10), lactase–phlorizin hydrolase (EC 3.2.1.23-62), maltase–glucoamylase (EC 3.2.1.20); and three peptidases: aminopeptidase A (EC 3.4.11.7), aminopeptidase N (EC 3.4.11.2) and dipeptidyl peptidase IV (EC 3.4.14.5). The final forms of the enzymes can be divided into at least two groups: the *sucrase–isomaltase type*, characterized as dimers, which are asymmetric in their hydrophilic parts, have two types of active site and anchor only on one subunit; and the *aminopeptidase N type*, characterized as dimers, which are symmetric in their hydrophilic part, have only one type of active site and anchor on both subunits. These enzymes are likely to be synthesized on rough endoplasmic reticulum and simultaneously glycosylated into endoglycosidase H-sensitive forms. They are later reglycosylated to endoglycosidase H-resistant forms, which have relative molecular masses similar to the final forms. Enzymes of the sucrase–isomaltase type seem to be synthesized with a polypeptide-chain length corresponding to the *sum* of both subunits, whereas enzymes of the aminopeptidase N type seem to be synthesized with a polypeptide-chain length corresponding to the constituent subunits themselves. Not much is known about the catabolism of these enzymes. The enzyme activities and the amounts of enzyme protein decrease at the top of the villi, probably due to release into the lumen. The subunits of aminopeptidase N are cleaved by pancreatic proteases to smaller peptides, and sucrase–isomaltase may lose its sucrase polypeptide, while both enzymes remain bound to the membrane.

1983 Brush border membranes. Pitman Books Ltd, London (Ciba Foundation symposium 95) p 50-72

The microvillar membrane of the small intestine contains a group of hydrolases, comprising glycosidases and peptidases, which have a relative molecular mass (M_r) of about 300 000. The M_r of the constituent polypeptides suggests a dimeric structure, at least in some phase of their life cycle. Pioneering work on this group of enzymes from the intestine was done on sucrase–isomaltase (Semenza 1981) and aminopeptidase N (see Kenny & Maroux 1982). These enzymes were shown to have their main mass located on the non-cytoplasmic side of the membrane, being anchored by only a small terminal segment.

In the belief that information on several of these enzymes would provide a general understanding of their structure and function, we have purified three glycosidases and three peptidases from the pig intestine by immunoadsorbent chromatography: sucrase–isomaltase (EC 3.2.48-10, Sjöström et al 1980); maltase–glucoamylase (EC 3.2.1.20, Sørensen et al 1982); lactase–phlorizin hydrolase (EC 3.2.23-62, Skovbjerg et al 1982); aminopeptidase N (EC 3.4.11.2, Sjöström et al 1978); aminopeptidase A (EC 3.4.11.7); and dipeptidyl peptidase IV (EC 3.4.14.5, Svensson et al 1978). Using specific antibodies to these enzymes we have been able to study certain aspects of their structure in the functional (final forms), biosynthetic (pro-forms) and degradation (degraded forms) phases. This paper summarizes our results and discusses them in relation to similar results from other research groups.

Functional phase

Many microvillar enzymes are dimers with a similar relative molecular mass

The M_r values of the constituent polypeptides of the purified enzymes are given in Table 1. All enzymes contain polypeptides in the M_r range of 125 000 to 170 000. Sucrase–isomaltase and maltase–glucoamylase also contain 260 000 and 245 000 M_r forms, respectively, and aminopeptidase N also shows 120 000 and 60 000 M_r forms. As we shall discuss later, the high M_r forms of sucrase–isomaltase and maltase–glucoamylase are precursors and, for aminopeptidase N, the 120 000 and 60 000 M_r forms are generated from the 160 000 M_r form.

The determination of M_r values of the enzymes residing in the membrane is difficult. The M_r data on solubilized enzymes may differ, as the aggregation state varies with the polarity of the medium because of the hydrophobic anchor. Some information may be obtained from gel filtration experiments in which the enzymes have had their anchor(s) removed by proteolysis (Table 1). The most obvious interpretation (perhaps with the exception of sucrase–isomaltase) is that these enzymes are dimers with their polypeptides held together by forces independent of interaction between anchors.

Microvillar enzymes have two modes of anchoring to the membrane

It has been known for some years (Semenza 1981, Kenny & Maroux 1982) that these enzymes are anchored to the membrane by short peptide segments,

TABLE 1 Apparent M_r values of the final forms of pig intestinal microvillar hydrolases

Enzyme	Molecular size of the hydrophilic form (Gel filtration) 0.05 M-Tris/HCl, 0.15 M-NaCl, 0.1% Triton X-100	M_r of the constituent polypeptides (PAGE in the presence of SDS)	
		Normal pig	Pig with disconnected pancreatic duct
Sucrase–isomaltase	370 000	265 000[a] 150 000 140 000	265 000[a]
Maltase–glucoamylase	260 000	245 000[b] 135 000 125 000	245 000[b]
Lactase–phlorizin hydrolase	280 000[c]	160 000[c]	160 000[c]
Aminopeptidase N	280 000	160 000[d] 120 000 60 000	160 000[d]
Aminopeptidase A	270 000	170 000	170 000
Dipeptidyl peptidase IV	260 000	140 000[e]	140 000

[a] Sjöström et al (1980); [b] Sørensen et al (1982); [c] Skovbjerg et al (1982); [d] Sjöström et al (1978); [e] Svensson et al (1978). PAGE, polyacrylamide gel electrophoresis; SDS, sodium dodecyl sulphate.

called anchors. The anchor-containing forms are called *amphiphilic* (or *amphipathic*), whereas the anchor-free forms, which may be produced experimentally, are designated the *hydrophilic* forms. Table 2 gives a summary of the existence of the anchors.

By comparison of the N-terminal amino acids or the amino acid sequences of the hydrophilic and amphiphilic forms of four of these enzymes, it has been concluded that they are inserted in the membrane via an N-terminal anchor

TABLE 2 Anchoring of microvillar hydrolases

Enzyme	N-terminal anchoring		C-terminal anchoring
	Presence	Number	Presence
Sucrase–isomaltase	+[a]	1[a]	−[a]
Maltase–glucoamylase	n.a.	max. 1	n.a.
Lactase–phlorizin hydrolase	n.a.	n.a.	n.a.
Aminopeptidase N	+[b]	2[c]	n.a.
Aminopeptidase A	+[b]	2[b]	n.a.
Dipeptidyl peptidase IV	+[b]	2[b]	−[b]

[a] Semenza (1981); [b] Kenny & Maroux (1982); [c] Norén & Sjöström (1980); Sjöström & Norén (1982). n.a., not analysed; –, not present.

(Semenza 1981, Kenny & Maroux 1982). Not much is known about the localization of the N-terminal amino acid in relation to the membrane but there is evidence, for some of the enzymes, that the anchors can be labelled from the cytoplasmic side and can thus span the membrane (Kenny & Maroux 1982). If the anchor spans only once it penetrates the membrane in the direction C-non-cytoplasmic to N-cytoplasmic, an orientation that has not been described for any other proteins known to penetrate the membrane only once.

There are some indications (glycosylation at threonine 11 and sequence homology with glycophorin in the N-non-cytoplasmic to C-cytoplasmic direction) that sucrase–isomaltase has its N-terminal on the non-cytoplasmic side and thus spans the membrane at least twice. For the other enzymes no such information is available. It is, however, interesting to note that amino acid 12 in rabbit aminopeptidase N is unidentified (Feracci et al 1982). This may be due to attached glycan chains. Table 3 shows a comparison of the N-terminal

TABLE 3 Comparison of the N-terminal sequence of rabbit isomaltase and rabbit aminopeptidase N

Enzyme	Sequence
Rabbit isomaltase[a]	Ala-Lys-Arg-Lys-Phe-Ser-Gly-*Leu*-Glu-Ile-*Thr-Leu*-Ile-
Rabbit aminopeptidase N[b]	Tyr-Ile-Ser-Lys-Ala-Leu-Gly-Ile-*Leu*-Gly-Phe- X -*Leu*-Gly-

[a] Sjöström et al (1982); [b] Feracci et al (1982).

amino acid sequences of sucrase–isomaltase (Sjöström et al 1982), and aminopeptidase N (Feracci et al 1982), assuming that position 12 in aminopeptidase N corresponds to position 11 in sucrase–isomaltase. Some homology is seen, indicating that the anchor of aminopeptidase N may also span twice.

Results on sucrase–isomaltase (Semenza 1981) and (kidney) dipeptidyl peptidase IV (Kenny & Maroux 1982) suggest that the final forms do not have any C-terminal anchor, but information on other microvillar enzymes is lacking. However, a hypothetical C-terminal anchor may be more easily cleaved than an N-terminal anchor during purification. During our work with hydrophobic labelling on aminopeptidase N (Norén & Sjöström 1980), we found that the anchor on the 120 000 M_r polypeptide was more easily cleaved during the preparation than was the anchor on the 160 000 M_r polypeptide. Moreover, most membrane proteins are inserted via a C-terminal segment. This may have a biosynthetic explanation, as one of the forces for penetration through the membrane—the protein synthetic motive force—stops when 30–40 amino acids are still covered by the ribosome (Sabatini et al 1982). The existence of C-terminal anchoring on at least some of these microvillar hydrolases is thus still possible.

Fig. 1 shows an electron micrograph of negatively stained reconstituted aminopeptidase N (Hussain et al 1981). It illustrates the morphology of the aminopeptidase molecules and their relation to the membrane. The shape of the molecules indicates dimers with dimensions corresponding to an M_r of about 270 000. This globular part of the molecule is separated from the membrane by a 5 nm gap, indicating that the anchor has two different domains: the *hydrophobic root*, buried in the bilayer, and the *hydrophilic junctional segment*, bridging the gap. Data on amino acid analysis of the anchor, which demonstrate both hydrophobic and hydrophilic amino acids

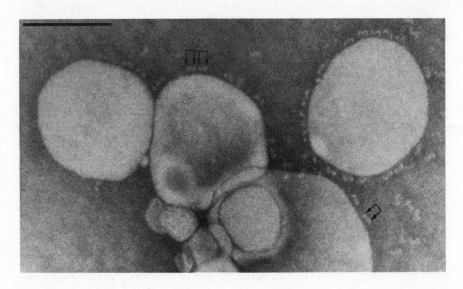

FIG. 1. Electron micrograph of negatively stained reconstituted aminopeptidase N. 2 mg of phosphatidylcholine were evaporated to a thin film, which was dissolved in buffer containing 20 mM-deoxycholate, and 80 μg aminopeptidase N was added. Detergent was then removed by dialysis. Arrow shows the reincorporated enzyme in profile. It appears to have a slightly narrowed waist, compatible with a dimeric structure, about 13.5 nm × 5.5 nm. Scale bar: 100 nm (Hussain et al 1981).

(Kenny & Maroux 1982), fit well with this model. The distance bridged by the junctional segment indicates an M_r of 2000–4000, depending on its secondary structure. Provided that the intramembranous peptide spans the membrane once and has no large cytoplasmic mass, the total M_r of the anchor is calculated at 4000–8000, which agrees with biochemical determinations (Kenny & Maroux 1982).

Since the enzymes are dimers they can have either one or two N-terminal anchors on each native molecule. For aminopeptidase N, we have demonstrated that both the 160 000 and the 120 000 M_r forms can be labelled with a hydrophobic label (Norén & Sjöström 1980). Because an immunological study of isolated subunits (Sjöström & Norén 1982) has demonstrated that only one type of 160 000 M_r polypeptide generates the 120 000 M_r polypeptide, aminopeptidase N is probably anchored to the membrane by both polypeptides in the dimer.

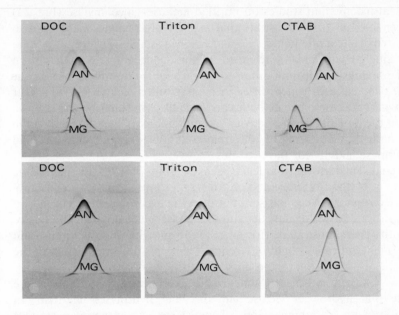

FIG. 2. Charge-shift crossed immunoelectrophoresis of single-chain amphiphilic maltase–glucoamylase (upper row) and single-chain hydrophilic maltase–glucoamylase (lower row). DOC, buffer contains 0.2% sodium deoxycholate and 0.1% Triton X-100; Triton, buffer contains 0.1% Triton X-100; CTAB, buffer contains 0.0125% cetyltrimethylammonium bromide and 0.1% Triton X-100; AN, hydrophilic aminopeptidase N; MG, single-chain maltase–glucoamylase. The experiment shows that the addition of charged detergents changes the mobility of amphiphilic but not hydrophilic single-chain maltase–glucoamylase in relation to hydrophilic aminopeptidase.

If dimers, which originate by cleavage of a single polypeptide, are to be anchored by both N-termini an intermediate hydrophobic segment must exist between the two different domains in the single-chain form. As the single-chain enzymes can be isolated in a hydrophilic form, having an M_r only 5000 smaller (Fig. 2), we suggest that these types of dimer (sucrase–isomaltase and maltase–glucoamylase) do not have any interposed segment and thus that they insert with one N-terminal anchor only.

Two characteristic groups also for the constituent polypeptides

It has been long known that sucrase–isomaltase is composed of two different polypeptides, one with sucrase and one with isomaltase activity (Semenza 1981). Heat-inactivation studies on purified maltase–glucoamylase (Fig. 3a) recently enabled us to demonstrate that maltase–glucoamylase also has two different active sites, one heat-labile and one heat-stable. This result is valid both for single-chain and for 'cleaved' maltase–glucoamylase. It has been reported previously that in addition to sucrase–isomaltase there are, in the intestine, two maltases which differ in heat stability (Semenza 1981). Our results suggest that these two activities occur on the same enzyme. Fig. 3a also shows that the amylopectinase activity is somewhat more heat-labile than the maltase activity, indicating a different relation between maltase and amylopectinase activity for the two sites.

Single-chain maltase–glucoamylase can be split *in vitro* by pancreatic proteases into the $125\,000$ and $135\,000\,M_r$ forms. Fig. 3(b,c) shows immunoelectrophoretic comparisons between the two polypeptides using two different antisera raised against denatured maltase–glucoamylase. In Fig. 3b, total identity is demonstrated. However, the result with the other antiserum (Fig. 3c) might indicate a slight difference. This is possibly a reflection of the two active sites, but further experiments need to be done.

Lactase–phlorizin hydrolase (Semenza 1981) also has two different active sites, one that hydrolyses lactose and one that hydrolyses phlorizin. In collaboration with G. Semenza and colleagues we have recently shown that the lactase activity could be totally blocked with conduritol-B-epoxide. As we have demonstrated polypeptides of only one M_r we cannot yet tell whether they are different.

The three peptidases seem to have only one type of active site each, and there is positive evidence for only one type of polypeptide chain in each of the enzymes. Aminopeptidase N is monomeric in the rabbit (Kenny & Maroux 1982), and the $160\,000\,M_r$ polypeptide of the pig enzyme exhibits immunological homogeneity (Sjöström & Norén 1982) when antibodies directed against the complete molecule are used. Aminopeptidase A has also been suggested to be homogeneous because only one N-terminal amino acid was found (Kenny & Maroux 1982). There is no information on dipeptidyl peptidase IV from the intestine, but the kidney enzyme, which is also a dimer, shows a homogeneous N-terminal sequence (Kenny & Maroux 1982). Table 4 summarizes some properties of the constituent polypeptides.

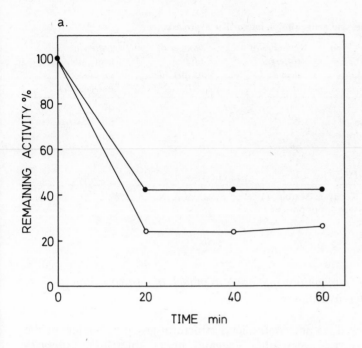

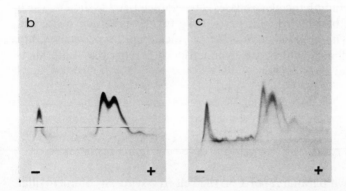

FIG. 3. (a) Heat-inactivation studies on maltase–glucoamylase. Purified maltase–glucoamylase was incubated at 55 °C and analysed for maltase (●) and amylopectinase (○) activities. (b,c) Crossed SDS–PAGE immunoelectrophoresis of a maltase–glucoamylase preparation containing 125 000, 135 000 and 245 000 M_r polypeptides, using two different antisera.

TABLE 4 Polypeptides and active sites in microvillar hydrolases

Enzyme	Number of different active sites	Number of different polypeptides	Different active site on different polypeptides
Sucrase–isomaltase	2[a]	2[a]	+[a]
Maltase–glucoamylase	2	2	n.a.
Lactase–phlorizin hydrolase	2[a]	n.a.	n.a.
Aminopeptidase N	1[b]	1[c]	–
Aminopeptidase A	1[b]	1[b]	–
Dipeptidyl peptidase IV	1[d]	1[b]	–

[a] Semenza (1981); [b] Kenny & Maroux (1982); [c] Sjöström & Norén (1982); [d] Svensson et al (1978). n.a. not analysed; –, not present.

Sucrase–isomaltase and aminopeptidase N as models of the two groups of intestinal microvillar hydrolases

Present knowledge does not contradict a structural grouping similar to the functional one for the microvillar enzymes under study. The *sucrase–isomaltase type*, including the glycosidases, are characterized as dimers which are asymmetric in their hydrophilic parts, have two types of active site and one anchor only. The *aminopeptidase N type*, including the peptidases, are characterized as dimers which are symmetric with regard to both their hydrophilic part and their anchor.

Biosynthetic phase

Primary translation product of sucrase–isomaltase and aminopeptidase N

There have been two parallel reports on the cell-free synthesis of microvillar hydrolases: sucrase–isomaltase (Wacker et al 1981) and aminopeptidase N (Danielsen et al 1982a). By the use of intestinal mRNA-directed protein synthesis *in vitro*, followed by purification with antibodies against sucrase–isomaltase, two polypeptides with M_r values of 270 000 and 240 000 were detected (Wacker et al 1981). In similar experiments we also found that the primary translation product of the enzyme was a doublet, with an M_r around 220 000. This corresponds to an enzyme with an M_r of 265 000 that has 22% glycosylation. We have at present no explanation for the occurrence of the doublet.

We have demonstrated that aminopeptidase N is synthesized as a $115\,000\,M_r$ polypeptide (Danielsen et al 1982a). This corresponds to a polypeptide with an M_r of 160 000 that has 28% glycosylation, and clearly suggests a separate synthesis of each of the two polypeptides in the final aminopeptidase. The biosynthetic mechanism for aminopeptidase N is thus different from that for sucrase–isomaltase and maltase–glucoamylase, which are synthesized as polypeptides with an M_r corresponding to the final dimer.

Microvillar hydrolases are co-translationally inserted in the membrane

Proteins, characterized as integral membrane proteins, have been reported to be synthesized either by ribosomes bound to the endoplasmic reticulum or by cytoplasmic ribosomes (Sabatini et al 1982). It seems as if glycosylated polypeptides are synthesized by membrane-bound polysomes, whereas the non-glycosylated ones are synthesized by cytoplasmic polysomes.

We have only indirect information about the site of synthesis of the microvillar hydrolases. In organ culture of explants using [35S]methionine labelling, the earliest detectable form of the enzymes was found to be associated with membranes rather than being in a soluble form, indicating that membrane insertion occurs co-translationally (Danielsen 1982).

No cleavage of the signal in aminopeptidase N?

Secretory and membrane proteins have, in their primary sequences, a signal that is responsible for the binding of the nascent chain to the membrane. For secretory proteins the signal is cleaved in most cases whereas, for membrane proteins, there are examples of both cleaved and non-cleaved signals.

Two principal hypotheses have been proposed for the co-translational insertion of membrane proteins: the linear model and the loop model. The latter seems more generally applicable and evidence favouring it is accumulating (Sabatini et al 1982). A likely consequence of the loop model seems to be that membrane proteins with cytoplasmically located N-terminal amino acids should have a non-cleaved signal, whereas those with non-cytoplasmically located N-terminal amino acids may have either cleaved or non-cleaved signals.

Fig. 4 shows a fluorograph of the earliest form of the enzyme seen in tunicamycin-treated organ-cultured intestinal explants (lane 1) and the cell-free translation product of aminopeptidase N (lanes 2–3). As tunicamycin is known to inhibit N-linked glycosylation, a direct comparison of the M_r values of the two polypeptides can give information about the possible cleavage of a signal. No differences in M_r can be detected, indicating that if signal cleavage occurs, the signal has an M_r less than 1500, a value smaller than most cleaved signals previously reported. Thus, a cleaved signal with a size corresponding to other known signals cannot be detected in aminopeptidase N.

These results represent the first information about signal segments in microvillar hydrolases and are consistent with at least three models of assembly.

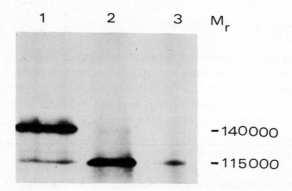

FIG. 4. Fluorographs of ^{35}S-labelled aminopeptidase N of various origins. Lane 1, purified from tunicamycin-treated organ-cultured intestinal explants. Lanes 2–3, purified after cell-free synthesis *in vitro*.

(1) The loop model, with the N-terminal amino acid located cytoplasmically: this mechanism would be analogous to that of the band III protein of the erythrocyte (Sabatini et al 1982).

(2) The loop model, with the N-terminal amino acid non-cytoplasmically located: in this case the mechanism resembles that of retinal opsin (Sabatini et al 1982). However, the transfer of the N-terminal part of aminopeptidase N through the membrane is difficult to conceive as there is an unblocked N-terminal and lysine in this region. Retinal opsin has no lysine and has a blocked N-terminal amino acid (Hargrave 1977).

(3) The linear model, in combination with a secondary insertion of the anchor, as suggested by Kenny & Booth (1978).

A 'high-mannose' glycosylation precedes a more 'complex' glycosylation

By preparative immunoadsorbent chromatography of Triton-solubilized calcium-precipitable membranes a new form of each enzyme was found, of lower

TABLE 5 Apparent molecular masses of different intracellular precursor forms of pig intestinal microvillar hydrolases

Enzyme	Primary translation product	Endoglycosidase H sensitive form	Endoglycosidase H resistant form
Sucrase–isomaltase	220 000[a] (doublet)	240 000[b,c,d,]	260 000[b,c,d]
Maltase–glucoamylase	n.a.	225 000[c,e]	245 000[c,e]
Lactase–phlorizin hydrolase	n.a.	150 000[c]	160 000[c]
Aminopeptidase N	115 000[a]	140 000[b,c,d] (doublet)	160 000[b,c,d]
Aminopeptidase A	n.a.	140 000[e]	170 000[e]
Dipeptidyl peptidase IV	n.a.	115 000[e]	140 000[e]

[a] Danielsen et al (1982a); [b] Danielsen et al (1981a); [c] Danielsen et al (1981b); [d] Danielsen (1982); [e] Danielsen et al (1983). n.a. not analysed. See also Table 1, p 157 for further details

M_r than that initially occurring in the membrane (Table 5, Danielsen et al 1981a, Danielsen et al 1981b). These new forms were all shown to be sensitive to treatment with endoglycosidase H, indicating that they have a so-called 'core' or 'high-mannose' glycosylation (Sabatini et al 1982). This core glycosylation is known to precede the more 'complex' glycosylation, and the change from core glycosylation to complex glycosylation is known to take place in the Golgi complex (Sabatini et al 1982).

By pulse–chase labelling with [^{35}S]methionine in organ-cultured intestinal explants we have demonstrated, for sucrase–isomaltase (Danielsen 1982), maltase–glycoamylase (Danielsen et al 1983), aminopeptidase N (Danielsen 1982), aminopeptidase A and dipeptidyl peptidase IV (Danielsen et al 1983), that these endoglycosidase H-sensitive forms are the earliest forms detectable, suggesting that this glycosylation occurs co-translationally.

We have no definitive information on whether there is a change in glycosylation after the enzymes have reached the microvillar membrane. The endoglycosidase H-resistant, intracellular forms are sensitive to neuraminidase. In our initial work on biosynthesis (Danielsen et al 1981a) these forms of aminopeptidase N, sucrase–isomaltase and maltase–glucoamylase had somewhat higher M_r values than their respective final microvillar forms, indicating a final trimming in the microvillar membrane. However, later results indicate that this difference is explained by variation between individual preparations, at least for sucrase–isomaltase and maltase–glucoamylase (Sørensen et al 1982).

Lactase–phlorizin hydrolase obviously follows another scheme

Fig. 5 shows the results of a pulse–chase labelling experiment with lactase–phlorizin hydrolase. A 190 000 M_r band and a 200 000 M_r band of equal intensity appeared earliest in the calcium-precipitable membranes after a 10-min pulse (Fig. 5a), whereas only the 160 000 M_r band could be seen in microvillar membrane fraction after continuous labelling (Fig. 5b). By using monensin, which results in vacuolization of the Golgi apparatus, and thereby disturbs its function, we observed the two bands of 190 000 and 200 000 M_r, indicating that both occur before the passage through the Golgi apparatus and therefore probably lack the complex glycosylation. (In parallel experiments, the complex glycosylation of other hydrolases was inhibited by monensin.) In the monensin-treated cells, a fuzzy 150 000 M_r band was also seen (Fig. 5c). The tentative interpretation of the experiments is as follows. The 200 000 M_r form is a high-mannose glycosylated form, containing both polypeptides of the final form in a single chain. This polypeptide is split, in the endoplasmic reticulum or Golgi complex, into two equally sized peptides of M_r 150 000, which correspond to the demonstrated intracellular precursor. This is finally reglycosylated to the 'complex' 160 000 M_r form in the Golgi apparatus. The 190 000 M_r band probably represents a less glycosylated form. The mechanism resembles that of kidney γ-glutamyltransferase, which has recently been described (Nash & Tate 1982).

Microtubules take part in the transport of the enzymes to the membrane

In general little is known about the mechanism of transport from endoplasmic reticulum to plasma membrane. It has been suggested that precursors to the membrane proteins are transported in coated vesicles, but such a mechanism has been demonstrated only for the G protein of vesicular stomatitis virus (Sabatini et al 1982). We have an indication that microtubules are important for this transport because colchicine, in organ-cultured explants, does not interfere with the synthesis of the intracellular forms of aminopeptidase N or sucrase–isomaltase, although it severely inhibits their appearance in the microvillar membrane.

What is the structure of the address for the plasma membrane?

The address for correct cellular transport must reside in the primary sequence, probably in the juxtamembranous part. For addressing only, a

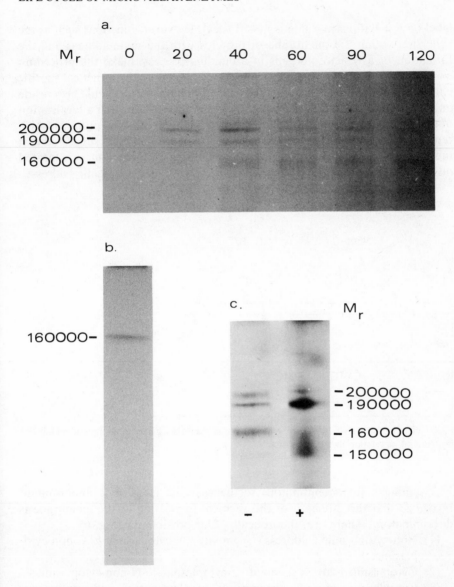

FIG. 5. Pulse–chase labelling experiments in organ-cultured intestinal explants. (a) Lactase–phlorizin hydrolase from Ca^{2+}-precipitable membranes at different times (min) of chase after a 10-min pulse period. (b) Lactase-phlorizin hydrolase in a Triton-solubilized homogenate after continuous labelling for 20 h. (c) Lactase–phlorizin hydrolase in Triton-solubilized homogenate after continuous labelling for 90 min, in the absence (−) and presence (+) of monensin.

label on the cytoplasmic side is most logical. However, functions such as the collection within the membrane of proteins with the same address and the formation of a vesicle, perhaps in a budding process, make the procedure complex, and it probably requires the participation of a hypothetical specific endoplasmic membrane protein. This means that an address could also reside on the non-cytoplasmic side of the peptide chain. In fact, such a localization of the label has recently been suggested from studies on some proteins which remain in the endoplasmic reticulum (Okada et al 1982). It is suggested that they are not transported further because the majority of their mass is located on the cytoplasmic side, and because they lack a non-cytoplasmic address.

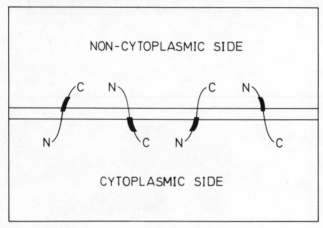

FIG. 6. Theoretical possibilities for the location of an address segment of an integral membrane protein and its relation to the membrane.

Assuming a juxtamembranous segment as the label, it is important to recognize that the direction of the segment in relation to the membrane is discriminatory. There are, theoretically, four possibilities (Fig. 6):

(1) Non-cytoplasmic address segment: N-cytoplasmic-to-C-non-cyto-plasmic;
(2) Cytoplasmic address segment: C-cytoplasmic-to-N-non-cytoplasmic;
(3) Cytoplasmic address segment: N-cytoplasmic-to-C-non-cytoplasmic; and
(4) Non-cytoplasmic address segment: C-cytoplasmic-to-N-non-cyto-plasmic.

Of the proteins shown to span the membrane only once, none spans in the direction: N-cytoplasmic-to-C-non-cytoplasmic. Therefore, only (2) and (4), above, are possible for a more general model.

It is interesting to note that sucrase–isomaltase and glycophorin have a highly homologous segment with a localization according to model (4) (Sjöström et al 1982). This segment is also very well preserved in the glycophorins isolated from different species. The suggested model of aminopeptidase N in relation to the membrane (Feracci et al 1982), with the N-terminus on the cytoplasmic side and a free C-terminus, is impossible to fit into a general model for the address in relation to the membrane. Perhaps the enzyme spans the membrane twice, as sucrase–isomaltase does, or it may, additionally, have a C-terminal insertion. Sequence studies on the N- and C-termini of the different microvillar hydrolases provide an excellent opportunity to look for sequence homologies of the suggested type, making it possible to support or reject the hypothesis, i.e. that the address segment is located on the transition zone between membrane and non-cytoplasmic side in the direction N-non-cytoplasmic-to-C-cytoplasmic.

Degradation phase

Microvillar enzymes may be degraded by different mechanisms

The mechanisms for the catabolism of individual membrane proteins are not well characterized. However, for the regulation of the amount of these enzymes in the microvillus membrane the degradation phase is as important as the biosynthetic phase. Theoretically, membrane proteins may be catabolized by four different mechanisms:

(1) *Degradation in the membrane*
The main mass of the enzyme is still bound to the membrane, but proteolytic attack(s) result(s) in breaks in the peptide chain, with possible loss of enzymic activity. The fragments thus generated may remain bound to the molecule by non-covalent forces, or they may be released into the lumen.

(2) *External delivery*
 (a) *Solubilization.* This mechanism originally suggested by Alpers & Tedesco (1975) implies a proteolytic attack at the junctional peptide with release of a hydrophilic, active enzyme. We have recently studied the enzyme activity and the immunological reactivity along the crypt–villus axis of the intestine for aminopeptidase N, dipeptidyl peptidase IV, sucrase and lactase (Skovbjerg 1981). A close correlation between the two measurements was found, indicating that the earlier observed decrease in enzyme activity at the top of villi is not due to specific enzymic inactivation or release of cells or cell fragments, but rather to a solubilization of the enzymes.

 (b) *Budding.* In organ-culture experiments we always find accumulation of enzymic activities in the medium (Danielsen et al 1982b). We have shown that about 90% of the aminopeptidase activity in the medium is membrane-bound, indicating that budding may be important in maintaining a constant enzyme activity in the microvillus membrane. Electron microscopic evidence for the formation of vesicles has been presented previously (Berteloot et al 1981, Misch et al 1980).

(3) *Endocytosis*

It is well known that the microvillar membrane does endocytose. However, it has recently been argued on various grounds that there is no transport of microvillar proteins by this mechanism in the intestine (Berteloot et al 1981, Blok et al 1981). Perhaps this route is more important in microvillar membranes of organs where external loss of membrane proteins is unlikely.

Structure of degraded forms

Degradation may be regarded as a late post-translational modification because, when the transformation is not accompanied by any changes in the specific enzymic activity, it may be impossible to distinguish between transformation from the pro-form to the final form and transformation from the final form to the degraded form.

To obtain information about the importance of pancreatic enzymes for the structure of the microvillar hydrolases, we have purified the different enzymes from pigs which, three days before removal of the intestine, had had their pancreatic duct(s) disconnected. By this approach we could show that: sucrase–isomaltase occurred as a 265 000 M_r band (instead of 150 000 and 160 000 M_r bands; Sjöström et al 1980); aminopeptidase N as a 160 000 M_r band (instead of 160 000, 120 000 and 60 000 M_r bands; Sjöström et al 1978); and maltase–glucoamylase as 245 000 M_r bands (instead of occasional findings of 125 000 and 135 000 M_r bands; Sørensen et al 1982). The other three microvillar hydrolases were unaffected (Table 1).

The single-chain sucrase–isomaltase which, despite there being no activation accompanying the cleavage of the 265 000 M_r band, has been called pro-sucrase–isomaltase, has been further characterized structurally by us in collaboration with Dr G. Semenza (see also this volume, p 92–112).

In crossed immunoelectrophoresis of human biopsies, the sucrase–isomaltase precipitate regularly has an extra cathodal spur, exhibiting partial identity with the main precipitate (Skovbjerg et al 1979). By histochemical staining methods we could show that the extra spur represented isomaltase, which was not associated with sucrase. As sucrase–isomaltase is bound to the membrane via the isomaltase polypeptide, it is likely that this phenomenon represents a type of degradation where either the sucrase has been totally degraded or the binding to the isomaltase has been destroyed, with the consequent release of sucrase into the intestinal lumen.

The polypeptide composition of maltase–glucoamylase differs from preparation to preparation (Sørensen et al 1982). Some normal preparations show the 245 000 M_r band only, whereas others have approximately half the enzyme transformed into the 135 000 and 125 000 M_r bands. The steady-state concentration is obviously different from that of sucrase–isomaltase, where normally only small amounts of the single-chain form may be found. The cleavage site in maltase–glucoamylase is probably not readily hydrolysed by pancreatic proteases or, alternatively, there is a more rapid synthesis of maltase–glucoamylase.

We have further characterized the degradation of aminopeptidase N (Sjöström & Norén 1982). By raising antibodies against the separated, denatured polypeptides, we were able to analyse the polypeptide composition without a preceding purification. The results clearly showed that the cleavage process occurs *in vivo*. Furthermore, by densitometric scannings of polyacrylamide gels with very rapidly purified aminopeptidase N we showed that there is always more of the 60 000 M_r band than of the 120 000 M_r band, on a molar basis. This suggests that part of the 120 000 M_r band is further degraded while still bound to the membrane.

General conclusion

The intestinal microvillar membrane is a good model system for studying the life cycles of stalked, integral membrane proteins. In spite of the similarity of the functional forms, i.e. dimers with M_r values of around 300 000, two structural groups may be distinguished: the *sucrase–isomaltase type*, characterized as dimers, which are asymmetric in their hydrophilic parts, have two types of active sites and anchor on one polypeptide only; and the *aminopeptidase N type*, characterized as symmetric dimers.

Both groups are probably synthesized on membrane-bound ribosomes and are glycosylated. They are then transported and reglycosylated via the Golgi apparatus. Enzymes of the sucrase–isomaltase type are synthesized with a polypeptide-chain length corresponding to the *sum* of the constituent polypeptides, whereas enzymes of the aminopeptidase N type are synthesized with a polypeptide-chain length corresponding to the constituent polypeptides themselves. Sucrase–isomaltase and maltase–glucoamylase are cleaved in the microvillar membrane. Lactase–phlorizin is probably cleaved in the endoplasmic reticulum or Golgi complex. The possibility of purifying large amounts of several membrane proteins with the same functional localization, for use in studies of sequence homology, will aid in determining which segments have important biological functions (e.g. address for transport).

As far as is known, solubilization and release of membrane into the intestinal lumen are more important in degradation than endocytosis, but studies on the metabolic rates of individual enzymes remain to be done.

Acknowledgements

This work was supported by the Danish Medical Research Council (512–20074, 512–15590, 512–20564, 12–2214), the Danish Natural Research Council (11–1615, 11–2306, 11–0482), the Carlsberg Foundation, P. Carl Petersen's Fund (B 1160) and the Novo Foundation.

REFERENCES

Alpers DH, Tedesco FJ 1975 The possible role of pancreatic proteases in the turnover of intestinal brush border proteins. Biochim Biophys Acta 401:28-40

Berteloot A, Chabot J-G, Hugon JS 1981 Turnover of mouse intestinal brush border membrane proteins and enzymes in organ culture. A direct evaluation from studies on the evolution of enzyme activities during the culture. Biochim Biophys Acta 678:423-436

Blok J, Mulder-Stapel AA, Ginsel LA, Daems WT 1981 Endocytosis in absorptive cells of human small-intestinal tissue: horse-radish peroxidase, lactoperoxidase and ferritin as markers. Cell Tissue Res 216:1-13

Danielsen EM 1982 Biosynthesis of intestinal microvillar proteins. Pulse–chase labelling studies on aminopeptidase N and sucrase–isomaltase. Biochem J 204:639-645

Danielsen EM, Sjöström H, Norén O 1981a Biosynthesis of intestinal microvillar proteins. Putative precursor forms of microvillus aminopeptidase and sucrase–isomaltase isolated from Ca^{2+}-precipitated enterocyte membranes. FEBS (Fed Eur Biochem Soc) Lett 127:129–132

Danielsen EM, Skovbjerg H, Norén O, Sjöström H 1981b Biosynthesis of intestinal microvillar proteins. Nature of precursor forms of microvillar enzymes from Ca^{2+}-precipitated enterocyte membranes. FEBS (Fed Eur Biochem Soc) Lett 132:197-200

Danielsen EM, Norén O, Sjöström H 1982a Biosynthesis of intestinal microvillar proteins. Translational evidence *in vitro* that aminopeptidase N is synthesised as a M_r-115 000 polypeptide. Biochem J 204:323-327

Danielsen EM, Sjöström H, Norén O, Bro B, Dabelsteen E 1982b Biosynthesis of intestinal microvillar proteins. Characterisation of intestinal explants in organ culture and evidence for the existence of pro-forms of the microvillar enzymes. Biochem J 202:647-654

Danielsen EM, Sjöström H, Norén O 1983 Biosynthesis of intestinal microvillar proteins. Pulse–chase labelling studies on maltase–glucoamylase, aminopeptidase A and dipeptidyl peptidase IV. Biochem J, in press

Feracci H, Maroux S, Bonicel J, Desnuelle P 1982 The amino acid sequence of the hydrophobic anchor of rabbit intestinal brush border aminopeptidase N. Biochim Biophys Acta 684:133-136

Hargrave PA 1977 The amino-terminal tryptic peptide of bovine rhodopsin. A glycopeptide containing two sites of oligosaccharide attachment. Biochim Biophys Acta 492:83-94

Hussain MM, Tranum-Jensen J, Norén O, Sjöström H, Christiansen K 1981 Reconstitution of purified amphiphilic pig intestinal microvillus aminopeptidase. Mode of membrane insertion and morphology. Biochem J 199:179-186

Kenny AJ, Booth AG 1978 Microvilli: their ultrastructure, enzymology and molecular organisation. Essays Biochem 14:1-44

Kenny AJ, Maroux S 1982 Topology of microvillar membrane hydrolases of kidney and intestine. Physiol Rev 62:91-128

Misch DW, Giebel PE, Faust RG 1980 Intestinal microvilli: responses to feeding and fasting. Eur J Cell Biol 21:269-279

Nash B, Tate SS 1982 Biosynthesis of rat renal γ-glutamyl transpeptidase. J Biol Chem 257:585-588

Norén O, Sjöström H 1980 The insertion of pig microvillus aminopeptidase into the membrane as probed by [^{125}I] iodonaphthylazide. Eur J Biochem 104:25-31

Okada Y, Frey AB, Guenthner TM, Oesch F, Sabatini DD, Kreibich G 1982 Studies on the biosynthesis of microsomal membrane proteins. Site of synthesis and mode of insertion of cytochrome b$_5$, cytochrome b$_5$ reductase, cytochrome P-450 reductase and epoxide hydrolase. Eur J Biochem 122:393-402

Sabatini DD, Kreibich G, Morimoti T, Adesnik M 1982 Mechanisms for the incorporation of proteins in membranes and organelles. J Cell Biol 92:1-22

Semenza G 1981 Intestinal oligo- and disaccharidases. In: Randle PJ et al (eds) Carbohydrate metabolism and its disorders. Academic Press, London, vol 3:425-479

Sjöström H, Norén O 1982 Changes of the quaternary structure of microvillus aminopeptidase in the membrane. Eur J Biochem 122:245-250

Sjöström H, Norén O, Jeppesen L, Staun M, Svensson B, Christiansen L 1978 Purification of different amphiphilic forms of a microvillus aminopeptidase from pig small intestine using immunoadsorbent chromatography. Eur J Biochem 88:503-511

Sjöström H, Norén O, Christiansen L, Wacker H, Semenza G 1980 A fully active, two-active-site, single-chain sucrase–isomaltase from pig small intestine. Implications for the biosynthesis of a mammalian integral stalked membrane protein. J Biol Chem 255:11332-11338

Sjöström H, Norén O, Christiansen LA et al 1982 N-terminal sequences of pig intestinal sucrase–isomaltase and pro-sucrase–isomaltase. Implications for the biosynthesis and membrane insertion of pro-sucrase–isomaltase. FEBS (Fed Eur Biochem Soc) Lett, in press

Skovbjerg H 1981 Immunoelectrophoretic studies on human small-intestinal brush-border proteins. Relation between enzyme activity and immunoreactive enzyme along the villus–crypt axis. Biochem J 193:887-890

Skovbjerg H, Sjöström H, Norén O 1979 Does sucrase–isomaltase always exist as a complex in human intestine? FEBS (Fed Eur Biochem Soc) Lett 108:399-402

Skovbjerg H, Norén O, Sjöström H, Danielsen EM, Enevoldsen BS 1982 Further characterisation of intestinal lactase–phlorizin hydrolase. Biochim Biophys Acta 707:89-97

Sørensen SH, Norén O, Sjöström H, Danielsen EM 1982 Amphiphilic pig intestinal microvillus maltase/glucoamylase: structure and specificity. Eur J Biochem 126:559-568

Svensson B, Danielsen M, Staun M, Jeppesen L, Norén O, Sjöström H 1978 An amphiphilic form of dipeptidyl peptidase IV from pig small-intestinal brush-border membrane. Eur J Biochem 90:489-498

Wacker H, Jaussi R, Sonderegger P et al 1981 Cell-free synthesis of the one-chain precursor of a major intrinsic protein complex of the small-intestinal brush border membrane (pro-sucrase–isomaltase). FEBS (Fed Eur Biochem Soc) Lett 136:329-332

DISCUSSION

Hauri: What were your two different approaches to studying the biosynthesis of lactase?

Sjöström: In the organ culture system we noticed, by pulse–chase labelling, that the lactase had an M_r of 200 000, which was higher than the M_r of the polypeptides of final lactase, thus suggesting a single-chain precursor. Such a precursor could not be found by purification from the calcium-precipitated membrane from ordinary intestines, probably because of a low steady-state concentration.

Smith: Are these enzymes active, in terms of their ability to hydrolyse substrate, from the endoplasmic reticulum stage onwards?

Sjöström: As far as we know, yes. The purification of the enzymes from the calcium-precipitated membranes is followed by assay of the enzymic activity.

Smith: Do you test for activity on endoplasmic reticulum membranes?

Sjöström: No; we have not purified those membranes specifically.

Curthoys: What proportion of the total enzyme would be in the biosynthetic route?

Sjöström: For aminopeptidase N, it is 3–4% by enzymic measurements. However, we know little about the topology of the enzyme in relation to the vesicles and the leakiness with respect to substrate.

Louvard: Since you have a specific antibody against the high M_r form, which should not recognize the B and C form, have you tried to do immunocytochemistry on a section of intestine to see if the high M_r form goes to the basolateral membrane?

Sjöström: The high M_r form also reacts with B and C, which *can* be distinguished from each other, but all antibodies interact with A.

Louvard: But if A is the longest form, you should be able to make an A-specific antibody.

Sjöström: We cannot, because B and C are contained in A.

Louvard: But A has an extra polypeptide segment, and it is longer than B & C. So it must have an antigenic determinant which is not on B & C.

Sjöström: In our experiments there is no indication that an extra peptide is split off when A is hydrolysed to B and C.

Inoue: Interaction between intestinal brush border membranes and pancreatic juice can be prevented by T-tube drainage. Do you see any changes in the subunit structure of the enzyme if animals receive such operations?

Sjöström: Yes; we did this type of experiment by surgical disconnection of the pancreatic duct, three days before removal of the intestine. As the life-time of the enterocytes is of a similar duration, the procedure should result in only the new enterocytes failing to make contact with pancreatic proteases.

Inoue: Did you observe the large molecular form of the enzymes as the predominant components?

Sjöström: Yes, for maltase–glucoamylase and for sucrase–isomaltase, but not for lactase–phlorizin hydrolase, which is obviously split intracellularly.

Alpers: I don't think elastase would affect the intracellular splitting.

Inoue: Is pancreatic juice protease fully responsible for the processing mechanism of sucrase–isomaltase into smaller molecular mass components?

Sjöström: Yes.

Alpers: In the absence of pancreatic enzymes do you find only the unhydrolysed form of aminopeptidase?

Sjöström: Yes.

Alpers: Is aminopeptidase present in the fetal pig before delivery?

Sjöström: We can't tell that.

Alpers: There should, in fact, be no pancreatic enzymes there, and the degradation processes seem to be quite different, too. I believe the time of onset varies in different species.

Hermon-Taylor: Did antibody raised to the final forms of each enzyme you studied immunoprecipitate the corresponding precursor forms produced in cell-free translation systems?

Sjöström: So far we have most experience with aminopeptidase N. The precursor form after cell-free translation could be immunoprecipitated with antibodies raised both to final and to SDS/heat-denatured aminopeptidase N. The latter antibodies do not immunoprecipitate the native enzyme, so the primary translation product probably resembles only partially the final one with respect to conformation.

Schmitz: Have you tried to characterize the two possibly different active sites of glucoamylase to see whether they are different according to other criteria than their temperature of denaturation?

Norén: Yes, and we have done some experiments with Conduritol B-epoxide and found no difference in its rate of inhibition of maltase compared to amylopectinase activity. So we can't differentiate these activities with that particular reagent.

Sjöström: To study whether the two possible different active sites are localized on the two polypeptides of the split form, we plan first to heat-inactivate one of the active sites and then to use Conduritol B-epoxide to label the other.

Alpers: We've done that with glucose polymers of different sizes (2–9) and we could not see a difference in the native form, although we did not have separate chains (Kelly & Alpers 1973). We heat-inactivated first and then tested activity against a series of glucose oligomers and also could not see any difference.

Sjöström: The difference between maltase and glucoamylase activities in the two active sites is 10–20% and only a minor point. The main thing is the different heat-stability of the two sites, which have similar maltase and amylopectinase activity.

Louvard: Have you tried to compare the high M_r form in a kidney preparation, where the question of pancreatic enzyme is excluded?

Sjöström: We have not succeeded in measuring any maltase activity (in one kidney) although we know it should be present at least in the rabbit (Booth & Kenny 1976).

Louvard: You could do it for the aminopeptidase N, at least.

Sjöström: Wacker et al (1976) have already done this.

Maroux: What do you think your calcium-precipitated membrane fractions contain?

Sjöström: We have not characterized them and thus only have the information from Schmitz et al (1973) which suggests the presence of microsomal membranes, mitochondria and probably basolateral membranes. What is important in our work is that the membrane fraction is depleted of microvillus membranes.

Hauri: The endo-H sensitivity that you found is a good indication that you are dealing with intracellular membranes.

REFERENCES

Booth AG, Kenny AJ 1976 Proteins of the kidney microvillus membrane. Identification of subunits after sodium dodecyl sulphate/polyacrylamide-gel electrophoresis. Biochem J 159: 395-407

Kelly JJ, Alpers DH 1973 Properties of human intestinal glucoamylase. Biochim Biophys Acta 315: 113-120

Schmitz J, Preiser H, Maestracci D, Ghosh BK, Gerda JJ, Crane RK 1973 Purification of the human intestinal brush border membrane. Biochim Biophys Acta 323: 98-112

Wacker H, Lehky P, Vanderhaege F, Stein EA 1976 On the subunit structure of particulate aminopeptidase from pig kidney. Biochim Biophys Acta 429: 546-554

Specific labelling of the hydrophobic domain of rat renal γ-glutamyltransferase

THOMAS FRIELLE and NORMAN P. CURTHOYS

Department of Biochemistry, University of Pittsburgh School of Medicine, Pittsburgh, PA 15261, USA

Abstract The amphipathic form of γ-glutamyltransferase (EC 2.3.2.2) was reconstituted into unilamellar lecithin vesicles and labelled using the membrane-soluble reagent, 3-trifluoromethyl-3-(m-[^{125}I]iodophenyl)diazirine ([^{125}I]TID), which can be photoactivated. Label was incorporated exclusively into the large subunit of the transferase, but no label was found in the enzyme released from the vesicles by partial proteolysis with papain. Chromatography of the papain-treated vesicles on Sephadex LH-60 indicated that the [^{125}I]TID was bound to two peptides of low relative molecular mass. The [^{125}I]-TID-labelled peptides should constitute the hydrophobic membrane-binding domain. The transferase was also labelled by reductive methylation (Lys residues) or with immobilized galactose oxidase and NaB^{3}H$_4$ (Gal residues), incorporated into lecithin vesicles and treated with papain. Both procedures yielded a single [^{3}H]-labelled hydrophobic peptide that remained associated with the vesicles. After chromatography on Sephadex LH-60, the peptide labelled by the latter two procedures corresponds to the larger of the two [^{125}I]TID-labelled peptides. These results suggest that papain may cleave the hydrophobic domain into two peptides. The observed labelling is also consistent with the alternative possibility that the N-terminal hydrophobic domain is preceded by an initial sequence that contains both lysine and carbohydrate residues. The smaller of the two [^{125}I]TID-labelled peptides could be generated by removal of the hydrophilic segment from the transferase molecules that are reconstituted with the N-terminus exposed on the external surface of the vesicles.

1983 Brush border membranes. Pitman Books Ltd, London (Ciba Foundation symposium 95) p 73-91

γ-Glutamyltransferase (EC 2.3.2.2) is an amphipathic (or amphiphilic) membrane glycoprotein which, in rat kidney, is primarily associated with the brush border membrane of the proximal tubule cells (Glossman & Neville 1972). Purification of this enzyme, after its solubilization by proteolysis with papain or by treatment with Triton X-100, yields hydrophilic and amphipathic forms of the transferase, respectively (Hughey & Curthoys 1976). The two forms differ in their physical properties. The papain-purified enzyme is soluble in aqueous buffers and has a relative molecular mass (M_r) of 68 000. In contrast, the Triton-purified transferase binds to detergent micelles, undergoes aggregation in the absence of detergent, and can be reconstituted into lecithin vesicles (Hughey et al 1979). The M_r of the Triton-purified enzyme, after correction for the mass of bound detergent, was estimated to be 87 000 (Hughey & Curthoys 1976).

γ-Glutamyltransferase is composed of two non-identical subunits (Tate & Meister 1975). Analysis on polyacrylamide gel with sodium dodecyl sulphate (SDS) indicates that the small subunit of the transferase is not altered by proteolytic solubilization. The small subunits isolated from the two forms of γ-glutamyltransferase contain identical N-terminal threonine residues (Tsuji et al 1980). In contrast, Ferguson-plot analysis of their electrophoretic mobilities indicates that the large subunit of the Triton-purified enzyme has an M_r that is 20 000 greater than the large subunit of the papain-purified enzyme (Horiuchi et al 1978). In addition, the two forms of the large subunit contain different N-terminal amino acid residues (Tsuji et al 1980). These results suggest that the N-terminal segment of the large subunit contains a proteolytically sensitive hydrophobic domain that serves to anchor the transferase within the renal brush border membrane. Experiments with various affinity labels have established that the γ-glutamyl-binding domain of the transferase is localized to the small subunit (Tate & Meister 1977, Gardell & Tate 1980). An analysis of its proteolytic sensitivity and its interaction with specific Fab antibodies has established that the catalytic domain of γ-glutamyltransferase is asymmetrically oriented on the external surface of the renal brush border membrane (Tsao & Curthoys 1980).

Specific labelling was used to examine further the amphipathic structure of γ-glutamyltransferase. The membrane-permeable, photoactivatable probe, 3-trifluoromethyl-3-(m-[^{125}I]-iodophenyl)diazirine ([^{125}I]TID) (Brunner & Semenza 1981) was used to label specifically the hydrophobic domain that is integral to the membrane bilayer. Labelling of galactose residues by immobilized galactose oxidase and labelling of lysine residues by reductive methylation were used to label the hydrophilic residues that are peripheral to the membrane bilayer. These procedures also labelled a portion of the amino acid sequence that is contained within the membrane binding domain of γ-glutamyltransferase. These results suggest a model for the membrane association of rat renal γ-glutamyltransferase.

Methods

Triton X-100-purified γ-glutamyltransferase (Hughey & Curthoys 1976) was reconstituted into unilamellar lecithin (phosphatidylcholine) vesicles (Hughey et al 1979) and photolabelled with [^{125}I]TID according to the method of Spiess et al (1982). The [^{125}I]TID-labelled lipid was extracted by five repeated precipitations of the active enzyme with volumes of acetone at −20 °C. The [^{125}I]TID-labelled transferase was reconstituted into unlabelled vesicles and treated for 18 h at 37 °C with a 40:1 ratio of papain (to transferase) which had been activated by preincubation with 10 mM-dithiothreitol and 2.5 mM-EDTA for 15 min at 37 °C. The vesicles were then chromatographed on a Sepharose 4B column (10 × 500 mm), equilibrated in 10 mM-Tris-Cl, 100 mM-NaCl, 0.1 mM-EDTA and 0.02% sodium azide, at pH 7.2. γ-Glutamyltransferase was labelled by reductive methylation (Rice & Means 1971) and by immobilized galactose oxidase and NaB^{3}H$_4$ labelling (Morell et al 1966) without loss of enzymic activity. Enzyme labelled by these techniques was reconstituted and treated as described above. Sepharose 4B fractions containing the papain-treated vesicles were dialysed against distilled water, and were lyophilized and dissolved in a mixture of ethanol and 90% formic acid (in a 7:3 ratio). The samples were then applied to a Sephadex LH-60 column (20 × 500 mm) that had been equilibrated in the same ethanol:formic acid mixture (Gerber et al 1979).

The Triton X-100-purified transferase and the papain-generated enzyme were subjected to electrophoresis on a 10% polyacrylamide slab gel containing 0.1% SDS (Laemmli 1970). Peptides were subjected to electrophoresis on a 20% polyacrylamide slab gel containing 6 M-urea and 0.1% SDS (Ito et al 1980). [^{125}I]TID-labelled proteins and peptides were visualized by auto-radiography using Kodak X-0Mat AR-5 film and a DuPont intensifying screen.

Results

The amphipathic form of γ-glutamyltransferase was reconstituted into uni-lamellar lecithin vesicles and labelled using the membrane-soluble reagent [^{125}I]TID, which can be photoactivated. Greater than 99% of the reactive carbene generated by photolysis was incorporated into phospholipids and was extracted by repeated precipitation of the transferase with acetone. The [^{125}I]TID that was covalently bound to the transferase was found to be quantitatively associated with the large subunit of the enzyme (Fig. 1). The fully active [^{125}I]TID-labelled transferase was then reconstituted into unlabel-led vesicles. As shown in Fig. 2 (panel A), all the enzyme activity and the [^{125}I]-radioactivity elute from a Sepharose 4B column in fractions correspond-ing to the position where unilamellar vesicles elute. Unbound aggregates of the transferase would elute at approximately fraction 45 (Hughey et al 1979).

Reconstitution of the labelled transferase into lecithin vesicles should provide a convenient means of protecting the hydrophobic domain from

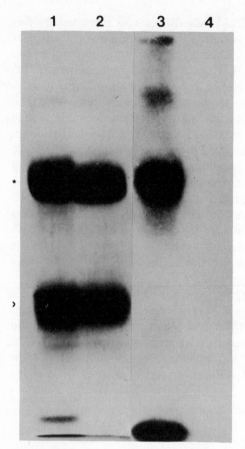

FIG. 1. Sodium dodecyl sulphate (SDS) polyacrylamide gel electrophoresis (PAGE) of [125I]TID-labelled γ-glutamyltransferase. Labelled transferase, and enzyme released by papain treatment of vesicles containing [125I]TID-labelled transferase, were subjected to electrophoresis on a 10% polyacrylamide slab gel and stained for protein (lanes 1 and 2, respectively). Lanes 3 and 4 are the corresponding autoradiograph. The label at the dye front of lane 3 represents residual labelled lipid not dissociated from the large subunit during acetone precipitation. The * and > indicate the large and small subunits of γ-glutamyltransferase, respectively.

proteolytic degradation. As shown in panel B of Fig. 2, papain treatment of the reconstituted [125I]TID-labelled transferase releases 90% of the enzyme activity. The released transferase elutes with a volume characteristic of the papain-purified form of γ-glutamyltransferase (Hughey et al 1979). Only 10% of the enzyme activity, but all the 125I-radioactivity, remains associated with the vesicles. The observation that none of the [125I]TID-labelled material is found associated with the papain-released enzyme, or in the retention volume

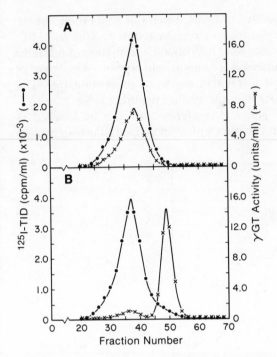

FIG. 2. Sepharose 4B chromatography of [^{125}I]TID-labelled γ-glutamyltransferase (γGT) reconstituted in lecithin vesicles and preincubated in the absence (panel A) or presence (panel B) of papain.

of the Sepharose 4B column, suggests that the peripheral domains of γ-glutamyltransferase are not labelled by the membrane-permeant probe. As shown in Fig. 1, both the large and small subunits of the enzyme released by papain treatment of vesicles that contain [^{125}I]TID-labelled transferase are devoid of ^{125}I-radioactivity. Thus, the labelled hydrophobic segment must remain associated with the papain-treated vesicles.

In order to isolate the hydrophobic domain of the transferase, the fractions from the Sepharose 4B column which contained the papain-treated vesicles were dialysed, lyophilized and then dissolved in ethanol:formic acid and chromatographed on Sephadex LH-60 (Fig. 3). The [^{125}I]TID-labelled transferase that is not released by papain treatment is excluded from this resin and elutes in the void volume of the column (40 ml). The Sephadex LH-60 chromatography does, however, resolve two [^{125}I]TID-labelled peptides that elute with volumes of 75 ml and 102 ml. The two peptides also migrate as discrete species when subjected to electrophoresis on a 20% polyacrylamide gel in the presence of 0.1% SDS and 6 M-urea. The Sephadex LH-60 column was calibrated with low-M_r standard proteins. From this calibration, the M_r values of the two hydrophobic peptides were estimated to be 8700 and 3400, respectively. The resolved peptides were hydrolysed in a mixture of 6 M-HCl and 50% propionic acid and analysed for amino acid content. The larger of the two peptides was observed to contain a greater proportion (68%) of hydrophobic amino acid residues than the smaller peptide (58%).

The amphipathic form of γ-glutamyltransferase can also be labelled in terminal galactose residues by incubation with immobilized galactose oxidase

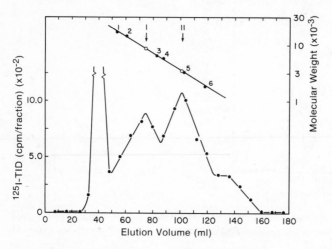

FIG. 3. Sephadex LH-60 chromatography of the vesicle-associated [^{125}I]TID-labelled peptides. Fractions from the Sepharose 4B column containing the papain-treated vesicles (Fig. 2) were pooled and chromatographed on Sephadex LH-60. The relative molecular masses of peptides I (larger) and II (smaller) were estimated relative to the elution of the following standard proteins: (1) myoglobin (17 100); (2) lysozyme (14 300); (3) aprotinin (6500); (4) insulin (5730); (5) glucagon (3490); (6) gramicidin D (1850).

followed by reduction with NaB^{3}H$_4$. The distribution of labelled galactose within the transferase was analysed by Sepharose 4B chromatography of labelled enzyme that had been reconstituted in lecithin vesicles and treated with papain (Fig. 4A). Papain treatment results again in the release of about 90% of the transferase activity. The released transferase contains only about 40% of the [^{3}H]-labelled galactose residues. Approximately 40% of the radioactivity is contained in a [^{3}H]galactose-labelled peptide that is recovered in the retention volume of the Sepharose 4B column, whereas 20% of the ^{3}H-label remains associated with the vesicle fractions. Trifluoroacetic acid (TCA) hydrolysis of the [^{3}H]galactose-labelled transferase, and of each of the fractions recovered from the Sepharose 4B column, followed by paper chromatographic analysis, established that in each case the label was incorporated into galactose residues.

The vesicle-associated [³H]galactose-labelled material was dissolved in ethanol:formic acid and subjected to Sephadex LH-60 chromatography (Fig. 5A). As observed in Fig. 3, the residual [³H]-labelled transferase elutes in the void volume. In addition, an [³H]galactose-labelled peptide elutes at 75 ml, corresponding to the larger of the two peptides labelled with [¹²⁵I]TID. The peak observed at 145 ml corresponds to free [³H]galactose that is released from oligosaccharide by the acidic conditions.

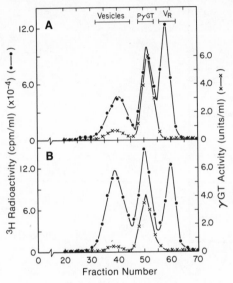

FIG. 4. Sepharose 4B chromatography of papain-treated vesicles containing γ-glutamyltransferase (γGT) prelabelled with galactose oxidase (panel A) or by reductive methylation (panel B). V_R, retention volume; PγGT, papain-solubilized γ-glutamyltransferase.

Fully active, [³H]-labelled transferase was also prepared by reductive methylation and then incorporated into lecithin vesicles. As shown in Fig. 4B, incubation with papain again causes release of 90% of the transferase activity. However, the vesicle fractions retain 35% of the [³H]-labelled material, and a [³H]-labelled peptide is also observed to elute in the retention volume of the column. The [³H]-labelled material that remains associated with vesicles was dissolved in ethanol:formic acid and chromatographed on Sephadex LH-60 (Fig. 5B). The residual transferase molecules that were not released by papain treatment were again recovered in the void volume. The vesicle-associated [³H]-labelled peptide generated by papain proteolysis eluted with a volume again characteristic of the larger of the two peptides labelled by [^{125}I]TID.

The vesicle-associated [^{3}H]-labelled peptide purified by Sephadex LH-60 chromatography, and the unfractionated peptide which elutes in the retention volume of the Sepharose 4B column, were characterized further. The relative hydrophobic–hydrophilic character of the two fractions was analysed by determination of their ability to partition between an aqueous phase and a

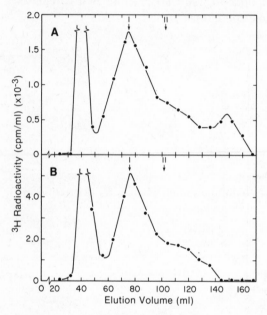

FIG. 5. Sephadex LH-60 chromatography of vesicle-associated peptides derived from γ-glutamyltransferase prelabelled with galactose oxidase (panel A) or by reductive methylation (panel B). The [^{3}H]-labelled material associated with the papain-treated vesicles (Fig. 4) was dissolved in ethanol:formic acid and chromatographed on a Sephadex LH-60 column.

series of aliphatic alcohols ranging from 1-butanol to 1-decanol. In each case, the peptide purified by Sephadex LH-60 chromatography quantitatively partitioned into the organic phase whereas the peptide in the retention volume quantitatively partitioned into the aqueous phase. In addition, only the LH-60 peptide could be reconstituted into lecithin vesicles. The association of the reconstituted [^{3}H]-labelled peptide with the vesicles was unaffected by treatment with 1 M-NaCl, indicating that this association is non-ionic. It is evident from these experiments that the peptide in the retention volume is hydrophilic whereas the LH-60 peptide is hydrophobic, and retains the ability to interact with a lipid bilayer.

Discussion

Previous experiments have established that [125I]TID specifically labels the hydrophobic domain of various proteins associated with the erythrocyte membrane (Brunner & Semenza 1981) and the hydrophobic domain of the intestinal sucrase–isomaltase complex (Spiess et al 1982). In these experiments, the addition of glutathione, which should scavenge any activated reagent released into the aqueous phase, had no effect on the extent of protein labelling. Therefore, the [125I]TID must partition completely into the lipid bilayer where the photogenerated carbene reacts rapidly and selectively with the intrinsic portion of the membrane proteins.

The photoactivated [125I]TID binds specifically to the large subunit of the reconstituted γ-glutamyltransferase, and the [125I]TID-labelled peptides produced by papain treatment are quantitatively retained within the vesicles. No label is contained in the released transferase or in the papain-generated hydrophilic peptides. These observations clearly establish that association of vesicles is achieved by integration of a limited segment of the large subunit of γ-glutamyltransferase into the hydrophobic interior of the lipid bilayer. The reconstituted transferase and the enzyme associated with isolated vesicles from the brush border of rat kidney exhibit a similar asymmetry of orientation (Tsao & Curthoys 1980), a similar sensitivity to papain and a similar temperature-dependent discontinuity in their energy of activation (Hughey et al 1979). Therefore, the mechanism of association characterized by using lecithin vesicles is likely to approximate closely the way in which γ-glutamyltransferase is associated with native membranes.

Protein proteolysis of the reconstituted [125I]TID-labelled transferase yields two distinct peptides that are labelled to a similar extent. If the two peptides represent separate regions of the membrane-binding domain, then a portion of the hydrophobic domain must be sufficiently exposed on the external surface of the vesicles to allow cleavage of at least one peptide bond by papain. Alternatively, reconstitution may occur, with the N-terminal sequence of the large subunit randomly positioned on either the internal or the external surface of the vesicle. In such a case, only the larger of the two [125I]TID-labelled peptides should contain the N-terminal sequence of the large subunit of γ-glutamyltransferase.

The larger of the two [125I]TID-labelled peptides can also be labelled by reductive methylation or with galactose oxidase and NaB^{3}H$_4$ treatment. Therefore, this larger peptide may contain an integral hydrophobic sequence and a second more hydrophilic sequence that is peripheral to the lipid bilayer. The peripheral sequence would contain the positively charged lysine residue(s) and the hydrophilic oligosaccharide chain which has a terminal galactose residue. The more hydrophilic segment of the larger peptide could either be derived from a portion of the connecting region which separates the membrane-binding domain from the hydrophilic domain of the large subunit or it could contain the N-terminal sequence.

The latter possibility is consistent with the analysis of the membrane-binding domain of the intestinal sucrase–isomaltase complex (Spiess et al 1982). This domain is localized to the N-terminus of the isomaltase subunit. Sequence analysis has established that the initial portion of this domain contains several positively charged residues and a threonine-linked oligosaccharide. This segment is followed by a sequence of at least 20 hydrophobic amino acids. It is thought that the initial hydrophilic segment containing the N-terminus is exposed on the external surface of the brush border membrane.

A more comprehensive analysis of the organization of the labelled peptides that are derived from the hydrophobic domain of the γ-glutamyltransferase will require sequence analysis of the isolated peptides and of the large subunit of the purified amphipathic form of the enzyme.

Acknowledgements

The [^{125}I]TID was synthesized and kindly provided by Dr Josef Brunner of The Eidgenossischen Technischen Hochschule, Zurich, Switzerland. This research was supported in part by grant AM 26012 from the National Institutes of Health.

REFERENCES

Brunner J, Semenza G 1981 Selective labeling of the hydrophobic core of membranes with 3-trifluoromethyl-3-(m-[^{125}I]iodophenyl)diazirine, a carbene-generating reagent. Biochemistry 20:7174-7182

Gardell SJ, Tate SS 1980 Affinity labeling of γ-glutamyltranspeptidase by glutamine antagonists. FEBS (Fed Eur Biochem Soc) Lett 122:171-174

Gerber GE, Anderegg RJ, Herlihy WC, Gray CP, Biemann K, Khorana HG 1979 Partial primary sequence of bacteriorhodopsin: sequencing methods for membrane proteins. Proc Natl Acad Sci USA 76:227-231

Glossman H, Neville DM Jr 1972 γ-Glutamyltranspeptidase in kidney brush border membranes. FEBS (Fed Eur Biochem Soc) Lett 19:340-344

Horiuchi S, Inoue M, Morino Y 1978 γ-Glutamyltranspeptidase: sidedness of its active site on renal brush border membrane. Eur J Biochem 87:429-437

Hughey RP, Coyle PJ, Curthoys NP 1979 Comparison of the association and orientation of γ-glutamyltranspeptidase in lecithin vesicles and in native membranes. J Biol Chem 254:1124-1128

Hughey RP, Curthoys NP 1976 Comparison of the size and physical properties of γ-glutamyltranspeptidase purified from rat kidney following solubilization with papain or Triton X-100. J Biol Chem 251:7863-7870

Ito K, Date T, Wickner W 1980 Synthesis, assembly into the cytoplasmic membrane, and proteolytic processing of the precursor of coliphage M13 coat protein. J Biol Chem 255:2123-2130

Laemmli UK 1970 Cleavage of structural proteins during the assembly of the head of bacteriophage T4, Nature (Lond) 227:680-685

Morell AG, van den Hamer CJA, Scheinberg IH, Ashwell G 1966 Physical and chemical studies on ceruloplasmin. Preparation of radioactive, sialic acid-free ceruloplasmin labeled with tritium on terminal D-galactose residues. J Biol Chem 241:3745-3749

Rice RH, Means GE 1971 Radioactive labeling of proteins in vitro. J Biol Chem 246:831-832

Spiess M, Brunner J, Semenza G 1982 Hydrophobic labeling, isolation and partial characterization of the NH_2-terminal membranous segment of sucrase–isomaltase complex. J Biol Chem 256:2370-2377

Tate SS, Meister A 1975 Identity of maleate-stimulated glutaminase with γ-glutamyltranspeptidase in rat kidney. J Biol Chem 250:4619-4627

Tate SS, Meister A 1977 Affinity labeling of γ-glutamyltranspeptidase and location of the γ-glutamyl binding site on the light subunit. Proc Natl Acad Sci USA 74:931-935

Tsao B, Curthoys NP 1980 The absolute asymmetry of orientation of γ-glutamyltranspeptidase and aminopeptidase on the external surface of the rat renal brush border membrane. J Biol Chem 255:7708-7711

Tsuji A, Matsuda Y, Katunuma N 1980 Studies on the structure of γ-glutamyltranspeptidase. Location of the segment anchoring γ-glutamyltranspeptidase to the membrane. J Biochem (Tokyo) 87:1567-1571

DISCUSSION

Norén: Was the galactose oxidase labelling done on γ-glutamyltransferase reconstituted into liposomes? That would reveal whether the sugar residue is outside or inside.

Curthoys: No. The Triton-purified enzyme was acetone-precipitated to remove most of the Triton, resuspended in a borate buffer, labelled and then reconstituted into liposomes.

Norén: Have you done TID-labelling (i.e. with [^{125}I]-3-trifluoromethyl-3-(*m*-iodophenyl diazirine) on microvillar vesicles and then studied the labelling pattern in the isolated enzyme? This could supplement the labelling studies done on the reconstituted system.

Curthoys: No, but that would be useful.

Louvard: A belief that carbohydrate can be accessible on the cytoplasmic side is interesting because it is against the current concept of asymmetric distribution of carbohydrate on the cell surface; it is important for biosynthesis.

Curthoys: For that reason, it would be important to compare the enzyme labelling achieved in isolated brush border membrane vesicles and in reconstituted liposomes. I would hesitate to draw a conclusion about the native orientation of the hydrophobic domain from experiments done on enzyme reconstituted in lecithin vesicles. The orientation of the membrane binding domain may be slightly different when reconstituted in an artificial lipid bilayer than when achieved as a result of the directed process of biosynthesis.

Semenza: It seems to me that γ-glutamyltransferase and sucrase–isomaltase are orientated in the membrane in similar positions. The point you raised is similar to that made by Professor Desnuelle earlier (p 31–32)—namely, that one must be cautious about drawing conclusions from the reconstituted system and applying them to the natural one. That is why we always use the two membranes in parallel for sucrase–isomaltase (i.e. 'native' brush border membrane vesicles and proteoliposomes); and although we have not found any difference, the same may not be true for other enzyme systems. Do you know anything about the amino acid sequence of this enzyme?

Curthoys: No; our information is limited to composition analysis, which shows that the various peptides contain about 55–70% hydrophobic residues. We have not yet attempted sequence analysis, but this is the only way to determine how the isolated peptides are arranged within the primary sequence of the protein.

Jørgensen: You said that peptide II (the smaller of the two [^{125}I]-TID-labelled peptides) had an M_r of about 2500, and you mentioned papain cleavage. Did you try using other proteolytic enzymes to see if this is an intra-membrane peptide to the extent that one cannot remove more of it from the surface?

Curthoys: We tested a variety of different proteases in our initial experiments, in an attempt to find a more specific protease that would release the catalytic domain from either brush border membrane vesicles or enzyme reconstituted into lecithin vesicles. We found that only papain and bromelain would release the catalytic domain. We have not, however, treated the isolated peptides that were reconstituted into lecithin vesicles with proteases other than papain.

Louvard: Maestracci (1976) reported that the proteolytic enzyme elastase is as efficient as papain at releasing intestinal hydrolases from the membrane.

Alpers: It has the same specificity.

Desnuelle: How did you correct the relative molecular mass for detergent binding; did you use radioactive detergent?

Curthoys: Yes; we used [^{3}H]-labelled Triton to determine the amount of detergent bound per mg of protein. Using this data and by measuring the Stokes radius, the sedimentation coefficient, and the partial specific volume of the Triton–protein complex, one can estimate the M_r of the amphipathic form of the transferase. The calculated amount of Triton bound per mole of enzyme corresponded closely to the M_r of a Triton micelle. In the Triton–protein complex, 53% of the mass was protein and 47% was detergent.

Alpers: In the electrophoresis of the larger peptide you had a band that travelled with the front and which might have been labelled phospholipid. Does that mean that you don't remove all the labelled phospholipid and, if so, do you have to test each preparation to see how much of the TID label is in the peptide?

Curthoys: Yes. Even after five acetone precipitations, some labelled lipid remains associated with the γ-glutamyltransferase.

Alpers: Are the natural vesicles impermeable enough for you to do differential labelling experiments?

Semenza: Yes, but it depends which reagent you want to use.

Curthoys: By using a large molecule such as galactose oxidase there should be no problem about permeability.

Louvard: Yes, although the natural vesicles *are* permeable to some smaller molecules.

Quaroni: Another problem may be that you have a mixture of closed and open vesicles. Even only 10% open vesicles would make a difference because of their more efficient labelling.

Alpers: The liposomes are a little cleaner.

Louvard: For that, you have an internal control, and the cytoskeletal protein shouldn't be labelled.

Quaroni: But cytoskeletal protein would not necessarily be in those vesicles; it depends on how they are prepared.

Inoue: γ-Glutamyltransferase is a heterodimeric glycoprotein enzyme and is highly enriched in brush border membranes of the kidney and other transmural tissues. We have studied its localization in basolateral and brush border membranes of rat kidney proximal tubules. More than 80% of renal arterial glutathione is extracted by a single pass through the kidney. Since only about 30% of plasma components with a small M_r can be filtered by a single pass, a peritubular extraction mechanism has been postulated (Häberle et al 1979). Peritubular extraction of plasma glutathione can be inhibited by AT-125, an affinity label of γ-glutamyltransferase (Anderson et al 1980). Thus, the peritubular handling of plasma glutathione seems to involve γ-glutamyltransferase.

We have studied subcellular localization of the transferase in the kidney by using histochemical and immunocytochemical methods. Light microscopic observation revealed that γ-glutamyltransferase activity is highest in the S1 segment of the proximal tubules. Using specific antibody against γ-glutamyltransferase and horseradish peroxidase-conjugated protein A, we studied the subcellular localization of the transferase by electron microscopy (Spater et al 1982). Dense deposits of 3,3'-diaminobenzidine (DAB) reaction product (oxidized DAB) can be seen in the brush border region of proximal convoluted tubules. The reaction product was also seen in the peritubular plasma membrane surface. No reaction product was observed in the thick ascending loop of Henle. Renal tissue treated with unimmunized serum showed no reaction product in the nephron structure. The enzyme activity has also been demonstrated in isolated renal microvessels and glomeruli (Das et al 1982).

Dr Maroux (p 34–49) showed the localization of aminopeptidase N in the brush border membranes and contraluminal membranes of the small intestine. Aminopeptidase N is also enriched in renal proximal tubules. In conjunction with γ-glutamyltransferase and dipeptidase, aminopeptidase is known to hydrolyse glutathione and its derivatives (Tsao & Curthoys 1980, Okajima et al 1981). Thus, these enzymes in the basolateral plasma membranes might function in glutathione extraction from the plasma. Quantitative aspects of the contraluminal metabolism of glutathione require further study. Apart from the mechanism of peritubular handling of plasma glutathione, basolateral membrane localization of γ-glutamyltransferase and other peptidases is also important for understanding the transfer mechanism of newly synthesized enzymes into brush border membranes.

Smith: Is the filtration of glutathione at the glomerulus sufficient to account for the total measured clearance of glutathione?

Inoue: About 20–30% of glutathione in the renal artery can be filtered by a single pass through the kidney. The filtered glutathione is rapidly hydrolysed by γ-glutamyltransferase and the peptidases. Renal extraction of plasma glutathione remains unchanged even after bilateral ureteral ligation. Plasma clearance of [^{14}C]inulin was inhibited by about 90% in ureter-ligated animals. This indicates a high capacity for the peritubular extraction mechanism. Since the turnover of γ-glutamyltransferase is very high, only a small amount of the enzyme in the renal peritubular membranes would be sufficient to metabolize renal arterial glutathione in the control as well as in the ureter-ligated animals. However, peritubular extraction of plasma glutathione may also involve uptake of intact glutathione by renal tubular cells. This possibility should be studied further.

Alpers: Some of the glutathione is secreted in the bile, and provides a considerable proportion of the liver's output.

Curthoys: In a normal animal the amount of glutathione secreted into the bile is low compared with the amount secreted into the plasma. However, in response to oxidative stress, large amounts of oxidized glutathione are produced and secreted preferentially into the bile. In such a case, the amount of oxidized glutathione translocated across the bile canalicular membrane becomes substantial.

Kenny: Dr Inoue, did you find the reaction product for γ-glutamyltransferase in only one region of the proximal tubule?

Inoue: We found the reaction product in the S1, S2 and S3 segments of the proximal tubules. It is difficult to quantitate the amount of the enzyme localized in different subcellular compartments by this immunohistochemical method.

Curthoys: Heinle & Wendel (1977) did experiments on individually dissected segments of proximal tubule. They found that the transferase activity is 3-fold greater in the S3 region than in the S1 region.

Hauri: Is there any indication that the enzyme in the basolateral membrane is different from that in the microvillus membrane? Do both enzymes split the same substrates?

Inoue: Since specific antibody was prepared using the papain-solubilized brush border membrane enzyme, the hydrophilic domains of the transferase in both plasma membrane surfaces possess common antigenicity. Kinetic analysis of the enzyme in the two membranes revealed no significant difference. The two enzymes in the brush border membranes and basolateral membranes may thus be identical.

Kenny: Are any brush border enzymes *not* also found in the basolateral membrane?

Semenza: It is actually very difficult to obtain a clean preparation of basolateral membrane which one can be sure is totally free of brush border membranes.

Alpers: I am unaware of any evidence that sucrase–isomaltase and lactase–phlorizin hydrolase are found in the basolateral membrane.

Quaroni: We cannot answer Dr Kenny's question at present. There is no doubt about the low amount of γ-glutamyltransferase in the basolateral membrane compared with that in the brush border membrane. The problem is that this low amount is within the margin of error of the techniques used.

Alpers: Would immunocytochemical techniques answer this more precisely?

Quaroni: Not really. Monoclonal antibodies against alkaline phosphatase do reveal some staining in the basolateral membrane which is much fainter than that in the brush border membrane. However, this too could be background staining or artifact, although I am fairly confident that it is not.

Alpers: Shields et al (1982) also have evidence for alkaline phosphatase in the basolateral membrane in suckling rats.

Quaroni: Antibodies against aminopeptidase, however, do not reveal any staining in the basolateral membrane but this may be because of the position of the antigen. Immunocytochemical techniques are known to have limitations.

Maroux: We cannot reveal aminopeptidase by immunofluorescence labelling, but histochemical labelling localizes the enzyme to a short region on the top of the lateral membrane (Feracci et al 1982). By contrast, in the preparation of basolateral membranes we can precipitate with specific antibody about 60% of the aminopeptidase activity and, simultaneously, 40% of the Na^+,K^+-ATPase activity of the preparation is precipitated. So the enzyme is localized over a large portion of the lateral membrane preparation, but we cannot say whether this is due to the redistribution of the enzyme that we found localized on top of the lateral membrane *in situ*.

Semenza: People studying transport have been unsuccessful over many years in demonstrating unequivocally any Na^+,K^+-ATPase in brush border membrane by various methods. However, some reports describe Na^+,K^+-ATPase at the bottom of the microvilli, as demonstrated e.g. by ouabain binding.

Jørgensen: This is probably a question of resolution of techniques. For example, immunocytochemical techniques will show some cross-reactivity of antibodies to Na^+,K^+-ATPase with the brush border membrane (Kyte 1976), perhaps because Na^+,K^+-ATPase has antigenic determinants in common with alkaline phosphatase. In contrast, the cytochemical stain for the ouabain-sensitive potassium phosphatase activity of Na^+,K^+-ATPase is absent from the luminal membrane of proximal tubules (Ernst 1975).

Quaroni: There may be different alkaline phosphatases. M. Neutra (unpublished) has shown, histochemically, that two forms are present in the fetal intestine of the rat.

Smith: How tight is a tight junction in relation to separating proteins completely? We always think in terms of insertion when we find a protein in one membrane or another but what about the possibility of a tiny amount of redistribution? In the intestine when cells migrate over a three-dimensional structure that is changing its shape, some tight junctions must be made and some broken, and redistribution could then occur in both directions. We need to know how efficient the membrane is at keeping different proteins apart.

Inoue: Is there evidence that any so-called 'basolateral membrane marker enzymes' are localized also in the luminal plasma membranes?

Quaroni: The techniques are not sufficiently well refined to answer this definitively. One can relatively easily exclude contamination of the basolateral membrane fraction with brush border membrane components, but intracellular vesicular membranes are more difficult to exclude because one has no available markers for many of them. Also, the Golgi complex is heterogeneous, and may distribute among different subcellular fractions. But within the limits of the techniques, we do have evidence (Hauri et al 1979) for incorporation of sucrase–isomaltase into the basolateral membrane before incorporation into the luminal membrane. The Dutch group (Blok et al 1981) has shown, by electron microscopic autoradiographic techniques, that with colchicine there is an increased incorporation of fucose-labelled glycoproteins in the basolateral membrane, which reproduces the results that we obtained with biochemical techniques (Quaroni et al 1979).

Louvard: We are dealing with how the biogenesis of polarity and the traffic in two directions is maintained. The first traffic of molecules is the one from the rough endoplasmic reticulum to the cell surface. But when membrane proteins reach the plasma membrane they do not stay there because extensive endocytosis takes place. In a canine kidney cell line (MDCK line), which is polarized in culture, we have studied aminopeptidase specifically (Louvard 1980). Rodriguez-Boulan & Sabatini (1978) showed that such a cell line can be infected with enveloped virus. Viruses of the vesicular stomatitis (VSV) type are expressed specifically on the basolateral membrane. In contrast, viruses of the influenza type are expressed specifically on the apical membrane. This observation provides a tool for the study of polarity. It suggests that the viral antigen in some way possesses either structural features that operate as 'sorting signals' or information equivalent to that of the cellular proteins so that the viral antigen can be sorted out by the same cell machinery. White et al (1981) showed that virus can be fused at low pH with the plasma membrane, and K. Matlin et al (unpublished observations) recently showed once that if VSV virions are fused with the apical membrane, the viral surface antigens are rapidly and uniformly redistributed over the apical membrane. The antigens are then taken into the cell rapidly by endocytosis and sorted out by the cell. Once internalized, these viral antigens reach the basolateral membranes rapidly and are cleared from the apical membranes. This shows that the mistake of antigen being placed in the wrong membrane can be corrected. This experiment indicates that the sorting processes may continue all the time: so it does not matter if a junction is leaky, or if lateral diffusion is taking place temporarily. Once the cell is able to repolarize, then such correction is possible by means of membrane internalization and selective membrane traffic.

Quaroni: Incorporation of virus into the basolateral membrane in the way you describe can simply represent a correction of an initial mistake in biosynthesis, which may have no major function in generating and maintaining cell polarization.

Louvard: It doesn't even have to be a mistake, but may be part of a physiological process. Transcytosis of immunoglobulin G (IgG) in the neonatal rat is one example.

Rodewald: There is good evidence that receptors can cross from one surface to the other, and the receptor for IgG is not the only one. This therefore presents a pathway by which other membrane proteins may cross accidentally or physiologically from one surface to the other.

Bretscher: How long does it take to clear the antigen totally from the apical membrane, Dr Louvard?

Louvard: It takes 15 min for clearing from the apical membrane, as observed by immunofluorescence or by radioimmunoassay. Within 30 min the antigen is transferred to the basolateral membrane.

Curthoys: Does the cell re-establish polarity by re-forming tight junctions or by establishing a transcellular ion gradient?

Louvard: That is a difficult question, which we have tried to address. On this MDCK cell line in suspension we found that surface antigens such as aminopeptidase and Na^+,K^+-ATPase are uniformly distributed on the plasma membrane. If one lets the cells become attached to a substratum, they rapidly spread and attach tightly to the support which seems to coincide with an accumulation of α-actinin, a cytoskeletal protein, at the cell border (D. Louvard et al, unpublished results). We cannot establish which process comes first. We know that some types of junction are needed to re-establish the surface polarity, but I don't know if this accumulation of α-actinin is a consequence of the polarization.

Booth: In the human placenta a brush border is separated from a basal membrane, with no junctions at all and no lateral membranes either. Yet this system can maintain polarity; alkaline phosphatase is present in the brush border and Na^+,K^+-ATPase is present in the basal membrane. So one must think in terms of a membrane shuttle system rather than any involvement of junctions.

Smith: In an early eight-cell embryo with no tight junctions, microvilli are formed at the opposite pole from the point of contact with other blastomeres. If that cell is taken away, and the point of contact with the other cells is changed around, brush borders are formed opposite the point of contact with the other cell. In these conditions no junctions are necessary (Ziomek & Johnson 1980).

Bretscher: If the MDCK cells are plated out, so that they do not touch each other, and presented with the virus, do they internalize it or not?

Louvard: E. Rodriguez-Boulan is studying viral antigens and has observed that when a single cell is spread onto a glass surface, polarized expression of those viral antigens occurs. We then have to define the junctional complex in a slightly different way. Such a single attached cell is polarized: it has an apical membrane, which faces the medium and contains aminopeptidase (D. Louvard, unpublished data), and influenza viruses can be expressed specifically there. The basal membrane is in contact with the glass, but there are no lateral membranes. Conversely, Na^+,K^+-ATPase is found in the basal membrane also where the VSV are budding. So when we say 'tight junctions' it is too frequently a rather loose description; we should discriminate between the tight junction itself (*zonula occludens*), which is involved in the control of epithelial permeability, and the *zonula adherens*, located just underneath the *zonula occludens*, which may be the important structure for maintaining polarity.

Hauri: Techniques are not yet available to establish unequivocally the presence of brush border enzymes in the basolateral membrane. However, subcellular fractionation studies indicate a transient association of the sucrase–isomaltase precursor with the basolateral membrane fraction during biosynthesis (see Hauri, this volume). The absence of cleaved subunits in this fraction argues against contamination by brush border membranes. Furthermore, kinetic studies suggest that the presence of the sucrase–isomaltase precursor in the basolateral membrane fraction cannot be fully explained by a possible cross-contamination with membranes derived from the Golgi complex.

REFERENCES

Anderson ME, Bridges RJ, Meister A 1980 Direct evidence for inter-organ transport of glutathione and that the non-filtration renal mechanism for glutathione utilization involves γ-glutamyl transpeptidase. Biochem Biophys Res Commun 96: 848-853

Blok J, Ginsel LA, Mulder-Stapel AA, Onderwater JJM, Daems WT 1981 The effects of colchicine on the intracellular transport of ^{3}H-fucose-labelled glycoproteins in the absorptive cells of cultured human small-intestinal tissue. Cell Tissue Res 215: 1-12

Das PD, Misra RP, Welbourne TC 1982 Renal γ-glutamyl transpeptidase: in situ antiluminal localization. J Histochem Cytochem 30: 148-152

Ernst SA 1975 Transport ATPase cytochemistry: ultrastructural localization of potassium-dependent and potassium-independent phosphatase activities in rat kidney cortex. J Cell Biol 66: 586-608

Feracci H, Bernadac A, Gorvel JP, Maroux S 1982 Localization by immunofluorescence and histochemical labeling of aminopeptidase N in relation to its biosynthesis in rabbit and pig enterocytes. Gastroenterology 82: 317-324

Häberle D, Wahlländer A, Sies H 1979 Assessment of the kidney function in maintenance of plasma glutathione concentration and redox state in anaesthetized rats. FEBS (Fed Eur Biochem Soc) Lett 108: 335-340

Hauri HP, Quaroni A, Isselbacher KJ 1979 Biogenesis of intestinal plasma membrane: posttranslational route and cleavage of sucrase-isomaltase. Proc Natl Acad Sci USA 76: 5183-5186

Heinle H, Wendel A 1977 The activities of the key enzymes of the γ-glutamyl cycle in microdissected segments of the rat nephron. FEBS (Fed Eur Biochem Soc) Lett 73:220-224

Kyte J 1976 Immunoferritin determination of the distribution of $(Na^+ + K^+)$ATPase over the plasma membranes of renal convoluted tubules. II: Proximal segment. J Cell Biol 68: 304-318

Louvard D 1980 Apical membrane aminopeptidase appears at site of cell-cell contact in cultured kidney epithelial cells. Proc Natl Acad Sci USA 77: 4132-4136

Maestracci D 1976 Enzymic solubilization of the human intestinal brush-border membrane enzymes. Biochim Biophys Acta 433: 469-481

Okajima K, Inoue M, Morino Y 1981 Topology and some properties of the renal brush border membrane-bound peptidase(s) participating in the metabolism of S-carbamidomethyl glutathione. Biochim Biophys Acta 675: 379-385

Quaroni A, Kirsch K, Weiser MM 1979 Synthesis of membrane glycoproteins in rat small intestinal villus cells. Biochem J 182: 213-221

Rodriguez-Boulan E, Sabatini DD 1978 Asymmetric budding of viruses in epithelial monolayers: a model system for study of epithelial polarity. Proc Natl Acad Sci USA 75: 5071-5075

Shields HM, Bair FA, Bates ML, Yedlin ST, Alpers DH 1982 Localization of immunoreactive alkaline phosphatase in the rat small intestine at the light microscopic level by immunocytochemistry. Gastroenterology 82: 39-45

Spater HW, Poruchynsky MS, Quintana N, Inoue M, Novikoff A 1982 Immunocytochemical localization of γ-glutamyltransferase in rat kidney with protein A–horseradish peroxidase. Proc Natl Acad Sci USA 79: 3547-3550

Tsao B, Curthoys NP 1980 The absolute asymmetry of orientation of γ-glutamyl transpeptidase and aminopeptidase on the external surface of the rat renal brush border membrane. J Biol Chem 255: 7708-7711

White J, Matlin K, Helenius A 1981 Cell fusion by Semliki Forest, influenza, and vesicular stomatitis viruses. J Cell Biol 89: 674-679

Ziomek CA, Johnson MH 1980 Cell surface interaction induces polarization of mouse 8-cell blastomeres at compaction. Cell 21: 935-942

Biosynthesis and assembly of the largest and major intrinsic polypeptide of the small intestinal brush borders

GIORGIO SEMENZA, JOSEF BRUNNER and HANS WACKER

Laboratorium für Biochemie der ETH, ETH-Zentrum, CH-8092 Zürich, Switzerland

Abstract The sucrase–isomaltase complex (SI) of the small intestinal brush border membrane accounts for approximately 9–10% of the intrinsic protein. The isomaltase subunit alone interacts with the membrane directly, via a highly hydrophobic segment at its N-terminal region. This segment has a helical conformation for more than 85% and crosses the membrane twice, the N-terminus being located at the outer, *luminal* side of the membrane. The sucrase subunit is attached to the membrane solely via its interactions with the isomaltase subunit. The sucrase–isomaltase complex is synthesized as a single, very long ($M_r \sim 260\,000$) polypeptide chain (pro-SI, carrying the two sites of sucrase and isomaltase in an already enzymically active form), with the isomaltase portion corresponding to the N-terminal part of pro-SI. Pro-SI is processed into 'final' SI by pancreatic proteases. Recently the cell-free translation of pro-SI has been achieved *in vitro*. From a detailed knowledge of the anchoring of SI (and pro-SI) in the membrane it has been possible to suggest one particular mechanism as the most likely for the synthesis, insertion and assembly of pro-SI.

1983 Brush border membranes. Pitman Books Ltd, London (Ciba Foundation symposium 95) p 92-112

Negatively stained small intestinal brush border (Johnson 1967, Nishi et al 1968) and brush border membrane vesicles are studded with a great number of particles which have been identified as digestive enzymes. These particles protrude from the luminal side of the membrane. Carefully controlled papain treatment removes them from the brush border membrane without affecting the apparent 'unit membrane' structure and width (at thin sectioning; see Nishi & Takesue 1978) and without affecting either the active or the passive permeabilities (Tannenbaum et al 1977) of the membrane.

By definition, these enzymes are 'integral' proteins, as they are not detached from the membrane by aqueous solutions of low or high ionic strength, whereas detergents and proteolytic treatment *can* detach them. However, of the protein mass, only a small portion interacts with the membrane fabric; most of the enzymes, including their active sites, protrude towards the intestinal lumen. For such integral membrane proteins, the name 'stalked intrinsic protein' has been suggested (Brunner et al 1978, 1979).

As the detailed positioning of small intestinal and kidney brush border hydrolytic enzymes (plus γ-glutamyltransferase) becomes better known it seems that most if not all of the enzymes are anchored to the membrane fabric via a hydrophobic segment located at the N-terminal region of one or more polypeptide chains. However, the mere existence of a hydrophobic segment at the N-terminal region of the polypeptide chain should not be taken *per se* as the demonstration of its being involved in the anchoring to the membrane, and even less of its being the sole anchor of the protein (see also Kenny & Maroux 1982). Fig. 1 illustrates this point. It is imperative that other criteria than simply

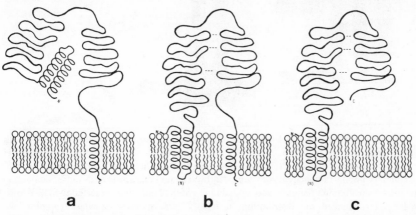

FIG. 1. Possible positioning of a stalked intrinsic membrane protein having a hydrophobic segment at the N-terminal region (marked N). (a) The protein is anchored via another hydrophobic segment at the C-terminal region (marked C), and the hydrophobic segment at the N-terminal region is not involved in any interaction with the hydrophobic core of the membrane fabric. (b) The protein is anchored via two hydrophobic anchors, one at the N-terminal, the other at the C-terminal region. (c) The protein is anchored solely via a hydrophobic segment located at the N-terminal region.

a hydrophobic sequence at the N-terminal region be provided. At least three approaches have been used, as follows.

(1) Proteolytic solubilization does not modify the C-terminal region(s): thus the C-termini are not located at the cytosolic side. This criterion was fulfilled for the small intestinal sucrase–isomaltase (Brunner et al 1979) and for dipeptidylpeptidase IV of the kidney cortex (Macnair & Kenny 1979).

(2) Recently a highly hydrophobic photolabel has been developed (the carbene generator 3-trifluoromethyl-3-(m[^{125}I]iodophenyl)-diazirine, TID, (Brunner

& Semenza 1981) which partitions almost totally in the hydrophobic phase of
the membrane and thus allows one to probe the hydrophobic core selectively.
In the small intestinal brush border membrane TID labels only the isomaltase
subunit of the sucrase–isomaltase complex (Fig. 2) and, within the isomaltase,

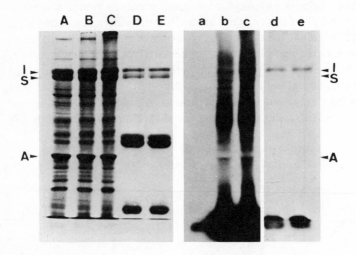

FIG. 2. Distribution of radiolabel among proteins of brush border membranes labelled with
[^{125}I]TID. Brush border membrane vesicles (2 mg of protein/ml; 50 mM-sodium phosphate, pH
7.5) equilibrated with 10 μCi of [^{125}I]TID (10 Ci/mmol) were irradiated for various lengths of time.
Non-covalently bound radioactivity was removed by repeated extraction with buffer containing
1% bovine serum albumin. Samples were boiled in 2% SDS (2 min) and subjected to SDS-PAGE
(8.4 × 2.7). To visualize the distribution of label in the sucrase–isomaltase complex, we
solubilized labelled brush border membranes in 2% Triton X-100 and the enzyme complex was
precipitated with anti-sucrase–isomaltase antibodies. Washed immunoprecipitates were denatured in SDS and run on the same gel. The gel was stained with Coomassie brilliant blue R-250
(lanes A to E) and the dried slab gel was autoradiographed (lanes a to e). Lanes A to C, brush
border membranes exposed to irradiation for 0 s (A), 15 s (B), and 120 s (C). Lane D, immunoprecipitate of sucrase–isomaltase from brush border membranes labelled in the absence of glutathione. Lane E, immunoprecipitate of sucrase–isomaltase from brush border membranes labelled
led in the presence of glutathione (20 mM). Lanes a to e represent the corresponding autoradio-
graphs. The positions of the subunits of sucrase–isomaltase (I, isomaltase; S, sucrase) and A, actin,
are indicated by arrows. The Coomassie blue-stained bands in the lower half of D and E originated
from the antibodies. (From Spiess et al 1982.)

only the segment that remains behind in the membrane during proteolytic
solubilization. The part of the protein that is solubilized by controlled papain
digestion (a treatment which does not affect the C-terminal regions of either
subunit) is not labelled by TID (Fig. 3). Thus, isomaltase interacts with the

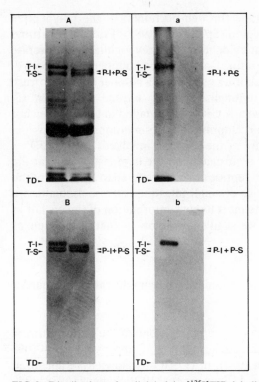

FIG.3. Distribution of radiolabel in [^{125}I]TID-labelled sucrase–isomaltase. TID-labelled and albumin-washed brush border membrane vesicles were either solubilized by Triton X-100 or treated with papain. After centrifugation (30 min, 100 000 × *g*), sucrase–isomaltase complex was precipitated with anti-sucrase–isomaltase antiserum and the immunoprecipitates were washed with buffer (0.15 M-NaCl, 10 mM-sodium phosphate, pH 7.5) containing 1% Triton X-100. The precipitates were subjected to SDS-PAGE (8.4 × 2.7). (A, left) immunoprecipitate from Triton X-100-solubilized sucrase–isomaltase (Coomassie blue-stained). (A, right) immunoprecipitate from papain-solubilized sucrase–isomaltase (Coomassie blue-stained). (a) autoradiography of the dried gel A. (B, left) sucrase–isomaltase isolated from [^{125}I]TID-labelled proteoliposomes by gel filtration on Sephadex G-100. (B, right) sucrase–isomaltase solubilized from radiolabelled proteoliposomes by papain and separated from peptidoliposomes and papain by gel filtration on Bio-Gel A-5m. (b) autoradiography of the dried gel B. Each gel contained identical amounts (sucrase activity) of detergent- and papain-solubilized sucrase–isomaltase. Positions of the subunits of detergent-solubilized (T-I and T-S) and papain-solubilized (P-S and P-I) sucrase–isomaltase complex are marked by *arrows*. TD, tracking dye front. The heavily stained (Coomassie blue) bands in A are due to immunoglobulins. P-S and P-I, the sucrase and isomaltase subunit (respectively) of papain-solubilized sucrase–isomaltase complex; T-S, Triton–sucrase, and T-I, Triton–isomaltase subunits, as obtained from Triton-solubilized sucrase–isomaltase complex. (From Spiess et al 1982.)

hydrophobic layer of the membrane through portion(s) of the polypeptide chain other than the C-terminal region (Spiess et al 1982). Frielle & Curthoys (this volume) are providing similar evidence for kidney γ-glutamyltransferase (EC 2.3.2.2). Using a nitrene generator, 1-azido-4-[^{125}I]iodobenzene, Booth et al (1979) were able to label the anchoring portions of a number of kidney brush border enzymes. Interestingly enough, another nitrene generator (5-[^{125}I]iodonaphthyl 1-azide; Bercovici & Gitler 1978) failed to label the anchor of sucrase–isomaltase (J. Brunner, unpublished observations), perhaps because of the extremely inert nature of the segment involved; see Fig. 5.)

(3) A third type of evidence may be provided by the demonstration that the transmembrane portion of the polypeptide chain is confined to a portion of the N-terminal region only. In the case of small intestinal sucrase–isomaltase a strong indication is provided by the most likely conformation of the anchor at the N-terminal region, which, as we shall show below, is that of two helixes connected by a β-turn.

Detailed positioning of the sucrase–isomaltase complex in the brush border membrane

The small intestinal sucrase–isomaltase complex is one of the major intrinsic proteins of the brush border membrane, accounting for approximately 8–10% of its protein content (Kessler et al 1978). In 1979 it was shown to be anchored in the membrane as depicted in Fig. 4 (Brunner et al 1979, Semenza 1978, 1979

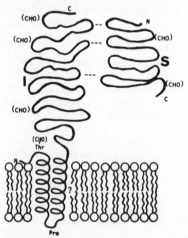

FIG. 4. Positioning of sucrase–isomaltase in the small intestinal brush border membrane as suggested by Brunner et al (1978) (see also Semenza 1978, 1979a,b). Note: the drawing is not to scale and is intended to convey the major features only. (CHO), carbohydrate chains. (From Semenza 1981a.)

a,b; see reviews by Semenza 1981 a,b, and by Brunner et al 1982). That is: the sucrase subunit does not interact detectably with the membrane fabric; only the isomaltase subunit is anchored to it; this 'anchor' is a part of the N-terminal region of the isomaltase polypeptide chain; and the four N- and C-termini of the two subunits are all exposed at the extracellular, luminal side of the membrane. Recent work has confirmed the correctness of the positioning depicted in Fig. 4 and has added further details. In discussing it, let us bear in mind the N-terminal sequence of the isomaltase subunit (Fig. 5) (Frank et al 1978, Sjöström et al 1982) which acts as the anchor. (For reasons still not identified, the amino acid residues 2 to 4 were found to differ from those published in 1978.)

(1) *Residue-11 is glycosylated* (Frank et al 1978, Sjöström et al 1982). The following neutral sugars at least are associated with this amino acid residue, in approximately molar ratios 1:1:1—galactose, glucose and fucose (H. Wacker et al, unpublished). Since glycosylation of membrane proteins is confined to the luminal compartment of the endoplasmic reticulum and of the Golgi membranes (see Hanover & Lennarz 1981, Sabatini & Kreibich 1976, Sabatini et al 1982), these data strongly indicate that residue 11 is located on the extracellular, luminal side of the membrane. Since the 1–11 sequence, even if stretched, is barely long enough to cross the membrane (and many of its residues are charged) it seemed unlikely that Ala-1 is located at a side of the membrane opposite to residue 11.

(2) *The N-terminus of isomaltase is located at the luminal side.* Direct evidence for this has been provided recently by the use of a new, little permeant acetimidate, 3-[dimethyl-2-(acetimidoxyethyl)ammonio]-propane-sulphonic acid (DAP) Table 1; Bürgi et al 1983). The degree of modification of the isomaltase N-terminus (Ala) by this reagent is the same, irrespective of whether the reaction is done on right-side-out brush border membrane vesicles (Klip et al 1979a) or on membrane fragments (obtained by deoxycholate extraction; Klip et al 1979b) because Ala-1 is as readily accessible to DAP that acts only from the luminal side as to DAP that acts from both sides. Ala-1 must, therefore, be located at the luminal side. Similar results were obtained with Ile-1 (the N-terminus of the sucrase subunit), which we know from other evidence to be located at the luminal side (Brunner et al 1979). If the isomaltase polypeptide chain has *both* termini at the luminal side, it must either not cross the membrane fabric or cross it an *even* number of times. In order to resolve this point, the following data on the isomaltase 'anchor' had to be collected.

(3) *The 'anchor' is some 60 amino acid residues long.* Having established by hydrophobic TID-labelling that all the anchoring portion remained associated with the membrane fabric during papain solubilization (Fig. 3, discussed above), we could isolate it by TID-photolabelling of sucrase–isomaltase, papain digestion and gel filtration on Sephadex LH-60 in ethanol–formic acid.

PARTIAL N-TERMINAL SEQUENCES OF ProSI AND OF ISOMALTASE AND SUCRASE POLYPEPTIDES

```
                                                                    ?
HOG ProSI   Ala-Arg-Lys-Ser-Phe-Ser-Gly-Leu-Gly-Ile-X-Leu-Val-Leu-Phe-Ala-Ile-Val-
                        Thr                         CHO
                                                    CHO
HOG I       Ala-Arg-Lys-Lys-Phe-Ser-Gly-Leu-Glu-Ile-X-Leu-Ile-Val-Leu-Phe-Ala-Ile-Val-Val-X-Ala-Leu-Val-Val-X-Ala-Ser-Lys-X-Pro-Ala-Val
                                                                                   ?           ?
                            ?   ?                   CHO
RAT ProSI^a Ala-Lys-Lys-Lys-Phe-Arg-Ala-Leu-Glu-Ile-X-Leu-Ile-Val-Leu-Phe-Ile-Ile-
                                                    CHO
RAT I^a     Ala-Lys-Lys-Lys-Phe-Ser-Ala-Leu-Glu-Ile-X-Leu-Ile-Val-Leu-Phe-Ile-Ile-Val-Ala-Ile-Ala-Ile-Ala-Leu-Val-Val-Leu-
                                                                                  ?
                                                        CHO
RABBIT I^b  Ala-Lys-Arg-Lys-Phe-Ser-Gly-Leu-Glu-Ile-Thr-Leu-Ile-Val-Leu-Phe-Val-Ile-Val-Leu-Phe-Ile-Ile-Val-Ile-Ala-Ile-Ile-Ala-Val-Leu-Ala-X-X-X-Pro-Ala-Val
                                                                                                          25      30       35
                                                       Val Lys-Tyr-His-Lys-Val-Leu-Glu-
HOG S       Ile-Lys-Leu-Pro-Ser-Asp-Pro-Ile-Pro-Thr-Leu-Arg-Met-Glu-    Thr-Asp-Tyr-Met-Leu-Glu-
                                                       Met
                               ?              ?        ?
RAT S^a     Ile-Lys-Leu-Pro-Ser-Asn-Pro-Ile-Arg-Thr-Leu-Arg-Thr-Leu-Arg-Val-Glu-Val-Thr-Tyr-X-Thr-Asn-Arg-Val-Leu-Gln-

RABBIT S    Ile-Asn-Leu-Pro-Ser-Glu-Pro-Glu-
                               Thr     Thr

                     1       5          10         15         20
```

```
HUMAN GLYCOPHORIN^a  -His-His-Phe-Ser-Glu-Pro-Glu-Ile-Thr-Leu-Ile-Ile-Phe-Gly-Val-Met-Ala-Gly-Val-Ile-
                      66          70          75          80          85
HOG GLYCOPHORIN^d    -Gln-Asp-Phe-Ser-His-Ala-Glu-Ile-Thr-Gly-Ile-Ile-Phe-Ala-Val-Met-Ala-Gly-Leu-Leu-
                      56          80          85          90          95
HORSE GLYCOPHORIN^e  -His-Asp-Phe-Ser-Gln-Pro-Ser-Val-Ile-Thr-Val-Ile-Ile-Leu-Gly-Val-Met-Ala-Gly-Ile-Ile
                      44          50          55          60
```

FIG. 5. Partial N-terminal sequences of pro-sucrase–isomaltase (pro-SI) and of isomaltase (I) and sucrase (S) polypeptides. (From Sjöström et al 1982.) Key: [a]Hauri et al (1982); [b]Frank et al (1978) and Sjöström et al (1982); [c]Furthmayr et al (1978); [d]Honma et al (1980); [e]Murayama et al (1982).

TABLE 1 Labelling of the N-termini of the sucrase–isomaltase complex, measured by using a little-permeant imidate

Conditions	Labelling (%) of the N-terminal of isomaltase (Ala) and of sucrase (Ile) with DAP[a]	
	Ala (%)	Ile (%)
Triton-solubilized SI (*in solution*)[b]	40	50
SI still bound to intact, *closed brush border vesicles*[b]	33 ± 4	58 ± 8
SI still bound to DOC[c]-*extracted membranes*[b]	35 ± 6	46 ± 8
SI incorporated in *proteoliposomes*[d]	73	69

[a]DAP, 3-[dimethyl-2-(acetimidoxyethyl)ammonio]-propane-sulphonic acid.
[b]10 min, pH 8.5. [c]DOC, deoxycholate. [d]20 min, pH 8.5

The peptide that we obtained, which was homogeneous in gel filtration, in SDS–PAGE and by determination of the N-terminus (Ala, by dansylation), had an apparent M_r of about 6500 (Spiess et al 1982). Thus, we know only about half its sequence (see Fig. 5).

(4) *Most of the 'anchor' has a helical configuration.* Circular dichroism spectra of the anchor in various detergents, 2-chloroethanol or in liposomes clearly showed it to have a very high helix[*] content of 75–85% or 100%, depending on the conditions (Fig. 6, Spiess et al 1982). The occurrence of a proline residue approximately in the middle of the anchor (position 35, Fig. 5) and the fact that the (unidentified) residues 32–34 are hydrophilic indicate that the anchor has a first stretch in helix configuration (from residue 12 to approximately 31), and then a β-turn near Pro-35, and then a helical domain again. Note that the 20 or so hydrophobic residues which follow Thr-11 can form a helix (α or 3_{10}) that is sufficiently long to span a hydrophobic layer 3.5 nm thick; so, too, are the 20–25 amino acid residues that follow Pro-35 and which must also be in a predominantly helical configuration. It is thus likely that the isomaltase anchor crosses the membrane twice, the Pro-35 and the neighbouring residues being located at the cytosolic side of the membrane. Indeed it is difficult, if not impossible, to accommodate otherwise within a membrane two helixes of this length connected by a β-turn.

---

[*]Our results (Spiess et al 1982) do not allow us to discriminate between an α-helical and a 3_{10}-helical configuration. For the purpose of the present discussion, however, this ambiguity is irrelevant.

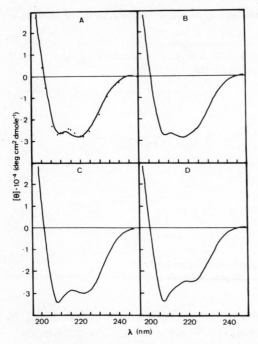

FIG. 6. Circular dichroism (CD) of the hydrophobic anchor peptide. (A) peptide incorporated in bilayers of egg phosphatidylcholine liposomes. For comparison, the CD spectrum calculated for 80% α-helix and 20% random coil structure, based on data of Greenfield & Fasman (1969) is shown (filled circles). (B) peptide solubilized in 0.5% (w/v) sodium cholate. (C) peptide in 2-chloroethanol–water, 9:1 (v/v). The peptide was transferred from ethanol–formic acid into chloroethanol–water by gel filtration on Sephadex LH-20 equilibrated and eluted with 2-chloroethanol. (D) peptide in 2% SDS. (From Spiesss et al 1982.)

Biosynthesis and membrane insertion of the sucrase–isomaltase complex

To explain the position of the two subunits (Fig. 4), their homologies and their common or related biosynthetic control mechanism, it was suggested in 1978 (Semenza 1979 a,b) that sucrase–isomaltase is synthesized and inserted in the membrane as a single very long (M_r at least 260 000!) polypeptide chain ('pro-sucrase–isomaltase') which is processed into the 'final' two-subunit complex by (extracellular) proteolysis. Since then, direct evidence has been obtained for an immunologically cross-reacting precursor (Hauri et al 1979) and, indeed, for a fully active pro-sucrase–isomaltase in brush borders not previously exposed to pancreatic protease(s) (Sjöström et al 1980, Hauri et al 1980, Danielsen et al 1981a, Montgomery et al 1981, Hauri et al 1982, Sjöström et al 1982). Subsequently, other brush border enzymes with two

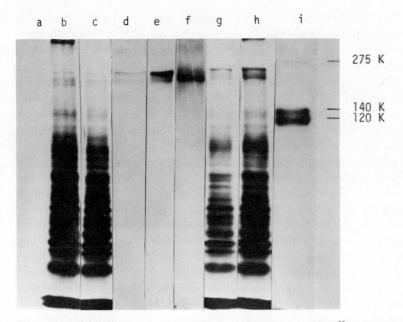

FIG. 7. *In vitro* synthesis of pro-SI (or a precursor of it). Fluorograph of ^{35}S-labelled polypeptides synthesized in a reticulocyte lysate pretreated with nuclease in the presence or absence of dog pancreatic microsomes, in response to total RNA extracted from rabbit intestinal mucosa. After translation, the synthesized polypeptides were precipitated with anti-SI-antiserum. The SDS-polyacrylamide gels (6%) were exposed for fluorography for 4 days (a–d,g,h) or 2 days (e,f): (a) control (no RNA, no microsomes); (b) translation mixture without microsomes; (c) as in (b) centrifugation after incubation (100 000 × g supernatant); (d) immunoprecipitate from (c); (e) mixture of the following three immunoprecipitates: (d) + immunoprecipitate from the 100 000 × g pellet (see c) + immunoprecipitate from (g) (see below); (f) translation mixture with microsomes, spun at 100 000 × g after the incubation (immunoprecipitate of the pellet); (g) translation mixture with microsomes, spun at 100 000 × g after the incubation (supernatant, no immunoprecipitation); (h) translation mixture with microsomes; (i) ^{125}I-SI (120 000, sucrase subunit; 140 000, isomaltase subunit). (From Wacker et al 1981.)

subunits have been shown to be synthesized similarly, as a single-chain pro-form: renal γ-glutamyltransferase, Nash & Tate 1982 (contrary to the glycosidases, only one of the two subunits in γ-glutamyltransferase carries an enzymically active site); intestinal glycoamylase, Danielsen et al 1981b; and the β-glycosidase complex, which is processed by intracellular rather than pancreatic proteases, Danielsen et al 1981b—see Sjöström et al, this volume. On the other hand, all brush border peptidases investigated so far seem to be synthesized and inserted as monomers (Danielsen et al 1981b; Sjöström et al, this volume).

Returning now to sucrase–isomaltase, *in vitro* cell-free translation of pro-sucrase–isomaltase has recently been achieved (Fig. 7) (Wacker et al 1981, Danielsen et al 1982). (Pro-sucrase–isomaltase is the largest identified membrane polypeptide chain successfully translated thus far in a cell-free system from total RNA.) In addition to providing a final piece of evidence that sucrase–isomaltase is synthesized as a one-chain precursor, the cell-free *in vitro* translation should facilitate the solution of problems related to the detailed mechanism of biosynthesis and membrane insertion. Before this could happen, however, the following questions on the positioning and structure of pro-sucrase–isomaltase would have to be answered.

(1) Does pro-sucrase–isomaltase begin with the isomaltase or with the sucrase portion? Fig. 5 shows the N-terminal sequences of rat (Hauri et al 1982) and hog (Sjöström et al 1982) pro-sucrase–isomaltases. Clearly, they are *identical* (not merely homologous!) to those of the corresponding isomaltase subunits. This identity strongly indicates that the isomaltase portion corresponds to the N-terminal part of pro-sucrase–isomaltase (Fig. 8).

(2) How many hydrophobic segments (and thus potential anchors) does pro-sucrase–isomaltase carry? In the original suggestion (Fig. 8, Semenza 1979 a,b) no statement was made about the possible existence of a hydrophobic segment at the C-terminal region and/or in the 'loop'.

At present we can rule out this latter possibility that a hydrophobic domain occurs between the sucrase and isomaltase portions of pro-SI, in the hypothetical loop indicated by 'L' in Fig. 8. In fact, the pro-SI occurring in the brush border membrane, but not yet processed by pancreatic proteases, can be prepared in either of two forms: an amphipathic (Triton-solubilized) pro-sucrase–isomaltase, and a non-amphipathic, totally water-soluble pro-sucrase–isomaltase (derived from the Triton-solubilized form, with the loss of the hydrophobic domain). The former (amphipathic) form shows charge-shift in electrophoresis in detergents; the latter (non-amphipathic) form does not. Both forms, however, are composed of a single polypeptide chain, that of the non-amphipathic pro-sucrase–isomaltase being only *slightly* smaller than that of the amphipathic enzyme. Thus, the loss of the hydrophobic domain, which conferred amphipathic properties to the original Triton-solubilized pro-sucrase–isomaltase, does not entail a drastic decrease in the length of the polypeptide chain: the original hydrophobic domain was not located, therefore, in the (hypothetical) loop occurring between the isomaltase and the sucrase portions ('L' in Fig. 8) (H. Sjöström et al, unpublished data).

We still have no final information about whether the other (hypothetical) hydrophobic segment in pro-sucrase–isomaltase carries, in addition to the hydrophobic anchor at the N-terminal region of the isomaltase portion, one more segment which is also hydrophobic (for example at the C-terminal region of the sucrase portion; see Fig. 8). We are at present using the hydrophobic photolabel TID, mentioned above, to compare the extent of

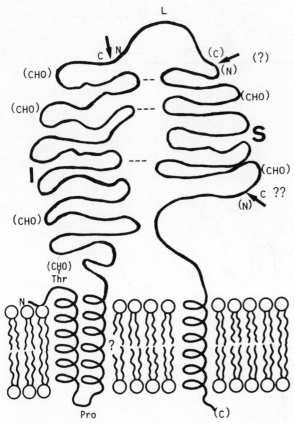

FIG. 8. Positioning of pro-sucrase–isomaltase in the brush border membrane as originally suggested by Semenza (1979a,b). Note: the drawing is not to scale and is intended to convey the major features only. I, isomaltase portion; S, sucrase portion (it is now established that the I portion does indeed correspond to the N-terminal half of pro-SI, as indicated—see Hauri et al 1982, Sjöström et al 1982); L, loop accessible to proteolytic attack (we now know definitely that this loop does not include a hydrophobic segment—H. Sjöström et al, unpublished); CHO, carbohydrate chains; N and C, N- and C-terminals, respectively, of pro-SI and/or final SI. Arrows show site of proteolytic attack.

label incorporated into pro-sucrase–isomaltase with that incorporated into sucrase–isomaltase under comparable conditions (H. Wacker et al, unpublished).

It is now possible to tackle some detailed questions. For example: is pro-sucrase–isomaltase synthesized with a pre-piece? Is the (still hypothetical)

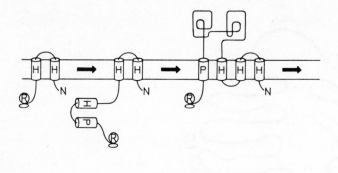

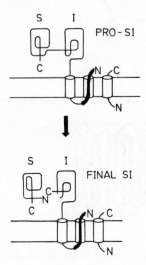

FIG. 9. Suggested sequence of events in the biosynthesis and insertion of pro-SI. The segments of known sequence (Fig. 5) are drawn in bold. R, ribosome; H, hydrophobic; P, polar; N, N-terminus; C, C-terminus. (From Sjöström et al 1982.)

pre-pro-sucrase–isomaltase synthesized as indicated in Fig. 9 (and as suggested by the 'loop' or 'hairpin' hypotheses—Austen 1979, DiRienzo et al 1978, Inouye & Halegoua 1980, von Heijne & Blomberg 1979, von Heijne 1980, Engelman & Steitz 1981, Sabatini et al 1982)? Or is this enzyme synthesized as a secretory protein and subsequently reincorporated into the membrane, e.g. from the lumen of the Golgi membranes (see Wickner 1979, 1980, Kenny & Maroux 1982)? What is the meaning, if any, of the homology (Frank et al 1978, Semenza 1979b) between the isomaltases and the glycophorins at the transition between extracellular compartment and hydrophobic segment in an 'N-out to

C-in' direction? This homology seems to be highly conserved in both the isomaltases and the glycophorins (Fig. 5). How do the glycosylation (see Sjöström et al, this volume) and the transfer from the Golgi membrane into the brush border (see Hauri, this volume) take place? This and similar systems may well provide some answers to the fundamental questions of membrane biosynthesis and polarity.

Acknowledgements

This work was supported by the Swiss National Science Foundation, Berne, grant No. 3.633-0.80. We want to express our sincere thanks to all those with whom we had the pleasure of collaborating, within and without our Department.

REFERENCES

Austen BM 1979 Predicted secondary structures of amino-terminal extension sequences of secreted proteins. FEBS (Fed Eur Biochem Soc) Lett 103:308-318

Bercovici T, Gitler C 1978 5- [^{125}I]Iodonaphthyl azide, a reagent to determine the penetration of proteins into the lipid bilayer of biological membranes. Biochemistry 17:1484-1489

Booth AG, Hubbard LML, Kenny AJ 1979 Proteins of the kidney microvillar membrane. Biochem J 179:397-405

Brunner J, Semenza G 1981 Selective labeling of the hydrophobic core of membranes with 3-trifluoromethyl-3-(m[^{125}I]iodophenyl)diazirine, a carbene-generating reagent. Biochemistry 20:7174-7182

Brunner J, Hauser H, Semenza G 1978 Single bilayer lipid–protein vesicles formed from phosphatidylcholine and small intestinal sucrase–isomaltase. J Biol Chem 253:7538-7546

Brunner J, Hauser H, Braun H, Wilson KJ, Wacker H, Semenza G 1979 The mode of association of the enzyme complex sucrase–isomaltase with the intestinal brush border membrane. J Biol Chem 254:1821-1828

Brunner J, Wacker H, Semenza G 1982 Sucrase–isomaltase of the small-intestinal brush border membrane: assembly and biosynthesis. In: Fleischer S, Fleischer B (eds) Methods in enzymology. Academic Press, New York, in press

Bürgi R, Brunner J, Semenza G 1983 Use of an impermeant imidoester for determining the sidedness of the N-termini of the small-intestinal sucrase–isomaltase. J Biol Chem, in press

Danielsen EM, Sjöström H, Norén O 1981a Biosynthesis of intestinal microvillar proteins. Putative precursor forms of microvillus aminopeptidase and sucrase–isomaltase isolated from Ca^{2+}-precipitated enterocyte membranes. FEBS (Fed Eur Biochem Soc) Lett 127:129-132

Danielsen EM, Skovbjerg H, Norén O, Sjöström H 1981b Biosynthesis of intestinal microvillar proteins. Nature of precursor forms of microvillar enzymes from Ca^{2+}-precipitated enterocyte membranes. FEBS (Fed Eur Biochem Soc) Lett 132:197-200

Danielsen EM, Norén O, Sjöström H 1982 Biosynthesis of intestinal microvillar protein. Biochem J 204:323-327

DiRienzo JM, Nakamura K, Inouye M 1978 The outer membrane proteins of gram-negative bacteria: biosynthesis, assembly and functions. Annu Rev Biochem 47:481-532

Engelman DM, Steitz J 1981 The spontaneous insertion of proteins into and across membranes: the helical hairpin hypothesis. Cell 23:411-422

Frank G, Brunner J, Hauser H, Wacker G, Semenza G, Zuber H 1978 The hydrophobic anchor of small-intestinal sucrase–isomaltase. N-terminal sequence of the isomaltase subunit. FEBS (Fed Eur Biochem Soc) Lett 96:183-188

Furthmayr H, Galardy RE, Tomita M, Marchesi VT 1978 The intramembranous segment of human erythrocyte glycophorin A. Arch Biochem Biophys 185:21-29

Greenfield N, Fasman GD 1969 Computed circular dichroism spectra for the evaluation of protein conformation. Biochemistry 8:4108-4116

Hanover JA, Lennarz WJ 1981 Transmembrane assembly of membrane and secretory glycoproteins. Arch Biochem Biophys 211:1-19

Hauri HP, Quaroni A, Isselbacher K 1979 Biogenesis of intestinal plasma membrane: posttranslational route and cleavage of sucrase–isomaltase. Proc Natl Acad Sci USA 76:5183-5186

Hauri HP, Quaroni A, Isselbacher K 1980 Monoclonal antibodies to sucrase–isomaltase: probes for the study of post-natal development and biogenesis of the intestinal microvillus membrane. Proc Natl Acad Sci USA 77:6529-6633

Hauri HP, Wacker H, Rickli EE, Bigler-Meier B, Quaroni A, Semenza G 1982 Biosynthesis of sucrase–isomaltase. Purification and NH_2-terminal amino acid sequence of the rat sucrase–isomaltase precursor (pro-sucrase–isomaltase) from fetal intestinal transplants. J Biol Chem 257:4522-4528

Honma K, Tomita M, Hamada A 1980 Amino acid sequence and attachment sites of oligosaccharide units of porcine erythrocyte glycophorin. J Biochem (Tokyo) 88:1679-1691

Inouye M, Halegoua S 1980 Secretion and membrane localization of proteins in Escherischia coli. CRC Crit Rev Biochem 10:339-371

Johnson CF 1967 Disaccharidase: localization in hamster intestine brush borders. Science (Wash DC) 155:1670-1672

Kenny AJ, Maroux S 1982 Topology of microvillar membrane hydrolases of kidney and intestine. Physiol Rev 62:91-128

Kessler M, Acuto O, Storelli C, Murer H, Müller M, Semenza G 1978 A modified procedure for the rapid preparation of efficiently transporting vesicles from small intestinal brush border membranes. Biochim Biophys Acta 506:136-154

Klip A, Grinstein S, Semenza G 1979a Transmembrane disposition of the phlorizin binding protein of intestinal brush borders. FEBS (Fed Eur Biochem Soc) Lett 99:91-96

Klip A, Grinstein S, Semenza G 1979b Distribution of sulfhydryl groups in intestinal brush border membranes. Localization of side-chains essential for glucose transport and phlorizin binding. Biochim Biophys Acta 558:233-245

Macnair RDC, Kenny AJ 1979 Proteins of the kidney microvillar membrane. The amphipathic form of dipeptidyl peptidase IV. Biochem J 179:379-395

Montgomery RK, Sybicki AA, Forcier AG, Grand RJ 1981 Rat intestinal microvillus membrane sucrase–isomaltase is a single high molecular weight protein and fully active enzyme in the absence of luminal factors. Biochim Biophys Acta 661:346-349

Murayama J-I, Tomita M, Hamada HA 1982 Primary structure of horse erythrocyte glycophorin HA. Its amino acid sequence has an unique homology with those of human and porcine erythrocyte glycophorins. J Membr Biol 64:205-215

Nash B, Tate SS 1982 Biosynthesis of rat renal γ-glutamyl transpeptidase. J Biol Chem 257:585-588

Nishi Y, Takesue Y 1978 Localization of intestinal sucrase–isomaltase complex on the microvillous membrane by electron microscopy using non-labeled antibodies. J Cell Biol 79:516-525

Nishi Y, Yoshida TO, Takesue Y 1968 Electron microscope studies on the structure of rabbit intestinal sucrase. J Mol Biol 37:441-444

Sabatini DD, Kreibich G 1976 Functional specialization of membrane-bound ribosomes in eukaryotic cells. In: Martonosi A (ed) The enzymes of biological membranes. John Wiley, New York, p 531-579

Sabatini DD, Kreibich G, Takashi M, Adesnik M 1982 Mechanisms for the incorporation of proteins in membranes and organelles. J Cell Biol 92:1-22

Semenza G 1978 The sucrase–isomaltase complex, a large dimeric amphipathic protein from the small intestinal brush border membrane: emerging structure–function relationships. In: Ahlberg P & Sundelf L-O (ed) Structure and dynamics of chemistry. (Symposia Universitatis Upsaliensis Annum Quingentesimum Celebrantis 12) Almqvist and Wiksell International, Stockholm, p 226-240

Semenza G 1979a The mode of anchoring of sucrase–isomaltase to the small intestinal brush-border membrane and its biosynthetic implications. In: Rapaport S, Schewe T (eds) Proceedings of the 12th FEBS Meeting, Dresden, 1978. Pergamon Press, Oxford, vol 53:21-28

Semenza G 1979b Mode of insertion of the sucrase–isomaltase complex in the intestinal brush border membrane: implications for the biosynthesis of this stalked intrinsic membrane protein. In: Development of mammalian absorptive processes. Elsevier/North-Holland, Amsterdam (Ciba Found Symp 70) p 133-146

Semenza G 1981a Molecular pathophysiology of small-intestinal sucrase–isomaltase. In: Peters T (ed) Clinics in gastroenterology. W.B. Saunders, Philadelphia, vol 10, p 691-706

Semenza G 1981b Intestinal oligo- and disaccharidases. In: Randle JP et al (eds) Carbohydrate metabolism and its disorders. Academic Press, London, vol 3:245-479

Sjöström H, Norén O, Christiansen L, Wacker H, Semenza G 1980 A fully active, two-active-site, single-chain sucrase–isomaltase from pig small intestine. J Biol Chem 255:11332-11338

Sjöström H, Norén O, Christiansen LA, Wacker H, Spiess M, Bigler-Meier B, Rickli EE, Semenza G 1982 N-Terminal sequences of pig intestinal sucrase-isomaltase and pro-sucrase-isomaltase. Implications for the biosynthesis and membrane insertion of pro-sucrase-isomaltase. FEBS (Fed Eur Biochem Soc) Lett 148:321-325

Spiess M, Brunner J, Semenza G 1982 Hydrophobic labelling, isolation and partial characterization of the NH_2-terminal membranous segment of sucrase–isomaltase complex. J Biol Chem 257:2370-2377

Tannenbaum C, Toggenburger G, Kessler M, Rothstein A, Semenza G 1977 High-affinity phlorizin binding to brush border membranes from small intestine: identity with (a part) of the glucose transport system, dependence on the Na^+- gradient, partial purification. J Supramol Struct 6:519- 533

von Heijne G 1980 Trans-membrane translocation of proteins. A detailed physicochemical analysis. Eur J Biochem 103:431-438

von Heijne G, Blomberg G 1979 Transmembrane translocation of proteins. Eur J Biochem 97:175-181

Wacker H, Jaussi R, Sonderegger P, Dokow M, Ghersa P, Hauri HP, Christen P, Semenza G 1981 Cell-free synthesis of the one-chain precursor of a major intrinsic protein complex of the small intestinal brush border membrane (pro-sucrase–isomaltase). FEBS (Fed Eur Biochem Soc) Lett 136:329-332

Wickner W 1979 The assembly of proteins into biological membranes: the membrane trigger hypothesis. Annu Rev Biochem 48:23-45

Wickner W 1980 Assembly of proteins into membranes. Science (Wash DC) 210:861-868

DISCUSSION

Quaroni: The N-terminal sequence of sucrase is very different from that of isomaltase. If it truly originated from gene duplication one would expect a greater similarity.

Semenza: We suggest a *partial* gene duplication, which would not encompass the anchor.

Quaroni: You should still find an identical sequence somewhere in isomaltase.

Semenza: Yes, but not necessarily in the anchoring portion. We surmise the presence of an original gene whose product split isomaltose and maltose. The enzyme except the anchor would have been partially gene duplicated, leading first to two identical sequences, each containing an active site for splitting both isomaltose and maltose. Subsequently, a point mutation at the 'distal' site could then have led to one site for maltase and isomaltase activity and another site for maltase and sucrase activity. In this scheme there is no need to assume that duplication of the anchor takes place. I cannot guess what might have been the advantage of synthesizing a single polypeptide of M_r 260 000 to be split afterwards, but we know nearly nothing about the mechanics of the first membrane insertion during biosynthesis.

Quaroni: If it turns out that most intestinal glycosidases are synthesized as single-chain precursors then it might be the same for lactase–phlorizin hydrolase, maltase–glucoamylase, etc. Gene duplication might be common in the intestine, and this could hardly be accidental.

Bretscher: Does the precursor with 260 000 M_r have the same enzymic activity as the final form?

Semenza: Yes. Sjöström et al (1980) have shown that it has the same immunological reactivity and the same enzymic reactivity as the 'final' sucrase–isomaltase.

Kenny: The use of the 'pro' nomenclature for pro-sucrase–isomaltase is not ideal because here it is used in a rather different sense from its use in the 'pro'-forms of secreted proteins.

Semenza: I realise that. We have never meant to imply that pro-sucrase–isomaltase is less active. However, other 'pro' forms of hydrolases are enzymically active, although less so than the 'final' forms, e.g. pro-carboxypeptidases.

Alpers: The use of the term 'pro'-sucrase–isomaltase implies that this substance has an extra piece that is added to the mature protein (of M_r 260 000) inserted in the membrane, but that is not so, and it gives a different meaning to the way you are using the word 'pro'.

Semenza: In fact there may be a trimming (e.g. by carboxypeptidases). The pro-sucrase–isomaltase with M_r of 260 000–270 000 can be split by minute amounts of pancreatic elastase into two bands which travel slightly less fast than the two bands of SI (Sjöström et al 1980). However, the presence of sugar residues makes it difficult to assess precisely (by SDS-PAGE) whether and by how much 'trimming' takes place.

Alpers: The splitting of pro-sucrase–isomaltase into sucrase and isomaltase may be the first step of degradation rather than the last step in synthesis. In that case the term 'pro' would certainly take on a different meaning.

Mooseker: In your results on cell-free synthesis, where you had the 260 000 M_r protein, there was a double band. Can you explain that?

Semenza: The faster of the two bands may arise from some biologically irrelevant proteolytic activity, or else it could reflect a processing that is biologically significant. At the moment we do not know.

Sjöström: I was surprised at the sizes of the primary translation products in relation to the glycosylated pro-sucrase–isomaltase. How much of the rabbit enzyme is glycosylated?

Semenza: About 15% (see Cogoli et al 1972).

Sjöström: Does this correspond to the M_r of the primary translation product?

Wacker: Yes. Of course with glycoproteins one is never sure what it means if one observes different mobilities on gels.

Sjöström: Our experiments gave a primary translation product that was a doublet and had an M_r of about 200 000. This fits well with a glycosylation of 15% of a pro-sucrase–isomaltase which, in the pig, has an M_r of about 260 000.

Louvard: Did you achieve translation in the presence of membrane?

Wacker: Yes, in the presence and in the absence of microsomal membranes. In the presence of membranes, the lower migrating band (the 'smaller' translation product) is more intense. One would expect exactly the opposite, i.e. a larger product, because core glycosylation should overcompensate an eventual loss of a postulated pre-piece. We cannot say what it really means. It could be some proteolytic activity, unrelated to translation, which we have introduced with the membranes.

Alpers: Why is it the opposite from what you would expect? You are assuming there will be glycosylation, but you don't know that. You could remove the true pre-piece (if we can use that term).

Wacker: It would be too small, as compared to the actual size of the polypeptide (240 000), for us to detect any difference on SDS-PAGE and it could not account for the observed difference in molecular mass of apparently 20 000.

Alpers: But you may also not be getting glycosylation with those membranes on that particular protein.

Wacker: That is possible.

Semenza: These data simply show that pro-SI can be synthesized *in vitro*, and I would not like to interpret our experiments further.

Louvard: Does the co-translated product co-migrate with a mature form expressed in the plasma membrane?

Wacker: No; it migrates further. The estimated M_r is 20 000 smaller, and this is much too big for what we normally know of pre-pieces. So it cannot account for so-called pre-pieces.

Booth: In your photolabelling, why did you choose a carbene instead of the nitrenes that are available?

Semenza: Carbenes are less specific. One cannot, in general, extract a proton from a C–H bond by using a nitrene, whereas one can insert the carbene arising from TID in cyclohexane. The reaction of photolysed TID is a fairly clean carbene reaction. In fact, the diazo isomer that is also formed can be expected to react sluggishly due to the electron withdrawal effect of the trifluoromethyl group.

Booth: What is its life-time compared to that of nitrene?

Semenza: Carbenes are supposed to react much faster. In addition, and perhaps most important, TID and the carbene arising from it are totally confined to the hydrophobic core. Glutathione does not act as a scavenger, for example (Brunner & Semenza 1981).

Rees: You mentioned that you used 3-[dimethyl-2-(acetimidoxyethyl)-ammonio]-propane-sulphonic acid (DAP) for labelling, and that you saw labelling of the alanine in isomaltase, and the isoleucine in sucrase, and that the whole molecule must therefore be outside. Did you use a control for any labelling inside the vesicles, e.g. by pre-loading the liposomes?

Semenza: We do not have a control in the liposome experiment but we do have one in the brush border vesicle experiment. These vesicles contain actin, which is only slightly labelled by DAP. But the real comparison must be done between fragmented membranes, in which the reagent has free access to whatever amino groups occur at both sides of the membrane, and closed membranes, in which the reagent is accessible mainly or solely from the outside, and yet the same degree of substitution is found in very mild conditions (see Table 1 in our paper).

Rees: One could pre-load the liposomes with something that is known to be impermeable.

Sjöström: In collecting evidence for the anchor penetrating the membrane twice you did not point out the homology between the first piece of the sucrase–isomaltase and a segment in the interior of glycophorin, known to span the membrane in the direction 'N-out' to 'C-in'. Don't you think this strengthens the argument?

Semenza: It fits the concept, but we really do not know what it means. I would not take that as major evidence.

Desnuelle: I would like to comment briefly on the effect of proline in the N-terminal sequence of isomaltase. I am not sure that proline alone can induce a β-turn in the chain; it merely makes a right angle for purely geometric reasons. β-turns require the succession of four residues in a conformation stabilized by several hydrogen bonds.

Semenza: I'm not basing this argument on proline-35 alone. Unfortunately we could not identify the three amino acids that come before Pro-35; but we do know that they are hydrophilic. The α-potential of a highly hydrophilic amino acid is fairly low, and proline is a strong α-breaker and a strong maker of β-turns. There is a strong likelihood of a β-turn occurring there. I wish we had a reagent capable of labelling this segment of the chain from the cytosolic side.

Mooseker: In your *in vitro* system, where you used the microsomal membranes, can you show association or insertion of the complex with the membranes? Has anybody looked at the effects of tunicamycin on the synthesis or insertion of any of these proteins in the intestine *in vitro* or in culture or in cell-free systems?

Semenza: This is one of the many things that we want to do. We also want to fractionate the RNA, and so on.

Norén: Danielsen (1982) from our laboratory has recently published data on the biosynthesis of the stalked microvillar enzymes. These enzymes are membrane-bound during biosynthesis. He also found that tunicamycin inhibits the final glycosylation.

Mooseker: Does tunicamycin interfere with proper insertion or not? Is it true that glycosylation is important for sorting but not for insertion?

Norén: If small intestinal mucosa is cultured in the presence of tunicamycin, the stalked enzymes are not expressed in the microvillar membrane even after 20 h of culture. However, the rate of synthesis is also slowed down. Provided that tunicamycin has no unknown effect directly on the intracellular protein transporting system, the results indicate that glycosylation plays a part in the intracellular transport of microvillar membrane proteins.

Hauri: Carbohydrates might have little to do with sorting of surface membrane proteins. From what is known about the biosynthesis of viral glycoproteins it is more likely that the carbohydrate moiety protects the protein backbone from proteolysis.

Louvard: Yes. E. Rodriguez Boulan, working on the polarized MDCK cell line that I mentioned earlier (p 89), treated the cells with tunicamycin and infected them with two types of virus. He observed that the virus found the way through the right membrane. The viral antigens were not glycosylated. However, these drugs are quite nasty and they slow down biosynthesis, too. So in this case one would favour the idea that glycosylation does not provide the information required to address the viral proteins to their correct location in the cell.

Quaroni: On the other hand, work by Herscovics et al (1980) on rat intestine has shown that there is a difference in the glycosidic portion of glycoproteins incorporated into the luminal and the basolateral membranes. Somehow, as the membrane proteins are synthesized, the type of glycosidic chain correlates with where the glycoproteins go. This may or may not be accidental. It may have nothing to do with determining the location.

Alpers: The major difference between the two forms of alkaline phosphatase—soluble and membranous—is in the carbohydrate moieties and not in the protein portion (Yedlin et al 1981).

REFERENCES

Brunner J, Semenza G 1981 Selective labeling of the hydrophobic core of membranes with 3-trifluoromethyl-3-(m[^{125}I]iodophenyl)diazirine, a carbene-generating reagent. Biochemistry 20: 7174-7182

Cogoli A, Mosimann H, Vock C, von Balthazar AK, Semenza G 1972 A simplified procedure for the isolation of the sucrase-isomaltase complex from rabbit intestine. Eur J Biochem 30: 7-14

Danielsen EM 1982 Biosynthesis of intestinal microvillar proteins. Pulse-chase labelling studies on aminopeptidase N and sucrase-isomaltase. Biochem J 204: 639-645

Herscovics A, Bugge B, Quaroni A, Kirsch K 1980 Characterization of glycopeptides labelled from D-(2-^{3}H)mannose and L-(6-^{3}H)fucose in intestinal epithelial cell membranes during differentiation. Biochem J 192: 145-153

Sjöström H, Norén O, Christiansen L, Wacker H, Semenza G 1980 A fully active, two-active-site, single-chain sucrase-isomaltase from pig small intestine. Implications for the biosynthesis of a mammalian integral stalked membrane protein. J Biol Chem 255: 11332-11338

Yedlin ST, Young GP, Seetharam B, Seetharam SS, Alpers DH 1981 Characterization and comparison of soluble and membranous forms of intestinal alkaline phosphatase from the suckling rat. J Biol Chem 256: 5620-5626

Use of monoclonal antibodies in the study of intestinal structure and function

ANDREA QUARONI*

Department of Medicine, Harvard Medical School, and Gastrointestinal Unit, Massachusetts General Hospital, Boston, Massachusetts 02114, USA

Abstract The hybridoma technique, originally developed by G. Kohler & C. Milstein, is a powerful new experimental approach for analysis of complex biological systems, and is particularly suited for identification and study of surface-membrane antigens. This technique has been used for the production of monoclonal antibodies to intestinal brush border membrane proteins. Spleen cells, obtained from BALB/c mice immunized with purified brush border membranes, were fused with NSI mouse myeloma cells, and hybrids were selected with a culture medium containing hypoxanthine, aminopterin and thymidine (HAT medium). Hybridoma cultures were screened for production of specific antibodies by radio-immunobinding assays and by immunofluorescent staining of intestinal frozen sections. Selected hybridoma cultures were cloned twice and used for the production of large amounts of antibodies, which were characterized. Nineteen monoclonal antibodies have been prepared to date, about half of them specifically staining the brush border membrane of mature enterocytes. Ten of the antibodies specifically immunoprecipitate surface-membrane proteins, which were analysed by sodium dodecyl sulphate slab-gel electrophoresis, by two-dimensional slab-gel electrophoresis, and by specific enzyme assays. Two antibodies were found to be specific for sucrase–isomaltase, one for an aminopeptidase, two for an isoenzyme of alkaline phosphatase that is present exclusively in the proximal small intestine, and one for maltase–glucoamylase. These monoclonal antibodies, and others prepared by similar techniques from mice immunized with a wide variety of intestinal subcellular fractions, should prove invaluable tools for the study of the biosynthesis of cell-surface proteins, the fetal and postnatal development of specific intestinal functions, and the process of cell differentiation in the intestinal epithelium.

1983 Brush border membranes. Pitman Books Ltd, London (Ciba Foundation symposium 95) p 113-131

Until recently, immunological techniques have received relatively limited application in the study of cell-surface membrane components, partly owing to the great complexity of most cellular membranes and partly to the difficulty

---

* now at Department of Biological Sciences, Section of Physiology, 820 Veterinary Research Tower Building, Cornell University, Ithaca, NY 14853, USA

in generating monospecific antisera without prior extensive purification of a specific membrane protein. The brush border membrane of the intestinal absorptive villous cells is, in this respect, exceptional, since it represents a highly specialized portion of the surface membrane and is composed of relatively few major protein components, many of which possess easily identifiable enzymic activities that have been purified to homogeneity and characterized in detail. Consequently, good polyclonal antisera have been produced to e.g. sucrase–isomaltase, aminopeptidase and lactase, and have been used extensively in the localization of these proteins by immuno-fluorescence and immunoelectron microscopy (Gitzelmann et al 1970, Doell et al 1965, Feracci et al 1982, Nishi & Takesue 1975) as well as in various biosynthetic studies (Hauri et al 1979, Sjöström et al 1980). However, a simple analysis of highly purified brush border membranes, e.g. by two-dimensional slab-gel electrophoresis, easily reveals in this membrane a large number of minor protein components, whose identity and function is still totally unknown. Among them are likely to be sugar and amino acid carriers, hormone receptors, and proteins involved in various cell–cell interactions or in other important cellular functions. Furthermore, other cell-surface fractions of the intestinal epithelial cells—the lateral and basal portions of the surface membrane of the absorptive villous cell and the surface membrane of the undifferentiated crypt cell, Goblet cell, Paneth cell, etc.—have few, if any, easily identifiable protein components, and this is the main reason why our knowledge of their structure and composition is still limited.

The development of a new technique for the production of monoclonal antibodies *in vitro* by lymphocyte hybrid cell lines (or hybridomas) was initially described by Kohler & Milstein (1975), and it has revolutionized almost every field of cell biology. Among its first and still most active applications has been the study of cell-surface membrane components, for which it offers unique advantages. This technique should prove extremely valuable for studying most intestinal cell-surface components: this paper discusses its use for the production of monoclonal antibodies to brush border membrane components, and its possible future uses in the study of intestinal structure and function.

Potential advantages of monoclonal antibodies for studying cell-surface antigens

The most important aspects of the hybridoma technique that can be applied to the study of the structure and function of cell-surface antigens are listed in Table 1. (1) The potential availability of an unlimited supply of antibodies with a defined and constant specificity is perhaps the most frequently

TABLE 1 Potential advantage of monoclonal antibodies in the study of cell surface antigens

(1) 'Unlimited' supply of antibodies with a defined specificity
(2) Specific antibodies can be prepared to rare and/or weak antigens
(3) Antibodies can be used to map different antigenic sites on a single protein (or protein complex), or to detect specific conformational changes
(4) Specific antibodies can be prepared by using complex antigen mixtures for immunization
(5) Monoclonal antibodies can be prepared to unknown antigens possessing specific biological functions (which can be assayed for), and then used to identify and purify the antigen(s) they recognize

mentioned advantage of monoclonal antibodies. This is valuable when the antibodies are to be used, e.g., in clinical assays, but large amounts of antibodies to a specific antigen are rarely needed in the study of cell-surface antigens. The reproducible properties and antigenic specificity of any given monoclonal antibody can, however, be great advantages for interpretation of its use under different experimental conditions. It can also be an asset to be able to thaw a specific hybridoma cell line at any time, even many years after its original production, and to prepare quickly as much well characterized antibody as required. (2) Membrane fractions used for immunization usually contain immunodominant antigens, to which monoclonal antibodies (as well as polyclonal antisera) can be preferentially and easily prepared. Weak or rare antigens will generate an immune response which can be undetectable in a polyclonal antiserum, but can be readily identified with properly designed screening procedures, when the multispecific response to a large number of different cell-surface antigens is resolved by cloning a large enough population of hybridomas. In this way, immunological techniques can be applied to the study of minor as well as major cell-surface components. The frequency of clones responding to non-immunodominant antigens can be greatly increased, if required, by fractionating the antigen mixture used for immunization with already available monoclonal antibodies (Springer 1981). (3) Since monoclonal antibodies are mostly specific for single antigenic sites on any given antigen, a set of independently derived monoclonal antibodies can be used, for example, to study the positioning of a membrane protein in the lipid bilayer, subunit interaction and peptide mapping, localization of active sites of enzymes or membrane receptors, and also to monitor specific conformational changes under different physiological conditions. The elegant studies of Tzartos et al (1981), Gullick et al (1981) and Mochly-Rosen & Fuchs (1981), who used monoclonal antibodies to the acetylcholine receptor, show the great potential of this technique. (4) The ability to produce monospecific monoclonal antibodies by using, for immunization, very complex antigen mixtures such as partially purified membrane fractions, or even whole cells, is perhaps the most important aspect of the hybridoma technique, and is central for its application to the study of cell-surface membrane components. A careful design of the antibody detection assays can, in most cases, easily identify the hybridoma cultures that produce antibodies to the antigens of interest, which can then be cloned to ensure monoclonality and, usually, monospecificity of the antibodies produced. (5) A property of the hybridoma technique that can be valuable in the identification of important, but still unknown, cell-surface membrane components is the possibility of producing monoclonal antibodies by using functional assays to screen the hybridoma cultures. For example, hybridoma culture supernatants can be tested for their ability to inhibit binding of hormones or other effector molecules to specific cellular receptors, or for their ability to inhibit uptake of nutrients or ions into membrane vesicles or intact cells. The monoclonal antibodies produced in this way can then be used to identify and purify the previously unknown antigen(s) that they recognize.

Preparation of monoclonal antibodies to brush border membrane antigens

The protocol and the general techniques used for the preparation of monoclonal antibodies to intestinal brush border membrane components are summarized in Fig. 1, and were similar or identical to those used in many previous studies. The details of this work have been published (Quaroni & May 1980, Hauri et al 1980) in part, and will also be described more completely elsewhere (A. Quaroni, unpublished results). In most cases, we used for immunization brush border membranes that were purified according to the method of Hopfer et al (1973) and were suspended in saline or phosphate-buffered saline (PBS, 10 mM phosphate buffer at pH 7.3, 0.154 M-NaCl), but successful fusions were also obtained after immunization with Triton X-100-solubilized brush border membrane proteins. The immunization protocol can be critical, particularly with purified soluble antigens, in determining the frequency of obtaining positive hybridoma cultures and, ultimately, the rate of successful production of monoclonal antibodies to any given antigen. The important variables are the amount of antigen administered, the route of immunization, and the number of and time between injections. With complex mixtures of particulate antigens, such as membrane fractions or whole cells, positive hybridoma cultures are almost always obtained in large numbers. However, by using different immunization protocols with brush border membranes, we have observed quite different patterns of antibody type and specificity in different fusions; this suggests that if monoclonal antibodies specific for a single membrane component are desired, the best immunization protocol must be sought. The protocol that consistently gave the best results in the preparation of monoclonal antibodies

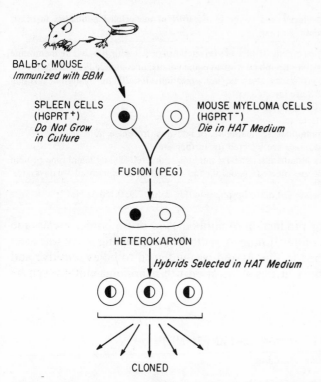

FIG. 1. Preparation of monoclonal antibodies to brush border membrane antigens (general scheme). BALB/c mice were immunized with purified brush border membranes (BBM) (Hopfer et al 1973) that were suspended in saline (100–200 μg membrane protein injected per mouse) and mixed with an equal volume of complete Freund's adjuvant (primary immunizations). Subsequent boosts, administered at 3 week to 4 month intervals, were given without Freund's adjuvant. Exactly 4 days after the last boost, spleen cells were obtained from the immunized mice and fused with mouse myeloma cells (HGPRT, hypoxanthineguanine phosphoribosyl transferase-deficient) using polyethylene glycol (PEG, average M_r 1500) as described by Galfre et al (1977). The myeloma cell line P3/NSI/1-Ag4-1 (NSI) was used in most experiments. After fusion, hybrid cells were selected with HAT (Littlefield 1964) medium (containing hypoxanthine, aminopterin and thymidine) and tested for antibody production. Cultures that were of interest were cloned twice by dilution plating (0.5 cells/well in 96-well Costar plates) with a feeder layer of mitomycin-C-treated 3T3 cells. The double-cloned hybridoma cell lines obtained were used for characterization of the immunoglobulins produced and of their antigenic specificity, and for the production of large amounts of antibodies after growth *in vivo* in ascitic form in Pristane-injected BALB/c mice.

to brush border membrane proteins is summarized in Table 2. After cell fusion and selection of the hybrid cells with HAT medium (containing 100 μM-hypoxanthine, 0.4 μM aminopterin and 16 μM thymidine), the hybridoma cultures (48 or 72 cultures were routinely obtained from each fusion)

TABLE 2 Immunization protocol used in the preparation of monoclonal antibodies to brush border membrane components

(1) *1st immunization*: Groups of 5 to 10 mice are injected i.p. or s.c. with 100–200 μg membrane protein suspended in 100 μl PBS mixed with an equal volume of complete Freund's adjuvant

(2) *1st boost:* Three to four weeks after 1st immunization, 100–200 μg membrane protein suspended in 100 μl PBS are injected i.p.

(3) Mice tails are bled 7–10 days after 1st boost
Antibody titers are determined
Sera are tested by immunofluorescent staining of intestinal frozen sections
The 2–3 best immunized mice are selected for further use

(4) *2nd boost:* Three to six months after the 1st immunization, 100–200 μg membrane protein suspended in 100 μl PBS are injected i.p. or i.v., and spleen cells are harvested 3–4 days later

PBS, phosphate-buffered saline (10 mM-phosphate buffer at pH 7.3, 0.154 M-NaCl).

were first screened for production of antibodies to brush border membrane antigens 10 to 15 days after fusion. A radio-immunobinding assay was used (schematically described in Fig. 2) and was designed to be as sensitive and reliable as possible, since at this stage of growth hybridoma cultures can be

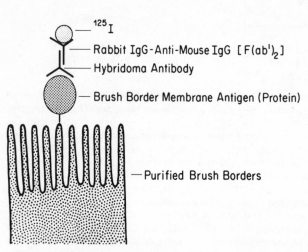

^{125}I

—— Rabbit IgG-Anti-Mouse IgG [F(ab')$_2$]

—— Hybridoma Antibody

—— Brush Border Membrane Antigen (Protein)

——Purified Brush Borders

FIG. 2. Radio-immunobinding assay: detection of hybridoma antibodies specific for brush border membrane antigens. Brush border caps, purified according to the method of Forstner et al (1968), were washed twice with TBS–0.2% bovine serum albumin (BSA), and then: (1) incubated at 4 °C for 90 min with 100 μl of hybridoma culture supernatants, containing 0.1% NaN$_3$, or fresh culture medium (controls); (2) spun (at 4000 r.p.m. in a Sorvall HS-4 rotor, at 4 °C for 10 min) and washed three times with 2.5 ml of Tris-buffered saline (TBS)–0.2% BSA; (3) incubated at 4 °C for 90 min with 50 μl TBS–1% BSA containing 2–5 × 10^5 c.p.m. of ^{125}I-labelled F(ab')$_2$ fragment of a rabbit IgG–anti-mouse IgG, affinity purified on a mouse IgG–Sepharose-4B column; (4) spun as above, washed three times with 2.5 ml of TBS–0.2% BSA; and (5) counted in a gamma counter.

heterogeneous. Cells derived from many different, independent fusion events may be present in the same culture, and the amounts of specific antibodies present in any culture can be very small. Affinity purification of the iodinated second antibody (an F(ab′)$_2$ fragment of rabbit immunoglobulin G-anti-mouse IgG) on a mouse IgG–Sepharose 4B column was essential to decrease

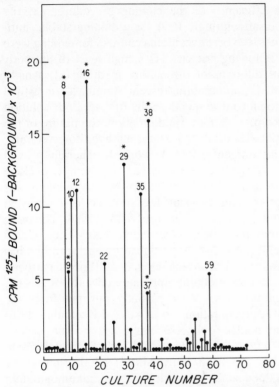

FIG. 3. Detection of monoclonal antibodies to brush border membrane antigens. Representative result obtained for the identification of hybridoma cultures that produce antibodies to brush border antigens by the radio-immunobinding assay described in Fig. 2. In this case, the hybridoma cultures produced (in fusion no. 5) were tested 16 days after fusion.

the non-specific (background) binding to an acceptable level. A representative result obtained using this assay in the screening of hybridoma cultures is shown in Fig. 3. Typically, about 30% of the cultures obtained from each fusion were positive in this assay, but only a few showed maximum binding (the assay was designed so that the amount of second (labelled) antibody, and not the amount of brush border membrane antigen, would be the limiting factor). These few more highly positive cultures were usually the only ones that were subsequently successfully cloned, and in later fusions they were the only ones considered for further use. All the hybridoma cultures had to be cloned to stabilize antibody production and to ensure monoclonality of the antibodies. Shortly after fusion and selection with HAT medium, hybridomas are very unstable, and many tend to stop growing or to segregate chromosomes during cell division, often losing the ability to produce specific antibodies. To increase the efficiency of the cloning procedure, i.e. the success rate (which can be disappointingly low) for obtaining stable, antibody-producing clonal cell lines, the best hybridoma cultures for cloning were chosen on the basis of the following criteria: (1) a high level of antibody production, tested at various dilutions of the culture medium; (2) a high, constant rate of growth; and (3) immunofluorescent staining of intestinal frozen sections, using hybridoma culture media as the first antibody solution for staining. This last test also provided information about the nature of the antigen(s) recognized by antibodies produced from each hybridoma culture, and the potential value of the antigen(s) for our work. It generally proved much easier and quicker to start a new fusion than to attempt to clone interesting but unstable hybridoma cultures or weak producers. Cloning was always done by dilution plating, and by using feeder layers of mitomycin C-treated 3T3 cells, as previously described (Quaroni & May 1980). Nineteen double-cloned hybrid cell lines have been obtained to date. Their clonal origin has been confirmed, and the antibody produced by each cell line has been characterized, as follows. (1) The double-cloned cell lines have been grown overnight in lysine-free culture medium supplemented with [^{14}C]lysine. Metabolically labelled antibodies have been partially purified from the culture medium by $(NH_4)_2SO_4$ precipitation, and analysed by double diffusion in agar gels and by immunoelectrophoresis, using heavy-chain specific rabbit anti-mouse IgG_1, IgG_{2a}, IgG_{2B}, IgG_3, IgA, IgM antisera, to determine the subclass of the antibodies produced. Surprisingly, all the antibodies produced by hybrid lines obtained so far belong to only two immunoglobulin types, IgG_1 or IgM. (2) The labelled immunoglobulins have been further purified by affinity chromatography on protein A–Sepharose-4B (for IgG_1 antibodies) or rabbit IgG–anti-mouse IgM-Sepharose 4B (for IgM antibodies) columns, and analysed by sodium dodecyl sulphate (SDS) slab-gel electrophoresis and by two-dimensional slab-gel electrophoresis. This last test has always revealed a single heavy chain and one or two light chains, as expected for monoclonal antibodies derived by fusion of spleen cells with the myeloma cell line P3-NSI-1-Ag4-1 (or NSI, which does not produce heavy chains, but produces a k light chain that can be expressed in the hybrids). After the clonal origin of each hybridoma has been confirmed, large amounts of monoclonal antibodies have been obtained from the ascites fluid of BALB/c mice injected i.p. with the hybrid cell lines. The mice were injected with Pristane two weeks before hybridoma injection to promote their growth in the ascites form rather than as solid tumours. Typically, monoclonal antibodies were present in the ascites fluid at a concentration of 10–100 mg/ml (for IgG_1) or 5–15 mg/ml (for IgM).

Identification and characterization of the antigens recognized by the different monoclonal antibodies

The tissue and cellular localization of the antigens for which the various monoclonal antibodies are specific was determined by fluorescent staining of frozen sections of rat jejunum. Many different staining patterns were observed (Fig. 4). About half the monoclonal antibodies stained totally specifically the brush border membrane of the villous cells (Figs. 4c, g, h), as expected, but some also stained the luminal membrane of both crypt and villous cells (BB4/42/1/10 and BB5/9/3/3), material in the intestinal lumen, perhaps mucus of glycocalyx components (Figs. 4d, e), the intestinal basement membrane and the serosa (Fig. 4f), or the muscularis mucosa and the luminal membrane of the crypt cells (Fig. 4i). While these results confirm the specialized composition of the intestinal brush border membrane, they also demonstrate that monoclonal antibodies can easily be obtained to cellular (or extracellular) antigens that are likely to be minor constituents of the antigenic mixture used for immunization. Ten of the antigens recognized by the different monoclonal antibodies could be identified after iodination, solubilization, and immunoprecipitation with monoclonal antibodies bound to Sepharose 4B, by SDS slab gel electrophoresis (see, e.g., Fig. 5). In most cases we observed more than one protein band corresponding to each immunoprecipitate. This is likely to be because many of the intestinal brush border membrane proteins are composed of different subunits, as are the antigens recognized by the monoclonal antibodies BB 3/34/12 (sucrase–isomaltase) and BB 8/2/8/1 (maltase–glucoamylase). Since many typical constituents of the brush border membrane are well known enzymes, the antigens bound to the different monoclonal antibodies were tested for various possible enzymic activities, as described in Fig. 6 legend. Thus, Fig. 6 shows that the monoclonal antibodies BB 3/34/12 and BB 5/8/40/90 (Hauri et al 1980) are specific for sucrase–isomaltase; BB 4/33/1/1 is specific for an aminopeptidase; BB 4/35/6/3 and BB 5/16/9/2 are specific for an isoenzyme of alkaline phosphatase present exclusively in the proximal small intestine (they were negative when tested for immunofluorescent staining of the distal small intestine); and BB 8/2/8/1 is specific for maltase–glucoamylase. The reasons for the apparent lack of specificity of the monoclonal antibodies BB 7/57/1/5 and BB 8/16/6/5 (which stain the intestinal mucosa in a very complex way, and

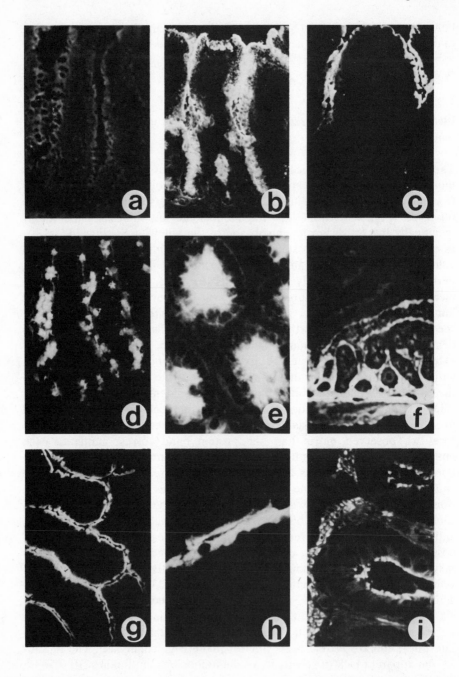

precipitate most, but not all, of the solubilized brush border membrane proteins (A. Quaroni, unpublished work) are unknown at present, but this observation points to the important notion that monoclonality is not always equivalent to monospecificity.

Conclusions

The wide application of hybridoma techniques to the study of vastly different problems, tissues and cellular systems underlines the many advantages of monoclonal antibodies over conventional polyclonal antisera. It also points to the fact that monoclonal antibodies are not simply better antibodies: they represent a new approach for studying problems that cannot be easily analysed by any other technique available at present. Possible future applications of this technique for the study of intestinal structure and function include: (1) a detailed study of surface-membrane changes during cell differentiation and fetal and postnatal development, including the study of cell-surface antigens devoid of enzymic activity, or possessing still unknown enzyme activities; (2) the mapping of different antigenic sites of various brush border membrane proteins, and their positioning in the membrane bilayer; (3) the identification and characterization of isoenzymes; (4) the study of the biosynthesis of surface-membrane components; (5) the purification of Golgi, lateral and basal membrane fractions, as well as any other cellular component of interest; and (6) the identification and characterization of subpopulations of crypt cells at different stages of differentiation. The approach and techniques we have used for preparing and characterizing monoclonal

(contd. on p 126)

FIG. 4. Immunofluorescent staining of intestinal frozen sections with monoclonal antibodies. Frozen sections of rat jejunum (2–4 μm thick) were incubated at room temperature for 30 min with monoclonal antibodies (ascites form, diluted 1 : 100 to 1 : 500 in phosphate-buffered saline, PBS) or with non-immune mouse serum (controls), washed three times (10 min each time) with PBS, incubated for 30 min with fluorescein isothiocyanate conjugated rabbit– or goat–anti-mouse IgG (diluted 1 : 25 in PBS), counterstained for 30 s with Evans blue (0.01% w/v in PBS), washed three times (10 min each time) with PBS, mounted in glycerol-PBS 9 : 1, and viewed in a Zeiss fluorescent microscope equipped with epifluorescence attachment. Pictures were taken with Kodak Tri X pan film (400 ASA) with exposure times of 5 s to 1 min. The staining patterns shown were obtained with: (a) non-immune mouse serum (control); (b) serum from a mouse immunized with brush border membranes; spleen cells from this mouse were subsequently used for fusion no. 4; (c) BB 4/33/1/1 (specific for aminopeptidase); (d) BB 8/16/6/5; (e) BB 7/57/1/5, (high magnification view of intestinal crypts); (f) BB 5/37/18/7; (g) BB 6/69/8/2; (h) BB 4/33/1/1 (high magnification view of a villus, illustrating specific staining of the brush borders); (i) BB 5/29/3/1. Original magnifications were: × 100 (Figs. 4a, b, c, d, f, g); × 160 (Fig. 4i) and × 400 (Figs. 4e, h).

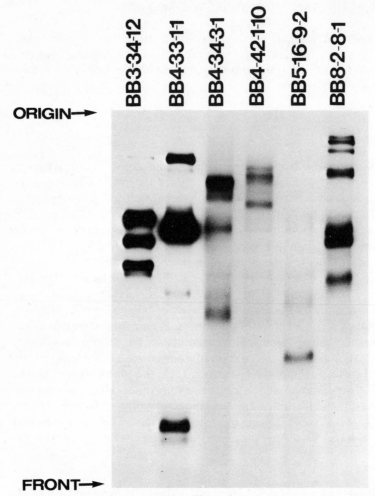

FIG. 5. SDS-slab gel electrophoresis of ^{125}I-labelled brush border membrane proteins specifically bound to insolubilized monoclonal antibodies. Purified brush borders prepared according to Forstner et al (1968) were incubated, in a total volume of 250 μl, with 5 mCi of ^{125}I (carrier-free), 25 μg lactoperoxidase, 1 unit glucose oxidase in 100 mM-KPO$_4$ at pH 7.6, 0.9% (w/v) NaCl, and 5 mM-glucose, for 15 min at room temperature. After extensive (10 × 50 ml) washing with PBS-I (PBS containing NaI instead of NaCl), brush border membranes were purified as described by Hopfer et al (1973), and solubilized in 500 μl of a solution containing 10 mM-NaPO$_4$ at pH 8.0, 1% (w/v) Triton X-100, 500 U/ml Trasylol, 1 mM-phenyl methylsulphonyl fluoride, 1 mg/ml trypsin inhibitor. After brief sonication, and incubation at 4 °C for 90 min, the solution was made up to 100 mM in NaCl, spun in an Eppendorf centrifuge for 30 min at 4 °C, and aliquots of the supernatant were incubated overnight at 4 °C in 1.5 ml Eppendorf centrifuge tubes with monoclonal antibodies bound to Sepharose 4B. After five washes with 1 ml of a solution containing 10 mM-NaPO$_4$ at pH 8.0, 100 mM-NaCl, 1 mg/ml trypsin inhibitor, 500 U/ml Trasylol, 1% (w/v) Triton X-100, and two washes with 1 ml H$_2$O, 100 ml of sample buffer (2% SDS, 10% glycerol, 62.5 mM-Tris-HCl at pH 6.8, 50 mM-dithiothreitol) was added to each tube. Bound, labelled membrane proteins were solubilized by incubation at 100 °C for 3 min, then the gel suspensions were applied to separate wells of a 7.5% polyacrylamide gel. After electrophoresis, labelled proteins were detected by fluorography.

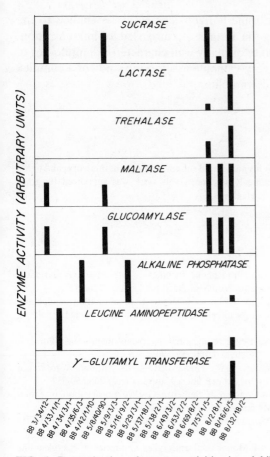

FIG. 6. Determination of enzyme activities in solubilized brush border membrane proteins specifically bound to insolubilized monoclonal antibodies. Solubilized brush border membrane proteins were incubated with monoclonal antibodies bound to Sepharose-4B as described in the legend to Fig. 5. After five washes with 1 ml of a solution containing 10 mM-NaPO$_4$ at pH 8.0, 100 mM-NaCl, 1 mg/ml trypsin inhibitor, 500 U/ml Trasylol, 1% Triton X-100, and two washes with 1 ml of the appropriate buffer, the Sepharose-4B beads were incubated as required for determination of various enzyme activities according to the following methods: sucrase, maltase, lactase, trehalase were determined according to the method of Messier & Dahlqvist (1966), with sucrose, maltose, lactose, trehalose (100 mM), respectively, as substrates; glucoamylase by the method of Schlegel-Haueter et al (1972), alkaline phosphatase according to Forstner et al (1968), with p-nitrophenylphosphate and β-glycerophosphate as substrates; aminopeptidase by the method of Roncari & Zuber (1969), and γ-glutamyltransferase according to Glossmann & Neville (1972).

antibodies to brush border membrane antigens can easily be applied to the above studies simply by changing the antigen mixture used for immunization, if required. Overall, the availability of many well characterized antibodies of constant specificity should be a very valuable asset in the study of a complex cellular system like the intestinal epithelium.

Acknowledgements

I am grateful to Dr Kurt J. Isselbacher for his advice and support throughout this work, and to Ms Katharina Kirsch for her excellent technical assistance. This work was supported by grant AM-25956 from the National Institutes of Health, USA.

REFERENCES

Doell RG, Rosen G, Kretchmer N 1965 Immunochemical studies on intestinal disaccharidases during normal and precocious development. Proc Natl Acad Sci USA 54:1268-1273

Feracci H, Bernadac A, Gorvel JP, Maroux S 1982 Localization by immunofluorescence and histochemical labeling of aminopeptidase N in relation to its biosynthesis in rabbit and pig enterocytes. Gastroenterology 82:317-324

Forstner GG, Sabesin SM, Isselbacher KJ 1968 Rat intestinal microvillus membranes. Purification and biochemical characterization. Biochem J 106:381-390

Galfre G, Howe SC, Milstein C, Butcher GW, Howard JD 1977 Antibodies to major histocompatibility antigens produced by hybrid cell lines. Nature (Lond) 266:550-552

Gitzelmann R, Bachi TH, Binz H, Lindenmann J, Semenza G 1970 Localization of rabbit intestinal sucrase with ferritin–antibody conjugates. Biochim Biophys Acta 196:20-28

Glossmann H, Neville DM 1972 γ-glutamyltransferase in kidney brush border membrane. FEBS (Fed Eur Biochem Soc) Lett 19:340-344

Gullick WJ, Tzartos S, Lindstrom J 1981 Monoclonal antibodies as probes of acetylcholine receptor structure. I: Peptide mapping. Biochemistry 20:2173-2180

Hauri HP, Quaroni A, Isselbacher KJ 1979 Biogenesis of intestinal plasma membrane: posttranslational route and cleavage of sucrase–isomaltase. Proc Natl Acad Sci USA 76:5183-5186

Hauri HP, Quaroni A, Isselbacher KJ 1980 Monoclonal antibodies to sucrase/isomaltase: probes for the study of postnatal development and biogenesis of the intestinal microvillus membrane. Proc Natl Acad Sci USA 77:6629-6633

Hopfer U, Nelson K, Perrotto J, Isselbacher KJ 1973 Glucose transport in isolated brush border membranes from rat small intestine. J Biol Chem 248:25-32

Köhler G, Milstein C 1975 Continuous cultures of fused cells secreting antibodies of predefined specificity. Nature (Lond) 256:495-497

Littlefield JW 1964 Selection of hybrids from matings of fibroblasts in vitro and their presumed recombinants. Science (Wash DC) 145:709-710

Messier M, Dahlqvist A 1966 A one-step ultramicro method for the assay of intestinal disaccharidases. Anal Biochem 14:376-392

Mochly-Rosen D, Fuchs S 1981 Monoclonal anti-acetylcholine receptor antibodies directed against the cholinergic binding site. Biochemistry 20:5920-5924

Nishi Y, Takesue Y 1975 Localization of rabbit intestinal sucrase on the microvilli membrane with non-labelled antibodies. J Electron Microsc 24:203-212
Quaroni A, May RJ 1980 Establishment and characterization of intestinal epithelial cell cultures. Methods Cell Biol 21B:403-427
Roncari G, Zuber H 1969 Thermophilic aminopeptidases from *Bacillus stearothermophilus*. I: Isolation, specificity and general properties of the thermostable aminopeptidase I. Int J Protein Res 1:45-61
Schlegel-Haueter S, Hore P, Kerry KR, Semenza G 1972 The preparation of lactase and glucoamylase of rat small intestine. Biochim Biophys Acta 258:506-519
Sjöström H, Norén O, Christiansen L, Wacker H, Semenza G 1980 A fully active, two-active-site, single-chain sucrase–isomaltase from pig small intestine. J Biol Chem 255:11332-11338
Springer TA 1981 Monoclonal antibody analysis of complex biological systems. J Biol Chem 256:3833-3839
Tzartos SJ, Rand DE, Einarson BL, Lindstrom JM 1981 Mapping of surface structures of electrophorus acetylcholine receptor using monoclonal antibodies. J Biol Chem 256:8635-8645

DISCUSSION

Kenny: Some of the relative molecular masses of these proteins from brush border of rat are rather different from those of proteins from the pig brush border.

Smith: Presumably you have tested these rare monoclonal antibodies against transport proteins and found nothing?

Quaroni: We have tested them but the problem is the assay. Just by mixing vesicles with antibodies (even the ones against alkaline phosphatase or sucrase) one does obtain measurable changes in transport activity in the vesicles, which is a general effect of monoclonal antibodies. We need a better assay for the effects of specific antibodies on transport in membrane vesicles.

Smith: Perhaps you have too much antigenic response to the glycolytic enzymes. One could strip those off before immunization to try to bring up these lesser components.

Quaroni: This approach has been used by Springer (1981) extensively. By passing the mixture of solubilized membrane proteins through a battery of different insolubilized antibodies, one can eliminate the immunodominant components from the antigen mixture which is then used for immunization.

Matsudaira: Because of the way that monoclonal antibodies work, if you obtain an immunoprecipitate is it due to there being repeated antigenic sites on the protein? Is it because the protein is oligomeric? If you did a western blot (Towbin et al 1979) to a gel would those same monoclonal antibodies stain only one band?

Quaroni: I have not done western blots using the monoclonal antibodies. The antibodies in our work were bound to beads, so what I have termed immunoprecipitation is actually immunoadsorption. After washing, the proteins bound to the beads were solubilized and added to the polyacrylamide gel. With fetal intestines or fetal transplants (Hauri et al 1982) one obtains a much simpler protein pattern, probably because of a generalized proteolytic activity which is responsible for splitting many surface proteins like the disaccharidases in the normal adult intestine. At least two of the antigens showed a very complex protein pattern. When we did the immunoprecipitation on fetal intestines we found a single spot or band in the gel.

Kenny: You seem to have avoided generating antibodies to the intermediate filaments that cause some of us considerable bother!

Quaroni: I do obtain many antibodies against basement membrane components, on the other hand!

Hauri: With monoclonal antibodies the success of the western blot technique depends predominantly on the antigen. We produced 24 monoclonal antibodies to rat liver cytochrome $P\text{-}450_b$ (U. Marti & H.P. Hauri, unpublished results), and 22 of them bound to the antigen which had been electrophoretically transferred from SDS-polyacrylamide gels to nitrocellulose blots. On the other hand, only two of 35 monoclonal antibodies to human brush border membranes could be identified by the western blot technique (H.P. Hauri, unpublished results). Thus, the technique with monoclonal antibodies is not always successful.

Booth: But you were doing the western blot from an SDS gel; if you had done it in a non-denaturing gel, taking a detergent supernatant e.g. Triton, and western-blotted that, you might have found that some of your antibodies recognized only the native protein.

Hauri: Without SDS you cannot get enough resolution. For brush border membrane, two-dimensional gels in the presence of SDS are required to separate all the membrane components.

Kenny: Drs Sjöström & Norén (1982) found that the antibodies that recognized the SDS-denatured proteins are different from those that recognize the native proteins.

Hauri: With the western blot technique one probably has partial renaturation due to the removal of SDS during the electrophoretic transfer and due to the immobilization of the antigen on nitrocellulose.

Kenny: But it would not be enough.

Hauri: It depends on the antigen.

Kenny: Is the immunization schedule important for selecting the major or minor antigens?

Quaroni: It is important, but nobody knows what exactly the rules are. I prefer a long immunization schedule, as does Dr Hauri, starting with a couple of boosts shortly after the first immunization, and then a final boost after five or six months.

Hauri: The immunization schedule not only depends on the actual amount but also on the antigenicity of the antigen. Thus, with cytochrome P-450$_b$ (a poor antigen) we needed a long immunization schedule in order to obtain monoclonal antibodies, while with microvillus membranes we have already been successful with a relatively short schedule.

Quaroni: We obtained similar results with short and long immunization schedules.

Hauri: You once mentioned that with long immunization schedules you obtained more IgM's and unwanted antibodies.

Quaroni: I got some IgM's, but I do not have enough experience to be certain that the immunization schedule had anything to do with that. It could have been accidental.

Booth: What would happen if you did not use any immunization schedule but just took the cells from the animal straight away? In other words, could these be endogenous antibodies?

Quaroni: No; without immunization one obtains very few, if any, hybridomas that secrete specific antibodies.

Louvard: I would agree with that for membrane protein but, for the basement membrane, everyone who has made monoclonal antibody always obtains a predominant reaction with filament. However, in several cases very few or none of these antigens have been injected into mice. What one obtains at the end of a hybridoma experiment may have nothing to do with what one has injected, and your monoclonal antibody to the basement membrane may well arise from such a situation.

Quaroni: I think that can happen occasionally with animals but I have never obtained any antibody against intermediate filaments, in the 15 fusions that I have done.

Louvard: When one infects an animal with complete Freund, one might obtain necrosis of the tissue. For example, recently we tried to obtain a monoclonal antibody against clathrin. We immunized with purified clathrin, and during the screening with immunofluorescence I observed that one of the hybridomas labelled microtubules. We checked, by immunoreplica techniques, what kind of antibody it was, and found it was specific for the α-subunit of tubulin.

Quaroni: That was my point; the key to everything is in the design of the screening assay. The immunization is important if you want antibodies against a *specific* antigen. In that case you may find that only a certain immunization schedule works. But if you are interested in surface membrane antigens in general and you design the assay to tell you which hybridomas are producing antibodies of interest for your work, the immunization schedule is rarely a relevant factor.

Kenny: So, if the schedule is important in obtaining an antibody to a particular antigen, what guidelines should be used?

Quaroni: I don't think the rules have been clearly established yet. When one uses two different animals or strains, the results may be very different. Mice have a limited immunoresponse, so one sometimes has to change the strain when the one initially chosen doesn't work with a particular antigen.

Jørgensen: Did the antibody used for staining the basolateral membrane also stain the brush border membrane?

Quaroni: Not in the small intestine. In the large intestine it does seem to stain the luminal (brush border) membrane as well. That needs to be confirmed. I don't think the immunofluorescence technique is good enough to answer the question completely.

Jørgensen: I am concerned about the specificity of your antibodies. You mentioned cases in which antibodies reacted with five different proteins—three glycosidases and two peptidases.

Quaroni: I think they are against glycosidic chains, in which case one would expect that they would react against many different components of the brush border membrane.

Jørgensen: But is the cross-reactivity related to monoclonal antibodies that have a particularly low affinity?

Quaroni: I don't think so. A monoclonal antibody may be totally specific for a certain antigenic site, but this site may be common to many different proteins.

Jørgensen: How many amino acid residues are in an antigenic site like that?

Quaroni: There could be four or five on different parts of the chain or they could all be in the same sequence.

Jørgensen: Is the low specificity related to antibodies against relatively few residues?

Quaroni: I don't know.

Alpers: You mentioned an antibody that recognized just sucrase and not isomaltase. Dr Semenza suggested (p 92–112) a possible point mutation on this enzyme. If it were like other point mutations on other enzymes one would expect cross-reaction of some sort. How would you explain that?

Semenza: Some antigenic determinants are identical and some are different. In my scheme I needed only one point of mutation, but there could be other mutations leading to changes of antigenic determinants.

Alpers: But no-one has yet used this antibody to, say, isolate the subunit and do peptide mapping.

Quaroni: No; the problem is in splitting the subunits. Hauri et al (1980) have done it by treatment with citraconic anhydride, but it is a very inefficient technique.

Sjöström: We have also done this. As the splitting into free subunits results in denaturation of the enzyme it requires antibodies against the denatured subunits. Sucrase–isomaltase was heat- and SDS-denatured and the subunits separated by chromatography on a hydroxyl apatite column. Polyclonal antibodies were raised in rabbits, and the purified IgG was coupled to Sepharose.

Using this we could separate the polypeptides by immunoadsorbent chromatography of the heat- and SDS-denatured protein.

Schmitz: What is the explanation for the antibody that specifically labelled the tip of the villi, and did this correlate with a known protein?

Quaroni: This could be due to degradation; at that point the cells start to age, so there may be degradation of some components of the luminal membrane. Or it could be something which is expressed only at that point during the life-cycle of the enterocytes. One must be careful in interpreting immunohistochemical data obtained with monoclonal antibodies, because they are totally specific for an antigenic site that may be easily changed during fixation. Although I like to believe the staining patterns I have obtained, they could be artifactual. So in the case you mentioned, for example, that particular antigen may be available for interaction with a given monoclonal antibody only in the dying cells present on the tip of the villi, but the antigen may actually be present also in enterocytes located in lower portions of the villi.

Hauri: The staining pattern of this particular antibody is comparable to that found for galactosyltransferase in the small intestine (E. Berger, personal communication). However I do not know of any characterized brush border protein that is exclusively localized at the very tip of the villus.

REFERENCES

Hauri HP, Quaroni A, Isselbacher KJ 1980 Monoclonal antibodies to sucrase-isomaltase: probes for the study of postnatal development and biogenesis of the intestinal microvillus membrane. Proc Natl Acad Sci USA 77: 6629-6633

Hauri HP, Wacker H, Rickli EE, Bigler-Meier B, Quaroni A, Semenza G 1982 Biosynthesis of sucrase-isomaltase. J Biol Chem 257: 4522-4528

Sjöström H, Norén O 1982 Changes of the quaternary structure of microvillus aminopeptidase in the membrane. Eur J Biochem 122: 245-250

Springer TA 1981 Monoclonal antibody analysis of complex biological systems. J Biol Chem 256: 3833-3839

Towbin H, Staehelin T, Gordon J 1979 Electrophoretic transfer of proteins from polyacrylamide gels to nitrocellulose sheets: procedure and some applications. Proc Natl Acad Sci USA 76: 4350-4354

Biosynthesis and transport of plasma membrane glycoproteins in the rat intestinal epithelial cell: studies with sucrase–isomaltase

HANS-PETER HAURI

Division of Clinical Pharmacology, Department of Medicine, University Hospital, Rämistrasse 100, CH-8091 Zurich, Switzerland

Abstract Sucrase–isomaltase (SI), an integral heterodimeric glycoprotein of the intestinal microvillus membrane, is synthesized as a single enzymically active precursor protein (pro-SI) of high relative molecular mass. After glycosylation in the Golgi complex pro-SI is transferred to the microvillus membrane where it is cleaved into the two subunits by pancreatic elastase. Pro-SI was purified by monoclonal antibody-affinity chromatography from microvillus membranes of fetal intestinal transplants in which SI is found exclusively in the non-cleaved precursor form. The N-terminal amino acid sequence of pro-SI was identical to that of the isomaltase subunit of SI which anchors the mature enzyme complex to the lipid bilayer, but it differed from the N-terminal sequence of the sucrase subunit of SI. This structural comparison indirectly gave insight into the mechanisms of membrane insertion and assembly of pro-SI during its biosynthesis. Subcellular fractionation studies indicate transient structural association of newly synthesized pro-SI with the basolateral membrane on its transfer from the Golgi complex to the microvillus membrane, suggesting that part of the basolateral membrane or its associated structures might be involved in the sorting-out processes of microvillar membrane proteins. This concept may have general relevance for the mechanisms of membrane insertion, intracellular transport and sorting of other microvillar membrane glycoproteins in the intestinal epithelial cell.

1983 Brush border membranes. Pitman Books Ltd, London (Ciba Foundation symposium 95) p 132-149

The intestinal epithelial cell (enterocyte) of the small intestine is characterized by a striking polarization of its surface membrane into at least two distinct structural and functional domains: the luminal surface or *microvillus membrane*—the site of various digestive and absorptive functions (Crane 1977, Semenza 1981a)—and the *basolateral membrane*, which is involved in cell-to-cell contact and adhesion to the basement membrane. Not surprisingly each of these two domains comprises a different set of proteins (Weiser et al 1978). Little is known, however, of the processes by which enterocytes and epithelial cells in general are able to generate and maintain this membrane polarity. From a methodological point of view the enterocyte has become an attractive model for studying these processes on a molecular basis. Subcellular fractionation techniques have been developed which allow the preparation of highly purified microvillus membranes (Hopfer et al 1973) from isolated enterocytes (Weiser 1973), and basolateral and Golgi membranes can be purified with minimal contamination by microvillus membranes (Weiser et al 1978). Polyclonal and monoclonal antibodies to various components of these membranes are now available (Hauri et al 1980, Quaroni & May 1980, see also Quaroni, this volume). With the ultimate goal of elucidating molecular mechanisms responsible for the sorting-out of newly synthesized membrane proteins we have studied the biosynthesis and post-translational fate of rat sucrase–isomaltase (SI) (a complex of sucrose α-glucohydrolase, EC 3.2.1.48, and oligo 1,6-glucosidase, EC 3.2.1.10), a typical marker of the microvillus membrane.

The majority of transmembrane proteins synthesized on membrane-bound polysomes have their N-terminus and the bulk of the polypeptide chain localized on the extracytoplasmic side. Close to the C-terminus these proteins possess a hydrophobic segment anchoring the protein to the lipid bilayer while the C-terminus itself protrudes on the cytoplasmic side (Engelmann & Steitz 1981). This situation applies to several viral glycoproteins, glycophorin, the membrane-bound forms of immunoglobulin heavy chains (Tyler et al 1982) and the heavy chain of the histocompatibility antigens (reviewed in Kreil 1981, Sabatini et al 1982). The mechanism of *biosynthesis* and *translocation* of these proteins has been established and it is in many respects similar to that for secretory proteins, apart from the interruption of the extrusion process. In contrast to these examples, the *anchoring* of SI (like that of other enzymes present in microvillar membranes of enterocytes and kidney epithelial cells; see Kenny & Maroux 1982) to the lipid bilayer is different. SI is anchored to the microvillus membrane via a very hydrophobic amino acid sequence near the N-terminus only of its isomaltase subunit (Frank et al 1978, Brunner et al 1979). The sucrase subunit carries no anchor and is held in place solely by non-covalent interactions with its corresponding isomaltase on the luminal side of the microvillus membrane. This topology raises a number of interesting questions concerning the mechanism by which SI, and microvillus membrane proteins in general, are assembled within the lipid bilayer of endoplasmic reticulum and by which they subsequently reach the luminal cell membrane. Are the enzyme subunits synthesized individually or as a common precursor? What post-translational modifications occur? By which pathway are newly synthesized microvillar proteins transferred to their final destination? What is the structural basis for the sorting-out of surface proteins destined for different membrane compartments? Some of these questions are addressed in this paper.

Biosynthesis and post-translational cleavage of sucrase–isomaltase

The biosynthesis of SI was initially studied by metabolic labelling with [³H]fucose *in vivo* followed by isolation of SI with a monospecific polyclonal antibody (Hauri et al 1979). Fluorograms of sodium dodecyl sulphate (SDS)–polyacrylamide gels, run with such immunoprecipitates from Golgi or basolateral membranes isolated 30 min after labelling, showed a single immunoreactive glycoprotein (P) of high relative molecular mass (M_r) but no radioactive subunits (Fig. 1). P progressively disappeared and was absent

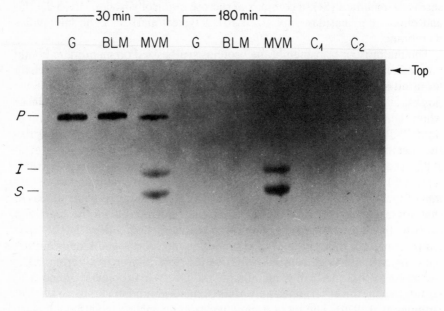

FIG. 1. Biosynthesis of sucrase–isomaltase (SI) *in vivo*. [³H]fucose-labelled Golgi membranes (G), basolateral membranes (BLM) or microvillus membranes (MVM) were solubilized with Triton X-100 and immunoprecipitated with a polyclonal antibody to SI. The immunoprecipitates were separated on sodium dodecyl sulphate–polyacrylamide gel electrophoresis (SDS–PAGE) under reducing conditions and were analysed by fluorography. The fluorogram shows the radioactivity patterns obtained 30 and 180 min after labelling. C_1, control: microvillus membranes from 12-day-old suckling rats (which do not yet synthesize SI) 60 min after fucose labelling. C_2, control: Golgi membranes 30 min after fucose labelling using an antibody unrelated to SI (rabbit anti-human IgA). *P*, pro-SI: the precursor of SI. *I*, isomaltase subunit; *S*, sucrase subunit (from Hauri et al 1979).

after 3 h. In contrast, immunoprecipitates from microvillus membranes isolated 30 min after labelling exhibited three bands, one of which was in the position of P and the two others were comigrating with the subunits of SI. Later P disappeared, while the intensities of the subunits increased. These results lead us to conclude that P (later called pro-SI) was a precursor that was cleaved into the subunits in the microvillus membrane. A precursor–product relationship was further substantiated by flow kinetics of pro-SI from Golgi to surface membrane (see below) and by the *in vitro* cleavage of pro-SI into two subunit-like fragments by pancreatic elastase (Hauri et al 1979). The demonstration of a common precursor of SI provided the experimental basis for a hypothesis of Semenza (1978), who speculated that the unusual topology of SI might be related to proteolytic cleavage of a single-chain precursor composed of both sucrase and isomaltase.

We next addressed the question of whether the cleavage of pro-SI by elastase is the mechanism by which the enzyme complex is activated or whether pro-SI is already enzymically active. Sucrase activities measured in Golgi membranes were the same with or without elastase treatment but the overall activities were so low that no conclusive answer could be obtained. We therefore had to find ways to exclude pancreatic enzymes from the gut. For this purpose fetal intestines were transplanted subcutaneously on the back of syngeneic 50 g rats (Leapman et al 1974). In these conditions the transplants undergo a maturation process comparable to the post-translational development *in situ*, and they show normal sucrase and isomaltase activities after a few weeks (Hauri et al 1980, Montgomery et al 1981a). However, the protein pattern (Fig. 2a) and the pattern of [³H]fucosylated glycoproteins (Fig. 2b) of microvillus membranes prepared from the transplants differed strikingly from the patterns obtained with normal intestinal microvillus membranes. The most prominent changes were the apparent absence of the sucrase and isomaltase subunits and the presence of a prominent high M_r component in the transplants. An analysis of immunoprecipitates obtained with the antibody to SI showed that this latter protein component was pro-SI and that no free subunits were indeed present in the transplants (Fig. 2a and 2b). Furthermore it was found that this non-processed SI was enzymically fully active (Hauri et al 1979, Hauri et al 1980). This finding was confirmed for the rat by Montgomery et al (1981b). Sjöström et al (1980), using a different approach, reported similar results for the SI isolated from hogs whose pancreatic ducts had been ligated.

We obviously had to prove that the precursors of SI in intestinal Golgi membranes of adult rats and in microvillus membranes of intestinal transplants were identical. Both precursors can be split by elastase to yield two subunit-like glycopeptides, each of similar but not identical mobilities on SDS–polyacrylamide gels (Fig. 3). The 'isomaltase' fragment from Golgi

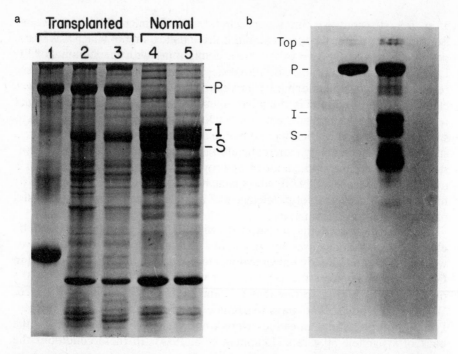

FIG. 2. (a) Protein patterns of microvillus membranes from adult and transplanted fetal intestines on SDS–PAGE. 1, immunoprecipitate with a polyclonal antibody to SI of microvillus membranes from transplanted fetal intestines; 2 & 3, patterns obtained from microvillus membranes of two different transplants; 4 & 5, patterns obtained from microvillus membranes of two different adult intestines (H. P. Hauri, unpublished results). (b) Pattern of [^{3}H]fucosylated glycoproteins of the microvillus membranes from fetal intestinal transplants (fluorogram): *left lane*, immunoprecipitate with a polyclonal antibody to SI (same sample as shown in (a), lane 1); *right lane*, pattern obtained with the whole microvillus membrane fraction (same sample as shown in (a), lane 2). P, pro-SI; I, isomaltase subunit; S, sucrase subunit (H. P. Hauri, unpublished).

membranes comigrated with the isomaltase subunit of SI; the 'sucrase' fragment, however, had a higher apparent M_r than the sucrase subunit of SI. In contrast, the 'isomaltase' fragment of pro-SI from transplants had a lower apparent M_r than the isomaltase subunit, while the 'sucrase' fragment comigrated with the sucrase subunit. Any interpretation of these results has to take into account the different orientation of pro-SI in Golgi and microvillus membranes. Hence, the accessibility of elastase to the precursor may differ in these two membrane fractions despite the fact that both membranes were exposed to the same concentration of elastase for an identical length of time. Nevertheless, these data suggest that the two

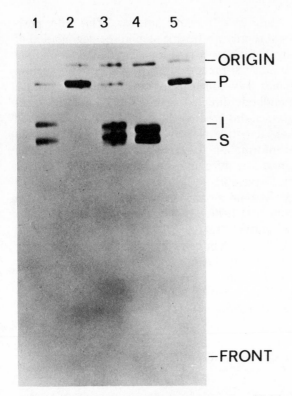

FIG. 3. Comparison of pro-SI from adult intestines (Golgi membranes) and from fetal intestinal transplants (microvillus membranes) by SDS–PAGE. SI-related proteins were immunoprecipitated from [³H]fucose-labelled membranes with a polyclonal antibody to SI. The fluorogram shows: 1, immunoprecipitate with microvillus membranes of an adult intestine 60 min after injection of [³H]fucose; 2, immunoprecipitate with Golgi membranes from an adult intestine 15 min after injection of [³H]fucose; 3, same as in lane 2 but the Golgi membranes were treated with porcine elastase prior to solubilization and immunoprecipitation; 4, immunoprecipitate with microvillus membranes from fetal intestinal transplants (60 min after injection of [³H]fucose) treated with elastase; 5, same as in lane 4 but without elastase treatment. P, pro-SI; I, isomaltase subunit; S, sucrase subunit (from Hauri et al 1982).

precursors are identical. *In vitro* elastase may not only cleave the precursor (as with pro-SI from Golgi) but, with more aggressive conditions (applying to pro-SI from transplants), it may also remove part of the newly generated N- or C-terminus of the sucrase subunit and the hydrophobic anchor of the isomaltase subunit (Hauri et al 1982). However, more work has to be done to establish unequivocally the structural identity of the two pro-forms. The physiological role of the splitting of pro-SI into subunits in the microvillus membrane of the normal enterocyte remains unclear. This late post-translational modification could represent the first step in the degradation of the enzyme or it could be a signal for proper positioning at the enzyme's final location. The presence of one *single* SI-precursor comprising both the sucrase and the isomaltase portions has now conclusively been established with a subunit-specific monoclonal antibody directed against sucrase. Pro-SI, purified on an affinity column to which this antibody had been coupled, exhibited both sucrase and isomaltase activities (Hauri et al 1980). Monoclonal antibodies also provided new information about the site of SI synthesis along the crypt–villus axis both in the mature intestine and during normal or precociously induced postnatal development (Hauri et al 1980). Contrary to previous observations with polyclonal monospecific antibodies (Doell et al 1964, Dubs et al 1975, Quaroni et al 1979c), monoclonal antibodies failed to detect SI in the crypts, which strongly suggests that only the differentiated villus cells, and not the proliferating crypt cells, are capable of synthesizing SI. Furthermore we found that SI is cleaved into subunits as soon as it appears for the first time at the base of the villi, on day 19. Similarly, most of the SI was found in the processed form when SI was precociously induced by cortisone acetate in nine-day-old suckling rats.

Mechanism of insertion deduced from the disposition of pro-SI in the microvillus membrane

The orientation of an integral membrane protein with respect to the lipid bilayer may offer insight into the mechanism of its insertion into the membrane during biosynthesis. Thus a comparison of the N-terminal amino acid sequence of pro-SI with that of the isolated subunits of the mature dimeric enzyme complex might reveal whether the sucrase or the isomaltase portion of pro-SI is synthesized and translocated first. Purification of 3–4 mg of pro-SI from 200 fetal intestinal transplants was achieved by using a two-step procedure. First, the enzyme antibody–complex was isolated by monoclonal antibody-affinity chromatography on protein A–Sepharose CL-4B (Fig. 4). In a second step, pro-SI was additionally purified by preparative SDS–PAGE (Fig. 5). In an analogous procedure the individual subunits of the mature SI from adult intestines were purified (Fig. 5). The N-terminal amino acid sequences given in Fig. 6 show the identity of pro-SI with the isomaltase subunit, whereas the N-terminal sequence of the sucrase subunit was different. In an independent study, H. Sjöström, O. Norén, H. Wacker et al (unpublished results) have obtained the same identity for hog pro-SI. This identity clearly shows that the isomaltase portion carrying the membrane anchor is synthesized prior to synthesis of the bulk of the protein destined to

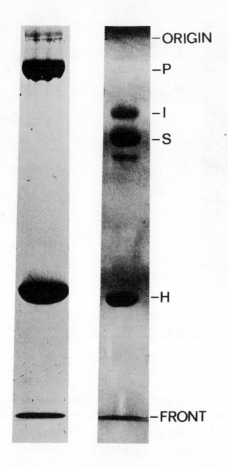

FIG. 4. Purification of SI and pro-SI by monoclonal antibody affinity chromatography on a protein A–Sepharose CL-4B column. The SDS–PAGE shows the protein patterns of eluted immunocomplexes obtained from fetal intestinal transplants (left lane) or adult intestines (right lane). P, pro-SI; I, isomaltase subunit; S, sucrase subunit; H, heavy chain of the monoclonal antibody to sucrase (from Hauri et al 1982).

be localized on the luminal side of the microvillus membrane. Because position 11 is glycosylated (as with the isomaltase from rabbits—see Frank et al 1978) we can assume that the N-terminus of SI and pro-SI is located at the extracellular side. This was conclusively demonstrated recently for the N-terminus of the rabbit isomaltase subunit (R. Bürgi, J. Brunner, G. Semenza, unpublished). Furthermore, the same workers have shown that the peptide chain between Thr 11 and the bulk of the protein on the luminal side

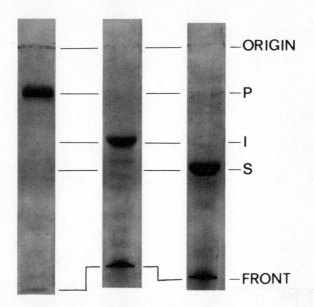

FIG. 5. Analysis of pro-SI (left lane), the isomaltase subunit (middle lane) and the sucrase subunit (right lane), purified by preparative SDS–PAGE. P, pro-SI; I, isomaltase subunit; S, sucrase subunit (from Hauri et al 1982)

of the microvillus membrane crosses the lipid bilayer twice. On the basis of the disposition of pro-SI (and mature SI) in the microvillus membrane, we propose the following mechanism for its biosynthesis and membrane insertion (Fig. 8; see also Hadorn et al 1981, Semenza 1981b, Hauri et al 1982, Semenza et al, this volume). A signal sequence (not yet demonstrated) would be synthesized first and would facilitate extrusion of the short hydrophilic sequence 1–11 (Fig. 6) until the hydrophobic sequence that follows stops the transfer process. Another short hydrophilic sequence remaining on the cytoplasmic side would follow up to a hydrophobic sequence reinitiating the

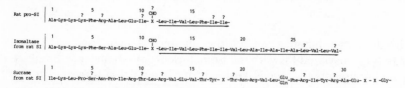

FIG. 6. N-terminal sequences of pro-SI, from fetal intestinal transplants, and of the isolated subunits of SI from adult small intestines. Ambiguities are indicated by a question mark, or by two residues being given (from Hauri et al 1982). Underlined sequences are part of the hydrophobic anchor.

extrusion process of the rest of pro-SI. However, the exact mechanism of insertion awaits further analysis. In particular, it would be interesting to know if, during insertion, the N-terminus of pro-SI is indeed preceded by a signal sequence (as indicated in Fig. 8) or if part of the membrane anchor itself represents an uncleaved signal sequence. A major step towards this goal is the

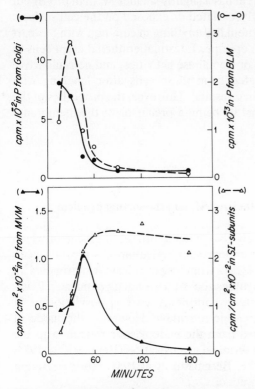

FIG. 7. Flow kinetics of [³H]fucose-labelled pro-SI from Golgi to surface membranes, and the appearance of newly synthesized sucrase and isomaltase subunits in the microvillus membrane. The Golgi membranes, basolateral membranes (BLM) or microvillus membranes (MVM) were isolated at various times after injection of [³H]fucose. Solubilized membranes were immuno-precipitated with the polyclonal antibody to SI and the precipitates were separated by SDS–PAGE. Total radioactivity was quantitated from gel slices (from Hauri et al 1979).

recent achievement *in vitro* of translation of the mRNA coding for SI (Wacker et al 1980). The proposed model of the biosynthesis of SI is in contrast to what has been proposed by Cezard et al (1979), who reported the presence of soluble sucrase and isomaltase subunits in the cytosol. They suggested that these subunits may represent precursors for the fully formed membrane enzyme at some stage of the intracellular assembly process. This

observation is not easily explained but mechanical dislodgement and proteolytic cleavage of pro-SI have also to be considered. Another possibility to
explain this discrepancy may be offered by the recent finding of a soluble
protein that cross-reacts immunologically with the monoclonal antibody to SI
(A. Quaroni, personal communication) in intestinal epithelial crypt cells and
intestinal organ cultures. This protein has a slightly smaller M_r than pro-SI but
is neither enzymically active nor glycosylated or exposed on the cell surface.
At present it is unknown if this protein has anything in common with SI apart
from sharing a similar or identical epitope. Intestinal epithelial crypt cells in
culture do not exhibit any sucrase or isomaltase activities, and no radioactive
pro-SI could be immunoprecipitated from these cells after labelling with
[³H]fucose (H. P. Hauri, unpublished results). However, the properties of the
cross-reacting protein argue against its being a precursor of the membrane-
bound SI.

Intracellular pathway of newly synthesized SI, and the sorting problem

Indirect evidence for an incompletely glycosylated form of SI precursor which
is presumably associated with the endoplasmic reticulum has recently been
presented by Danielsen et al (1981a), from organ-culture experiments in
which the sensitivity of newly synthesized SI to endoglycosidase H was
followed. As with other membrane glycoproteins, core glycosylation of SI
seems to take place in the endoplasmic reticulum. However, the mode of
transport of intestinal glycoproteins from the endoplasmic reticulum to the
Golgi complex, which is the site of terminal glycosylation (Bennett et al 1974,
Hauri et al 1979, Green et al 1981, Bergmann et al 1981, Roth & Berger
1982), has not yet been studied in detail.

How is newly synthesized SI transported from the Golgi complex to the
microvillus membrane? An unexpected finding was the association of
[³H]fucose-labelled pro-SI with the basolateral membrane (Fig. 1). Flow
kinetics of pro-SI from Golgi to surface membranes (Fig. 7) showed that
pro-SI was maximally labelled in the Golgi membranes after 15 min, in the
basolateral membranes after 30 min, and in the microvillus membranes after
45 min. This time-course suggested that pro-SI was transferred from the Golgi
to the microvillus membranes via the basolateral membrane. Several lines of
evidence seem to support such a concept, which was originally proposed by
Quaroni et al (1979a, b).

(1) Quaroni et al (1979a) observed that microvillar glycoproteins in villus
and crypt cells were transiently associated with the basolateral membrane

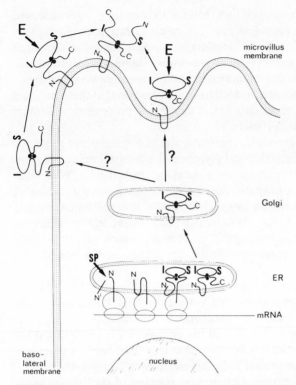

FIG. 8. Proposed membrane insertion, intracellular pathway and surface processing of newly synthesized sucrase–isomaltase. I, isomaltase portion (in pro-SI) or isomaltase subunit (in SI); S, sucrase portion (in pro-SI) or sucrase subunit (in SI); N, N-terminus; N', N-terminus of the postulated signal sequence; C, C-terminus; SP, signal peptidase; E, pancreatic proteases (e.g. elastase); ?, it is not unequivocally established whether pro-SI is transferred directly from the Golgi complex to the microvillus membrane or via the basolateral membrane.

fraction prior to their transfer to the microvillus membranes. This redistribution process was greatly inhibited by colchicine, suggesting that microtubules are involved in the polarization of the enterocyte (Quaroni et al 1979b). Data obtained by electron microscopical autoradiography are in agreement with this suggestion (Pavelka & Ellinger 1980, Blok et al 1981).

(2) Feracci et al (1982), using a histochemical approach in conjunction with ultra-thin frozen sections, have recently demonstrated enzymically active aminopeptidase N underneath the terminal web and in the upper part of the lateral membrane. Already their previous studies on the subcellular fractionation had revealed the presence of significant amounts (5–7%) of microvillus hydrolases in the basolateral membrane (Colas & Maroux 1980).

(3) Using a kidney epithelial cell line (MDCK), Louvard (1980) observed that aminopeptidase, when cross-linked at the apical surface with monospecific antibodies, was internalized, and it subsequently reappeared in the apical membrane at the region of intercellular junctions. Immunoelectron microscopy data confirmed a recycling of internalized aminopeptidase via the upper part of the basolateral membrane and led to the suggestion that the junctional complex might be involved in guiding apical membrane proteins to their final location (Reggio & Louvard 1980).

Despite these pieces of evidence, the existence of a basolateral route for the transfer of newly synthesized apical glycoproteins is by no means proven, and at present it can serve only as a working hypothesis. While the fractionation studies cannot fully exclude a possible cross-contamination of the basolateral membrane fraction by other intracellular membrane compartments (e.g. apical vesicles), morphological studies might not be sensitive enough to visualize trace amounts of glycoproteins which are transiently associated with the basolateral membrane en route to the microvillus membrane.

We are currently investigating the basolateral route by using a basolateral membrane-specific monoclonal antibody (A. Quaroni & H. P. Hauri, unpublished). This antibody recognizes two proteins of different apparent molecular masses in the basolateral membrane of the enterocyte. It will be used for the purification of the basolateral fraction and will thus help to elucidate whether pro-SI indeed is associated with this membrane compartment.

Fig. 8 schematically summarizes our present concept of the biosynthesis, assembly and intracellular pathway of SI. This scheme may also apply to some other microvillar hydrolases. Evidence for a common precursor of the two subunits has been presented for intestinal maltase–glucoamylase (Danielsen et al 1981b) and kidney γ-glutamyltransferase (Nash & Tate 1982). Another candidate, although not yet studied in detail, might be the heterodimeric intestinal enzyme enterokinase. It has become apparent, however, that the subunits of aminopeptidase N (Danielsen et al 1981a, 1982) and those of lactase–phlorizin hydrolase (Danielsen 1981b) are synthesized individually. It is obvious, therefore, that at least two different modes of subunit assembly exist for microvillar enzyme glycoproteins.

Acknowledgements

This work was supported by Grants No. 3.056.0.81 and 3.893.0.81 from the Swiss National Science Foundation, by the Barell Foundation of the Hoffmann-La Roche Company and the Sandoz Foundation for Biomedical Research. I thank Drs A. Quaroni, E. E. Rickli, G. Semenza and H. Wacker for their enthusiasm in collaborating in various phases of this project, Dr U. A. Meyer for reading the manuscript and Mrs M. Bucher for excellent secretarial help.

REFERENCES

Bennett G, Leblond CP, Haddad A 1974 Migration of glycoprotein from the Golgi apparatus to the surface of various cell types as shown by radioautography after labelled fucose injection into rats. J Cell Biol 60:258-284

Bergmann JE, Tokuyasu KT, Singer SJ 1981 Passage of an integral membrane protein, the vesicular stomatitis virus glycoprotein, through the Golgi apparatus en route to the plasma membrane. Proc Natl Acad Sci USA 78:1746-1750

Blok J, Ginsel LA, Mulder-Stapel AA, Onderwater JJM, Daems WT 1981 The effect of colchicine on the intracellular transport of ^{3}H-fucose-labelled glycoproteins in the absorptive cells of cultured human small-intestinal tissue. Cell Tissue Res 215:1-12

Brunner J, Hauser H, Braun H et al 1979 The mode of association of the enzyme complex sucrase–isomaltase with the intestinal brush border membrane. J Biol Chem 254:1821-1828

Cezard J-P, Conklin KA, Das BC, Gray GM 1979 Incomplete intracellular forms of intestinal surface membrane sucrase–isomaltase. J Biol Chem 254:8969-8975

Colas B, Maroux S 1980 Simultaneous isolation of brush-border and basolateral membrane from rabbit enterocytes. Presence of brush-border hydrolases in the basolateral membrane of rabbit enterocytes. Biochim Biophys Acta 600:406-420

Crane RK 1977 Digestion and absorption: water-soluble organics. Int Rev Physiol 12:325-365

Danielsen EM, Sjöström H, Norén O 1981a Biosynthesis of intestinal microvillar proteins. Putative precursor forms of microvillus aminopeptidase and sucrase–isomaltase isolated from Ca^{2+}-precipitated enterocyte membranes. FEBS (Fed Eur Biochem Soc) Lett 127:129-132

Danielsen EM, Skovbjerg H, Norén O, Sjöström H 1981b Biosynthesis of intestinal microvillar proteins. Nature of precursor forms of microvillar enzymes from Ca^{2+}-precipitated enterocyte membranes. FEBS (Fed Eur Biochem Soc) Lett 132:197-200

Danielsen EM, Norén O, Sjöström H 1982 Biosynthesis of intestinal microvillar proteins. Translational evidence *in vitro* that aminopeptidase N is synthesized as a M_r-115 000 polypeptide. Biochem J 204:323-327

Doell R, Rosen G, Kretchmer N 1964 Immunological studies of intestinal disaccharidases during normal and precocious development. Proc Natl Acad Sci USA 54:1268-1273

Dubs R, Gitzelman R, Steinmann R, Lindenmann J 1975 Catalytically inactive sucrase antigen of rabbit small intestine: the enzyme precursor. Helv Paediatr Acta 28:187-198

Engelman DM, Steitz TA 1981 The spontaneous insertion of proteins into and across membranes: the helical hairpin hypothesis. Cell 23:411-422

Feracci H, Bernadac A, Gorvel JP, Maroux S 1982 Localization by immunofluorescence and histochemical labeling of aminopeptidase N in relation to its biosynthesis in rabbit and pig enterocytes. Gastroenterology 82:317-324

Frank G, Brunner J, Hauser H, Wacker H, Semenza G, Zuber H 1978 The hydrophobic anchor of small-intestinal sucrase–isomaltase. N-terminal sequence of the isomaltase subunit. FEBS (Fed Eur Biochem Soc) Lett 96:183-188

Green J, Griffiths G, Louvard D, Quinn P, Warren G 1981 Passage of viral membrane proteins through the Golgi complex. J Mol Biol 152:663-698

Hadorn B, Green JR, Sterchi EE, Hauri HP 1981 Biochemical mechanisms in congenital enzyme deficiencies of the small intestine. Clin Gastroenterol 10:671-690

Hauri HP, Quaroni A, Isselbacher KJ 1979 Biogenesis of intestinal plasma membrane: posttranslational route and cleavage of sucrase–isomaltase. Proc Natl Acad Sci USA 76:5183-5186

Hauri HP, Quaroni A, Isselbacher KJ 1980 Monoclonal antibodies to sucrase–isomaltase: probes for the study of postnatal development and biogenesis of the intestinal microvillus membrane. Proc Natl Acad Sci USA 77:6629-6633

Hauri HP, Wacker H, Rickli EE, Bigler-Meier B, Quaroni A, Semenza G 1982 Biosynthesis of sucrase–isomaltase: purification and NH$_2$-terminal amino acid sequence of the rat sucrase–isomaltase precursor (pro-sucrase–isomaltase) from fetal intestinal transplants. J Biol Chem 257:4522-4528

Hopfer U, Nelson K, Perrotto J, Isselbacher KJ 1973 Glucose transport in isolated brush border membrane from rat small intestine. J Biol Chem 248:25-32

Kenny AJ, Maroux S 1982 Topology of microvillar membrane hydrolases of kidney and intestine. Physiol Rev 62:91-128

Kreil G 1981 Transfer of proteins across membranes. Annu Rev Biochem 50:317-348

Leapman SB, Deutsch AA, Grand RJ, Folkman J 1974 Transplantation of fetal intestine: survival and function in a subcutaneous location in adult animals. Ann Surg 179:109-114

Louvard D 1980 Apical membrane aminopeptidase appears at site of cell–cell contact in cultured kidney epithelial cells. Proc Natl Acad Sci USA 77:4132-4136

Montgomery RK, Sybicki MA, Grand RJ 1981a Autonomous biochemical and morphological differentiation in fetal rat intestine transplanted at 17 to 20 days of gestation. Dev Biol 87:76-84

Montgomery RK, Sybicki MA, Forcier AG, Grand RJ 1981b Rat intestinal microvillus membrane sucrase–isomaltase is a single high molecular weight protein and fully active enzyme in the absence of luminal factors. Biochim Biophys Acta 661:346-349

Nash B, Tate SS 1982 Biosynthesis of rat renal γ-glutamyl transpeptidase: evidence for a common precursor of the two subunits. J Biol Chem 257:585-588

Pavelka M, Ellinger A 1980 Effect of colchicine on the biosynthesis of plasma membrane glycoproteins in the rat intestinal epithelial cells as visualized by radioautography with ^{3}H-fucose. Eur J Cell Biol 22:259 (abstr)

Quaroni A, Kirsch K, Weiser MM 1979a Synthesis of membrane glycoproteins in rat small-intestinal villus cells. Redistribution of L-(1,5,6-^{3}H) fucose-labeled membrane glycoproteins among Golgi lateral basal and microvillus membranes in vivo. Biochem J 182:203-212

Quaroni A, Kirsch K, Weiser MM 1979b Synthesis of membrane glycoproteins in rat small-intestinal villus cells. Effect of colchicine on the redistribution of L-(1,5,6-^{3}H) fucose-labeled membrane glycoproteins among Golgi, lateral basal and microvillus membranes. Biochem J 182:213-221

Quaroni A, Wands J, Trelstad RL, Isselbacher KJ 1979c Epitheloid cell cultures from rat small intestine. Characterization by morphologic and immunologic criteria. J Cell Biol 80:248-265

Quaroni A, May R 1980 Establishment and characterization of intestinal epithelial cell cultures. Methods Cell Biol 21B:403-427

Reggio H, Louvard D 1980 An apical membrane protein, aminopeptidase, appears at the site of cell–cell contact in a culture of kidney epithelial cells. Eur J Cell Biol 22:271 (abstr)

Roth J, Berger E 1982 Immunocytochemical localization of galactosyltransferase in HeLa cells: codistribution with thiamine pyrophosphatase in trans-Golgi cisternae. J Cell Biol 92:223-229

Sabatini DD, Kreibich G, Morimoto T, Adesnik M 1982 Mechanisms for the incorporation of proteins in membranes and organelles. J Cell Biol 92:1-22

Semenza G 1978 The mode of anchoring of sucrase–isomaltase to the small intestinal brush border membrane and its biosynthetic implications. FEBS (Fed Eur Biochem Soc) Proc Meet 53:21-28

Semenza G 1981a Intestinal oligo- and disaccharidases. In: Randle PJ et al (eds) Carbohydrate metabolism and its disorders. Academic Press, London, vol 3:425-479

Semenza G 1981b Molecular pathophysiology of small-intestinal sucrase–isomaltase. Clin Gastroenterol 10:691-706

Sjöström H, Norén O, Christiansen L, Wacker H, Semenza G 1980 A fully active, two-active site, single-chain sucrase–isomaltase from pig small intestine. Implications for the biosynthesis of a mammalian integral stalked membrane protein. J Biol Chem 225:11332-11338

Tyler BM, Cowman AF, Gerondakis SD, Adams JM, Bernard O 1982 mRNA for surface immunoglobulin chains encodes a highly conserved transmembrane sequence and a 28-residue intracellular domain. Proc Natl Acad Sci USA 79:2008-2012

Wacker H, Jaussi R, Sonderegger P et al 1980 Cell-free synthesis of the one-chain precursor of a major intrinsic protein complex of the small-intestinal brush border membrane (pro-sucrase–isomaltase). FEBS (Fed Eur Biochem Soc) Lett 136:329-332

Weiser MM 1973 Intestinal epithelial cell surface membrane glycoprotein synthesis. I: An indicator of cellular differentiation. J Biol Chem 248:2536-2541

Weiser MM, Neumeier MM, Quaroni A, Kirsch K 1978 Synthesis of plasmalemmal glycoproteins in intestinal epithelial cells. Separation of Golgi membranes from villus and crypt cell surface membranes: galactosyltransferase activity of surface membrane. J Cell Biol 77:722-734

DISCUSSION

Inoue: Do you know any way by which the transient accumulation of brush border membrane proteins can be increased in basolateral plasma membranes?

Hauri: Yes. Quaroni et al (1979) have shown that colchicine treatment leads to an accumulation of newly synthesized brush border glycoproteins in the basolateral membrane fraction. This has later been corroborated by histo-autoradiography at the electron microscope level by several workers. On longer exposure to colchicine even the basolateral membrane develops micro-villus-like projections. Thus, colchicine apparently interferes with cell polarity.

Curthoys: Have you tried to determine if the pro-SI associated with the basolateral membrane fraction can be released by papain treatment?

Hauri: I haven't done this, but it should be possible because one can release it with elastase.

Maroux: We have tried to do this for aminopeptidase, and we can release it, but only at a slow rate, compared to that for the brush border membrane.

Sjöström: Were all the intestines from the same animal, in your experiments on the proteolytic transformation of pro-sucrase–isomaltase into final sucrase–isomaltase? There may be another reason why the products of *in vitro* hydrolysis of pro-sucrase–isomaltase were not exactly the same size as the polypeptides of final sucrase–isomaltase. We found variation in mobility in SDS–PAGE with different individuals, for both pro-sucrase–isomaltase and final sucrase–isomaltase. It may therefore be difficult to draw conclusions from these experiments if the preparations do not come from the same animal.

Hauri: We did not have this variation, probably because we used an inbred strain (Fisher rats).

Alpers: When you treated intestine with elastase your results on both transplants and normals showed subunits that were not identical to the micro-villus. But those were treated only with elastase and, although elastase may be the most active of the proteases, it is not the only one. Have you treated intestine with a mixture of the three major endopeptidases (trypsin, chymo-trypsin and elastase) to see if that reproduces the results?

Hauri: We have not used a mixture. Shapiro et al (1982) suggested that a mixture of trypsin and elastase might be more potent in the splitting process than elastase alone, but with trypsin alone we obtained degradation of pro-SI rather than cleavage.

Alpers: There are other examples of the same phenomenon—for instance, the luminal degradation of R-protein (Allen et al 1978) requires the combina-tion of the three endopeptidases.

Sjöström: We have not used a mixture but we have tested the three major pancreatic endopeptidases separately. All three result in splitting, but with a somewhat different pattern.

Alpers: It is conceivable that if you make a different polypeptide with, say, elastase it might be susceptible to trypsin, but the differences that one sees are not very great.

Semenza: We have examined the pro-sucrase–isomaltases of two species (rat and hog). Their N-terminal sequences are highly homologous but not identical (Hauri et al 1982, Sjöström et al 1982).

Schmitz: In this last processing step, have you any idea whether bacterial proteases will affect the splitting?

Hauri: I have evidence that bacteria are not involved in the splitting because SI is not cleaved even in infected transplants.

Rees: In your work with tritiated fucose *in vivo* you were seeing the precursor but not the subunits in the basolateral membrane. The possibility of the enzyme moving from the microvillar membrane to the basolateral mem-brane through tight junctions is therefore unlikely because if that were happening one would expect to see the individual subunits. Perhaps this is actually a sorting error rather than a diffusion process from the microvillar membrane.

Hauri: I was not saying that SI moves from the microvillus membrane to the basolateral membrane. Our working hypothesis is that the SI-precursor first moves to the basolateral membrane and subsequently is redistributed to the microvillus membrane where it is cleaved into its two subunits.

Rodewald: Your antibody for isolating the basolateral membrane could give you problems because of that, too. You may isolate not just basolateral membrane but also intracellular vesicles. It is not just a problem of differentiat-ing between apical and basolateral membrane in isolation.

Hauri: That's right; we have to be careful. However, one would expect that the basolateral antigen is exposed on the *inside* of vesicles that are derived from intracellular membranes, while it is exposed on the *outside* of basolateral membrane vesicles. So by using a basolateral membrane-specific antibody one should be able to discriminate between the two membrane compartments.

Curthoys: If the pro-SI were associated with an apical vesicle or an intracellular transport vesicle, you would expect that it would be oriented on the inside of that vesicle and that it would not be released by elastase.

Hauri: That is theoretically correct but, practically, one can never be sure that isolated membrane vesicles are completely sealed.

Alpers: That isn't necessarily true. For example, the receptor for intrinsic factor–cobalamin could get in by endocytosis of the already formed surface membrane, and the vesicle underneath the cell surface would have already been exposed. Your interpretation would be true only if the vesicle were coming from the inside of the cell and had never seen the luminal surface. But since endocytosis takes place, then even without contamination you could have an already exposed membrane.

REFERENCES

Allen RH, Seetharam B, Podell E, Alpers DH 1978 Effect of proteolytic enzymes on the binding of cobalamin to R proteins and intrinsic factor. J Clin Invest 61: 47-54

Hauri HP, Wacker H, Rickli EE, Bigler-Meier B, Quaroni A, Semenza G 1982 Biosynthesis of sucrase–isomaltase. Purification and NH_2-terminal amino acid sequence of the rat sucrase–isomaltase precursor (pro-sucrase–isomaltase) from fetal intestinal transplants. J Biol Chem 257: 4522-4528

Quaroni A, Kirsch K, Weiser MM 1979 Synthesis of membrane glycoproteins in rat small-intestinal villus cells. Effect of colchicine on the redistribution of L-(1,5,6-^{3}H)fucose-labelled membrane glycoproteins among Golgi, lateral basal and microvillus membranes. Biochem J 182: 213-221

Shapiro GL, Bulow SD, Conklin KA, Gray GM 1982 Conversion of single-chain sucrase precursor to the double chain sucrase-α-dextrinase (S-D) after its insertion in brush border. Gastroenterology 82: 1176 (abstract)

Sjöström H, Norén O, Christiansen LA et al 1982 Membrane anchoring and partial structure of small-intestinal pro-sucrase-isomaltase. A possible biosynthetic mechanism. FEBS (Fed Eur Biochem Soc) Lett 148:321-325

General Discussion I

Biosynthesis and assembly of brush border proteins

Some co-translational models for protein insertion into membranes

Desnuelle: Protein translocation across membranes is interesting because of its biological importance and the physicochemical problems raised by the passage of a largely hydrophilic molecule through a complex membrane structure, composed of a lipid bilayer sandwiched between two layers of charged groups. It is generally agreed that the principles governing co-translational translocation of secretory proteins and co-translational insertion of membrane proteins are similar, except of course that secretory proteins are discharged into the endoplasmic reticulum cisternae, while the membrane proteins remain bound to the membrane. Two categories of models have been proposed so far: those suggesting that special proteins in membranes facilitate the passage of the nascent chains; and those suggesting that all the information necessary for translocation is contained in the amino acid sequence of the chains.

The well known model proposed by Blobel & Dobberstein (1975) assumes that the leader sequence of the nascent chains somehow induces the formation across the membrane of an aqueous tunnel lined with endogenous proteins. The chains move forward along the tunnel until they are stopped by a so-called 'stop transfer' sequence. This process leads to the insertion of transmembrane proteins with an intra- and an extracytoplasmic segment, the relative sizes of which depend on the position of the 'stop transfer' sequence in the chain. The resulting 'N-out, C-in' arrangement has been experimentally checked in several cases. But it cannot apply to brush border hydrolases, including aminopeptidases, sucrase–isomaltase and dipeptidyl peptidase, which are known to be bound to the membrane by the N-terminus. Another characteristic of aminopeptidase and probably of other brush border enzymes is that they protrude almost completely from the extracytoplasmic face of the membrane so that the intracytoplasmic segment, if it exists, is very short.

Another model puts emphasis on the hydrophobicity of the leader sequence which should, in principle, allow direct transfer into the bilayer without expenditure of energy. According to the work of Inouye's group (see DiRienzo et al 1978), the rest of the growing chains form a 'loop' whose size increases as biosynthesis proceeds. At the end, the bulk of the chains has emerged from the extracytoplasmic face of the membrane. This model was initially proposed to explain translocation of secretory proteins. Therefore, the leader sequences were supposed to be cleaved by the signal peptidase (or 'signalase') and to remain inside the membrane in the form of short hydrophobic peptides, while the chains were discharged into the cisternae. But the signal peptidase may be absent sometimes, or ineffective. Then the proteins remain hung by the N-terminus, and they are almost completely outside since leader sequences are at or very close to the N-terminus.

More recently, a third model, the 'double helical hairpin' model, has been proposed by Engelman & Steitz (1981). Here, the leader sequence is assumed to form with the following segment of the chain two helixes able to penetrate into the bilayer. An alternative hypothesis is that the helix is not preformed in the cytoplasm and then inserted, but that it is progressively built where it is needed at the surface of the membrane. In this case, one might assume that the role of the leader sequence is to help translocation of the rest of the chain by virtue of physiochemical interactions between groups correctly distributed

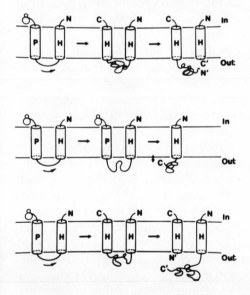

FIG. 1. (*Desnuelle*) The 'double helical hairpin' mechanism for co-translational protein insertion into membranes. *Top*: The leader sequence (hydrophobic, H) does not cross the bilayer. The rest of the chain, which is assumed to be polar (P), crosses the membrane until it is stopped by a stop transfer sequence. The signal peptidase cleaves the chain just after the leader sequence, resulting in an 'N-out, C-in' arrangement. The leader sequence remains inside the membrane. *Bottom*: Same scheme as above except that the signal peptidase cleavage occurs near the stop transfer sequence, resulting in an 'N-in, C-out' insertion. The stop transfer sequence remains inside the membrane. *Middle*: In the absence of a stop transfer sequence and a functional signal peptidase, the undegraded C-terminus of the chain emerges into the extracytoplasmic space and the chain is anchored by the N-terminus (adapted from Engelman & Steitz 1981).

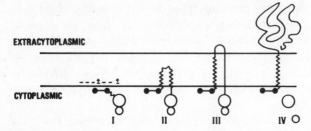

Fig. 2. (*Desnuelle*) Model for insertion of intestinal brush border aminopeptidase by the N-terminus. Zig-zag line shows hydrophobic sequence of about 20 amino acids; +, positive charges borne by the N-terminal tyrosine and the lysine at position 4; ±, negative charges or zwitterions of the inner phospholipid heads. I: Binding of the nascent chain by electrostatic interactions to the cytoplasmic face of the membrane. II: Direct transfer of the hydrophobic sequence into the lipid core of the membrane. III: Further growth of the chain by a still controversial mechanism. IV: Folding of the chain in the extracytoplasmic space (from Feracci et al 1982).

along the chain. As shown in Fig. 1, this model may explain several aspects of protein translocation, including discharge of secretory proteins and insertion by the 'N-out, C-in' or 'N-in, C-out' arrangement.

The mode of insertion proposed by Professor Semenza (see Semenza et al, this volume) for the isomaltase subunit of sucrase–isomaltase is probably compatible with one of the sophisticated versions of the Engelman–Steitz model. However, the low M_r values found for the anchoring peptides of aminopeptidases N and A by the isotope dilution technique led us to adopt a simpler version, illustrated in Fig. 2 (see Feracci et al 1982).

The presence of the two positive charges in the 'pre-piece' (also found in leader sequences) suggests that the very beginning of each nascent chain does not penetrate into the bilayer, but is stopped at the cytoplasmic face by electrostatic interactions. Then comes the hydrophobic segment, which may be transferred either as a 'loop' or as a 'double helical hairpin'. Finally, the protein emerges almost completely from the extracytoplasmic surface of the membrane and is bound by the N-terminus. The intracytoplasmic segment is composed of a few amino acids only. This model is so simple that it may appear naive. Nevertheless, it suggests that both electrostatic and hydrophobic interactions are necessary for proteins to be firmly bound to membranes. In serum lipoproteins, phospholipids are bound to the apoproteins by both their polar heads and their hydrophobic chains. The model is therefore consistent with the low M_r of the anchoring peptides of aminopeptidases N and A, with the asymmetric distribution of the molecules with respect to the membrane plane, and with the 'N-in, C-out' arrangement.

Semenza: In addition to the schemes you have summarized, John Kenny and Suzanne Maroux (1982) have suggested that the protein, e.g. sucrase–isomaltase, may be secreted into the cisternal space in rough endoplasmic reticulum or Golgi, and then be re-inserted through the hydrophobic segment into the membrane from the outside. Incidentally, I would like to mention the paper by Austen (1979), in which the formation of a loop during biosynthesis and insertion of membrane proteins was, I believe, suggested for the first time.

Hermon-Taylor: Brian Austen and David Ridd have recently prepared a novel 19-residue peptide whose amino acid sequence is predicted to confer secondary structural features commonly found in naturally occurring signal peptides. These include positively charged lysine and arginine residues near the amino terminus, a hydrophobic core with a tendency for α-helix formation, a β-turn near the C-terminus, acidic and basic residues on either side of the C-terminus and a small uncharged aliphatic residue on the carbonyl side of the potential signal peptidase cleavage point. This artificial consensus sequence inhibited the processing of bovine pituitary mRNA-directed pre-prolactin by dog pancreatic microsomes when added to cell-free translation systems in concentrations up to 50 μM. These findings further emphasize the importance of secondary structural features in the biological activity of signal peptides.

Sjöström: The Inouye model that Professor Desnuelle presented for the synthesis of aminopeptidase N does not include any cleaved signal. It seems that this could fit with our results from cell-free translation experiments in combination with tunicamycin-treated organ-cultured intestinal explants. There is no obvious need for cleavage of the signal for membrane proteins that have their N-terminal amino acid on the cytosolic side, and the combination of a cytosolic N-terminal amino acid and a non-cleaved signal may be a general phenomenon. The only other example known to me is band 3 protein of erythrocytes, which has its N-terminal on the inside and is synthesized without a cleaved signal.

Desnuelle: The Inouye model (DiRienzo et al 1978) was initially proposed for secretory proteins and this is why the leader sequence is cleaved in this model. But it can also be used for membrane proteins that are not cleaved and are bound by the N-terminus.

Alpers: We (Gordon et al 1982a,b) have compared the N-terminal sequences of rat intestinal prepro-apolipoprotein AI (prepro-apo AI) and pre-apolipoprotein AIV (pre-apo AIV). We have almost obtained the complete leader sequences, but we still don't have the entire sequence of pre-apo AIV (see Fig. 3).

With only a small shift in the assignment of the positions for pre-apo AIV compared with apo AI, 10 of the 18 amino acids are in identical positions. But, in addition, apolipoprotein AI has a propeptide (prepro-apo AI) of six amino acids. The post- and co-translational cleavage of prepro-apo AI occurs at an alanine residue, which is a good substrate for the leader sequence (two glutamines have never been seen at the end of a leader sequence, and that is not where signal peptidase splits). We don't yet know where cleavage occurs

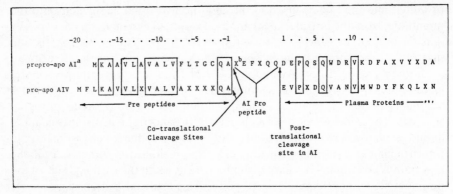

FIG. 3. (*Alpers*) Comparison of the N-terminal sequences of rat intestinal prepro-apo AI and pre-apo AIV. [a]As determined in Gordon et al 1982a,b. [b]X indicates that an assignment has not been made at this position.

between the product of the signal peptidase and the beginning of the mature protein as found in the plasma. This is a possible mechanism whereby things can be differentially sequestered in the intestine. Dr Semenza just mentioned the suggestion of Kenny & Maroux (1982) about proteins that have been put into the cisterna and then re-enter the membrane. That mechanism is proposed for mitochondrial proteins (which are synthesized on free ribosomes) but, to my knowledge, those are not glycoproteins. So I don't know how that mechanism relates to the glycosylated membrane proteins.

Semenza: Whereas cytochrome b_5 or cytochrome b_5 reductase does get inserted spontaneously into pre-formed liposomes, sucrase–isomaltase does not. Proteoliposomes are formed by sucrase–isomaltase with phosphatidylcholine only in the presence of detergent (Brunner et al 1978). This makes the later insertion into a pre-formed membrane less likely. But of course there may be a question of difference in lipid.

Alpers: The receptor for intrinsic factor–cobalamin can become inserted into pre-formed liposomes. Its complete form has a relative molecular mass of 222 000 (see also p 156).

Louvard: We are just beginning to understand the translocating machinery, and most of these models so far have been in terms of hydrophobicity. Meyer et al (1982), however, have purified a specific protein of the translocating machinery. Also, Walter & Blobel (1981) have recently described a protein that they call SRP (signal recognition protein), which is a complex of six polypeptides. SRP stops the translation of the protein after the synthesis of 70 amino acids has been completed. Presumably it can recognize the signal sequence of secretory proteins. Once this association is completed the complex formed can interact with a component specifically associated with a membrane of the rough endo-plasmic reticulum, the 'docking protein' (Meyer et al 1982). Once the insertion of the leading signal peptide into the membrane has been understood, the way the rest of the chain passes through the membrane may be resolved. We may expect to find other specific proteins which create some sort of aqueous pore, and provide specificity for transfer.

Desnuelle: These are interesting comments, but it is not easy for a physical chemist to accept the idea that nature synthesizes a hydrophobic leader sequence just to drill an aqueous tunnel across a membrane. But it may be true in some cases. Even if the leader sequence is directly transferred, with the first residues remaining inside, the steps of translocation that follow may require special proteins, as proposed by Blobel & Dobberstein (1975).

Smith: Another conceptual difficulty for people who are interested in transport arises from the fact that you cannot get a single hydrophobic amino acid across a bilayer at any significant rate unless you have a protein that is specific for carrying it. Spontaneous insertions of hydrophobic regions and passage across a bilayer can take place, in physicochemical terms, but how quickly does this happen? If it is a rapid mechanism, it is essential to consider seriously the proposals of Blobel & Dobberstein (1975).

Louvard: For insertion one also needs a specific transfer protein on the membrane (see Walter & Blobel 1981). There are two or possibly more components there.

Alpers: So Professor Desnuelle's suggestion is reasonable, but these other helpers are also needed, I would think.

Louvard: Not only for that, but one needs them also for specificity, or otherwise the protein will be inserted into the Golgi membrane.

Hauri: In addition, ribophorins (Sabatini et al 1981, 1982) appear to play a part in the translocation process.

Semenza: What is really needed is a good collaboration between physical chemistry and biochemistry to get a protein synthesized!

Rees: Is there any evidence for the ionic interaction that Professor Desnuelle proposes at the surface of the endoplasmic reticulum? Secondly, as I understand it, sucrase–isomaltase does not spontaneously insert into preformed liposomes, neither does it have the signal peptide removed. Therefore, would one not expect to see some sort of interaction of this enzyme with liposomes or vesicles?

Desnuelle: We have no experimental evidence that the charged groups remain at the intracytoplasmic surface of the membrane. However, two facts must be taken into account: (a) the transfer of these groups into the lipid bilayer would cost a great deal of energy; and (b) the groups are likely to interact with the phospholipid polar heads, which are predominantly negative at the inner membrane surface, at least in the erythrocyte (Verkleij et al 1973). Moreover, if some residues remain in the cytoplasm, where they might interact with other cytoplasmic components, the protein conserves its transmembrane character, even though it is almost completely outside.

Rees: I understand that, but I thought you were proposing that there was a spontaneous association of the hydrophobic leader sequence with the lipid bilayer. If so, why does one not see it in the case of proteins that still have their leader sequences present?

Hermon-Taylor: The presentation of a signal sequence to a membrane or another macromolecule as the nascent chain emerges from a ribosome is likely to differ substantially from the arrangement it may adopt in a completed preprotein where the specific accessibility of the signal sequence may no longer be assured. In a single round of translation in edeine-containing rabbit reticulo-cyte lysates, programmed with dog pancreatic mRNA, we have shown that enteropeptidase is capable of converting pretrypsinogen to trypsin only when the enzyme is added within about two minutes of the onset of translation, and that enteropeptidase has little effect on completed pretrypsinogen (Ridd et al 1982). This is likely to be because the Lys–Ile target bond on the C-terminal side of the tetra-aspartyl-containing activation peptide, only a few residues downstream from the signal sequence, becomes progressively inaccessible as the developing preprotein folds. The signal peptide itself may take part in the formation of secondary structure in the interior of the completed preprotein. Brian Austen and David Ridd have recently shown, however, that free synthetic signal peptide binds saturably to ribosome-depleted rough microsomes with a K_d of approximately 10^{-7} M.

Molecular sizes of brush border enzymes during assembly

Kenny: I have attempted, with the help of Drs Sjöström & Norén, to collect a table of the relative molecular masses of different forms of brush border enzymes. We have tried to list not only the final form but also some of the precursor forms, endo-H-sensitive and insensitive forms and, for a very few, the primary translation product (see Table 1). This might sharpen the focus of our discussion on the biosynthesis of the brush border enzymes.

Alpers: In addition, alkaline phosphatase (EC 3.1.3.1) seems to have a leader peptide that has an M_r of around 1000 (D.H. Alpers, unpublished work). We have not yet done glycosylated membrane experiments to confirm that value. The intrinsic factor–cobalamin receptor has an M_r of 220 000 and has no carbohydrate: it is unusual for a brush border protein because it is not glycosylated.

Hauri: Is that receptor initially synthesized as a soluble protein on free ribosomes? I would expect it to be so because it doesn't carry any carbohydrate.

Alpers: I don't know. That would be reasonable but to make 1 mg of it we

TABLE 1 *(Kenny) M*$_r$ **values of different forms of brush border enzymes**

Enzyme (and E.C. name)	E.C. no.	Relative molecular mass (M_r) in 1000's Final form	Endo-H insensitive	Endo-H sensitive	Primary translation products
Sucrase–isomaltase (sucrose α-D-glyco-hydrolase, oligo-1,6-glucosidase)	3.2.1.48 3.2.1.10	140,160[a,b] 275[c]	260[f,g,h]	240[f,g,h]	~275[a,d] 220(*)[e]
Maltase–glucoamylase (α-D-glucosidase)	3.2.1.20	245 130(*)[j]	245[g,i]	225[g,i]	—
Lactase–phlorizin hydrolase (β-D-galactosidase)	3.2.1.23 3.2.1.62	160	160[g]	150[g] 190[i],200[i]	—
Aminopeptidase N (aminopeptidase, microsomal)	3.4.11.2	160	160[f,g,h]	140(*)[f,g,h]	115[e]
Aminopeptidase A (aspartate amino-peptidase)	3.4.11.7	170	170[i]	140[i]	—
Dipeptidyl peptidase IV	3.4.14.– or 3.4.21.–	140	140[i]	115[i]	—
γ-Glutamyltransferase	3.2.2.2	51[k] 22[k]	78[k]	—	—

See also Table 5 in Sjöström et al, this volume. (*), doublet. [a]As estimated from SDS-PAGE. [b]Sigrist et al 1975; Brunner et al 1979. [c]M_r of the sucrase–isomaltase complex, as determined from its sedimentation behaviour; Spiess et al 1981. [d]As radioactive precursor from Golgi membranes: Hauri et al 1979; as pro-sucrase–isomaltase: Sjöström et al 1980, Hauri et al 1982; as *in vitro* translation product (pre-pro-sucrase–isomaltase): Wacker et al 1981. [e]Danielsen et al 1982. [f]Danielsen et al 1981a. [g]Danielsen et al 1981b. [h]Danielsen 1982. [i]E. M. Danielsen (unpublished). [j]Sørensen et al 1982. [k]Nash & Tate 1982. See individual references for species.

have to start with 5 kg of canine ileum, so we can't obtain cell-free translation products very readily!

Jørgensen: The mechanism of biosynthesis of the peptides of Na$^+$,K$^+$-ATPase (EC 3.6.1.3) has not been solved. This enzyme, of course, is not included in Table 1 because it is not a brush border enzyme. The results for the β-subunit appear to be consistent, while there are divergent data for the α-subunit. The β-subunit is synthesized in bound polysomes. Tunicamycin-sensitive glycosylation in the endoplasmic reticulum raises the M_r of the β-subunit from 38 000 to 45 000. Second-stage glycosylation in the Golgi is monensin-sensitive and raises the M_r further to 57 000. The α-subunit (M_r 106 000) was first reported to be synthesized on *free* polysomes with post-translational insertion, presumably with the β-subunit as receptor in the target membrane (Sabatini et al 1981, 1982). I believe that more recent results (D.D. Sabatini, personal communication, May 1982) suggest, however, that the α-subunit is synthesized on membrane-bound polysomes. The N-terminus of the α-subunit is cytoplasmic, with at least six and possibly eight transmembrane segments in the chain (see Jørgensen 1982).

Hauri: Our basolateral membrane protein defined by a monoclonal antibody has similar structural properties to Na^+,K^+-ATPase and it might indeed turn out to be the same enzyme. If so, then our results suggest that both subunits will be synthesized on membrane-bound ribosomes. We found this basolateral antigen in microsomes, in the Golgi apparatus and in basolateral membranes as individual subunits.

Distribution of enteropeptidase and aminopeptidase to non-brush border sites

Hermon-Taylor: We are most interested in the concept that brush border macromolecules might not be so confined to enterocyte membranes or to intestinal lumen as may have been imagined in the past. In collaboration with Robin Offord we developed a specific one-stage assay for enteropeptidase, based on the detection of the equimolar release of the activation peptides from α-N-tritiated trypsinogen (Magee et al 1981). This assay is independent of the presence of trypsin inhibitors and has allowed us to test for the enzyme in serum and bile with a detection limit of less than 0.5 ng enteropeptidase. In conscious animals, gentle luminal perfusion of the proximal duodenum even with warm saline and minimal distension results in the displacement of enteropeptidase into portal venous blood (Talbot et al 1982), and we have recently identified enteropeptidase in human bile. Blood-born enteropeptidase is rapidly cleared from the circulation by the liver, with a half-life of about 2.5 min (Grant et al 1979). The mechanism involves recognition of the peripheral sugars of the heavily glycosylated enzyme by hepatocyte receptors in a manner similar to that described for the clearance of asialoglycoproteins (Hudgin et al 1974). Chronic ethanol consumption in animals increases the amount of catalytically active enteropeptidase appearing in bile after intravenous administration (Grant & Hermon-Taylor 1982). The inappropriate sequestration of enteropeptidase from the duodenum into the blood, and its appearance in bile in catalytically active form, may be critical events in triggering acute necrotizing pancreatitis in humans.

Kenny: Is the enzyme recaptured by the enterocyte?

Hermon-Taylor: Probably not; however, enteropeptidase may pass from the enterocyte into portal blood in the absence of morphological evidence of mucosal damage. The mechanism of this transfer is unknown and requires further study.

Alpers: Is that the same enzyme as the brush border enzyme? We have the example of alkaline phosphatase.

Hermon-Taylor: We do not yet know the molecular form of catalytically active enteropeptidase excreted in bile, but we are attempting to characterize this by using [^{3}H]diisopropylphosphorofluoridate.

Alpers: It is interesting that the soluble alkaline phosphatase in the rat is also cleared by the liver, by a mechanism different from that for asialoglycoproteins (G.P. Young & D.H. Alpers, unpublished work).

Hauri: Your assay for measuring enteropeptidase activity appears to be similar to that developed by Hesford et al (1976). However, their assay is not entirely specific and evidently measures another as yet uncharacterized peptidase; is your assay specific?

Hermon-Taylor: We looked at the hydrolysis by enteropeptidase of the low M_r artificial substrate described by Hesford et al (1976). The assay, of course, depends on the colour developed after the release of 2-naphthylamine from tetra-L-aspartyl-lysyl-2-naphthylamide (Asp$_4$LysNNap). The substrate is susceptible to arylamidases which, unlike enteropeptidase, can be inhibited by 2–5 mM-Zn^{2+} in the assay buffer (Grant & Hermon-Taylor 1979). However, when trying to detect low levels of enteropeptidase activity in the presence of a high concentration of arylamidases (such as in bile) it is at times difficult to be certain that arylamidase inhibition is complete. The assay we developed (Magee et al 1981) uses the natural macromolecular substrate trypsinogen in the presence of trypsin inhibitors that detect the specific release of α-N-[^{3}H]-tetra-aspartyl activation peptides. This assay is specific for enteropeptidase; however, the two one-stage assays can be used together for the positive identification of enteropeptidase, since antibody to human enteropeptidase specifically inhibits cleavage of α-N-[^{3}H]-trypsinogen but not of Asp$_4$LysNNap. This is presumably because the low M_r substrate can still gain access to the active site of enteropeptidase in an immune complex with antibody directed against this domain of the molecule, whereas macromolecular trypsinogen cannot.

General functions of the enterocyte

Alpers: Drs J.I. Gordon, A.W. Strauss and I have isolated intact RNA from the enterocyte and translated it in both the wheatgerm and the reticulocyte lysate systems. The endogenous wheatgerm translation has the advantage over the reticulocyte lysate of not containing large endogenous messages at 40–

50 000 M_r. We have measured total jejunal RNA and found that two of the major mRNAs code for apolipoproteins AIV and AI, as identified by immunoprecipitation. Another abundant mRNA product that we have observed is calcium binding protein; and a doublet band, which is intestinal fatty acid binding protein, is seen at about 14 500 M_r. The so-called sterol carrier protein (the liver fatty acid binding protein, or protein Z) is made in much greater quantities in the intestine, compared to the liver. Many of these low M_r proteins in the intestine are actively translated, but estimation of the amount of message in a cell-free translation system depends on the efficiency of translation of the message, and smaller M_r messages may be translated more efficiently than the larger ones. These estimates are thus weighted *against* brush border proteins. We did not find a large content of mRNA for actin in the total enterocyte mucosa, but we have not done immunoprecipitation for that. When the fluorograph translation has been developed longer, many bands appear, but the amount of label in them is limited, even in a cell-free system. Immunoprecipitated alkaline phosphatase corresponds to a band that is about 0.05% of the total translatable mRNA. Sucrase–isomaltase cannot be detected in a small (50 µl) translation. Semenza et al (see this volume) have used a large-volume translation, and Dr Semenza has suggested that sucrase–isomaltase arises from a gene duplication. Liver or intestinal fatty acid binding proteins are similar in M_r, and have identical active sites, in that they seem to bind fatty acids in a similar way. We have now sequenced both proteins entirely through recombinant DNA techniques, and although the structures are fairly homologous at one end of the molecule, large areas of the molecule are not similar (see Fig. 3). The active site is probably at the N terminus where homology exists.

Quaroni: If you do cell-free translation with reticulocyte lysate do you see more translation of large messages?

Alpers: No, but only a slight increase. This suggests that we are not missing much mRNA in the wheatgerm. If we do the liquid RNA excess hybridization with the clone for apolipoprotein AIV (M_r 46 000) the percentage of translatable message is identical to that obtained from the cell-free translation data.

Quaroni: I am surprised that you see so little translation of larger messages, which makes me wonder if some of them are degraded.

Alpers: It is possible, but the RNA is shown to be intact by methylmercury denaturing gels, and the results are reproducible.

Quaroni: If you select mRNAs for apoliproproteins by hybridization to the corresponding cDNAs bound to cellulose, and then do cell-free translation, do you see single bands?

Alpers: One can hybrid-arrest by RNA/DNA hybridization first. We cannot completely hybrid-arrest the apolipoprotein AIV but our clone for that contains none of the structural part of the gene.

Quaroni: How large are the inserts?

Alpers: Our best studied examples to date are the fatty acid binding proteins. For the intestinal fatty acid binding protein the mRNA (by 'northern blot' analysis) is about 900 nucleotides long and the coding region has 558 nucleotides, so about 350 nucleotides are not translated.

Louvard: Have you tried to separate RNA on a sucrose sizing gradient to see if it is large? And have you translated the purified fraction?

Alpers: We plan to enrich for RNA. With the fatty acid binding protein we have enriched for RNA with a low M_r. The magnitude of the enrichment problem will be much greater for the RNA with a higher M_r.

Desnuelle: The fatty acid-binding proteins might function in lipid transport across membranes. Dietary triglycerides are hydrolysed by pancreatic lipase into more hydrophilic monoglycerides and free fatty acids, which can be assumed to insert spontaneously into the membrane. But we need to know how they get out. The fatty acid binding proteins might be considered to provide one of the internal pumps for these lipids.

Alpers: Their function is unknown. Both fatty acid binding proteins are acetylated at the N-terminus and are entirely intracellular. The intracellular concentration of fatty acid after giving 0.5 ml corn oil to a rat is about 100 mM, as calculated if it were free in solution. So the proteins may act (like calcium-binding protein) as a buffer that influences intracellular concentration of fatty acid.

REFERENCES

Austen BM 1979 Predicted secondary structures of amino-terminal extension sequences of secretory proteins. FEBS (Fed Eur Biochem Soc) Lett 103: 308-318

Blobel G, Dobberstein B 1975 Transfer of proteins across membranes. I: Presence of proteolytically processed and unprocessed nascent immunoglobulin light chains on membrane-bound ribosomes of murine myeloma. J Cell Biol 67: 835-851

Brunner J, Hauser H, Semenza G 1978 Single bilayer lipid–protein vesicles formed from phosphatidylcholine and small intestinal sucrase–isomaltase. J Biol Chem 253: 7538-7546

Brunner J, Hauser H, Braun H et al 1979 The mode of association of the enzyme complex sucrase-isomaltase with the intestinal brush border membrane. J Biol Chem 254: 1821-1828

Danielsen EM 1982 Biosynthesis of intestinal microvillar proteins. Pulse–chase labelling studies on aminopeptidase N and sucrase–isomaltase. Biochem J 204: 639-645

Danielsen EM, Sjöström H, Norén O 1981a Biosynthesis of intestinal microvillar proteins. Putative precursor forms of microvillus aminopeptidase and sucrase–isomaltase isolated from Ca^{2+}-precipitated enterocyte membranes. FEBS (Fed Eur Biochem Soc) Lett 127: 129-132

Danielsen EM, Skovberg H, Norén O, Sjöström H 1981b Biosynthesis of intestinal microvillar proteins. Nature of precursor forms of microvillar enzymes from Ca^{2+}-precipitated enterocyte membranes. FEBS (Fed Eur Biochem Soc) Lett 132: 197-200

Danielsen EM, Norén O, Sjöström H 1982 Biosynthesis of intestinal microvillar proteins. *In vitro* translational evidence that aminopeptidase N is synthesised as a M_r 115 000 polypeptide. Biochem J 204: 323-327

DiRienzo JM, Nakamura K, Inouye M 1978 The outer membrane proteins of gram-negative bacteria: biosynthesis, assembly, and functions. Annu Rev Biochem 47: 481-532

Engelman DM, Steitz TA 1981 The spontaneous insertion of proteins into and across membranes—the helical hairpin hypothesis. Cell 23: 411-422

Feracci H, Maroux S, Bonicel J, Desnuelle P 1982 The amino acid sequence of the hydrophobic anchor of rabbit intestinal brush border aminopeptidase N. Biochim Biophys Acta 684: 133-136

Gordon JI, Smith DP, Andy R, Alpers DH, Schonfeld G, Strauss AW 1982a The primary translation product of rat intestinal apolipoprotein A-I mRNA is an unusual preproprotein. J Biol Chem 257: 971-978

Gordon JI, Smith DP, Alpers DH, Strauss AW 1982b Proteolytic processing of the primary translation product of rat intestinal apolipoprotein A-IV mRNA. Comparison with preproapolipoprotein A-I processing. J Biol Chem 257: 8418-8423

Grant DAW, Hermon-Taylor J 1979 Hydrolysis of artificial substrates by enterokinase and trypsin and the development of a sensitive specific assay for enterokinase in serum. Biochim Biophys Acta 567: 207-215

Grant DAW, Hermon-Taylor J 1982 The biliary excretion of enterokinase is increased in rats with experimentally induced alcoholic fatty liver. Gastroenterology 82(2): 1073 (abstract)

Grant DAW, Magee AI, Meeks D, Regan C, Bainbridge DR, Hermon-Taylor J 1979 Identification of a defence mechanism in vivo against the leakage of enterokinase into the blood. Biochem J 184: 619-626

Hauri HP, Quaroni A, Isselbacher K 1979 Biogenesis of intestinal plasma membrane: posttranslational route and cleavage of sucrase–isomaltase. Proc Natl Acad Sci USA 76: 5183-5186

Hauri HP, Wacker H, Rickli EE, Bigler-Meier B, Quaroni A, Semenza G 1982 Biosynthesis of sucrase–isomaltase. Purification and NH_2-terminal amino acid sequence of the rat sucrase–isomaltase precursor (pro-sucrase–isomaltase) from fetal intestinal transplants. J Biol Chem 257: 4522-4528

Hesford F, Hadorn B, Blaser K, Schneider CH 1976 A new substrate for enteropeptidase. FEBS (Fed Eur Biochem Soc) Lett 71: 279-282

Hudgin RL, Pricer WE, Ashwell G, Stockert RJ, Morell AG 1974 The isolation and properties of a rabbit liver binding protein specific for asialoglycoproteins. J Biol Chem 249: 5536-5543

Jørgensen PL 1982 Mechanism of the Na,K-pump. Protein structure and conformations of the pure Na,K-ATPase. Biochim Biophys Acta 694: 1-42

Kenny J, Maroux S 1982 Topology of microvillar membrane hydrolases of kidney and intestine. Physiol Rev 62: 91-128

Magee AI, Grant DAW, Hermon-Taylor J, Offord RE 1981 Specific one-stage method for assay of enterokinase activity by release of radiolabelled activation peptides from α-N-[^{3}H]acetyltrypsinogen and the effect of calcium ions on the enzyme activity. Biochem J 197: 239-244

Meyer DI, Krause E, Dobberstein B 1982 Secretory protein translocation across membranes—the role of the 'docking protein'. Nature (Lond) 297: 647-650

Nash B, Tate SS 1982 Biosynthesis of rat renal γ-glutamyltranspeptidase. J Biol Chem 257: 585-588

Ridd DH, Hermon-Taylor J, Austen BM 1982 Enterokinase as a model for co-translational processing. Biochem Soc Trans 10: 46-47

Sabatini DD, Colman D, Sabban E et al 1981 Mechanisms for the incorporation of proteins into the plasma membrane. Cold Spring Harbor Symp Quant Biol 46: 807-818

Sabatini DD, Kreibich G, Morimoto T, Adesnik M 1982 Mechanisms for the incorporation of proteins in membranes and organelles. J Cell Biol 92: 1-22

Sigrist H, Ronner P, Semenza G 1975 A hydrophobic form of the small intestinal sucrase–isomaltase complex. Biochim Biophys Acta 406: 433-446

Sjöström H, Norén O, Christiansen L, Wacker H, Semenza G 1980 A fully active, two-active sites, single-chain sucrase–isomaltase from pig small intestine. Implications for the biosynthesis of a mammalian integral stalked membrane protein. J Biol Chem 255: 11332-11338

Sørensen SH, Norén O, Sjöström H, Danielsen EM 1982 Amphiphilic pig intestinal microvillus maltase/glucoamylase: structure and specificity. Eur J Biochem 126:559-568

Spiess M, Hauser H, Rosenbusch JP, Semenza G 1981 Hydrodynamic properties of phospholipid vesicles and of sucrase–isomaltase–phospholipid vesicles. J Biol Chem 256: 8977-8982

Talbot RW, Grant DAW, Hermon-Taylor J 1982 Displacement of enterokinase into portal venous blood and bile during luminal perfusion of the proximal small intestine. Gastroenterology 82(2): 1192 (abstract)

Verkleij AJ, Zwaal RFA, Roelofsen B, Comfurius P, Kastelijn D, Van Deenen LLM 1973 The asymmetric distribution of phospholipids in the human red cell membrane. A combined study using phospholipases and freeze-etch electron microscopy. Biochim Biophys Acta 323: 178-193

Wacker H, Jaussi R, Sonderegger P et al 1981 Cell-free synthesis of the one-chain precursor of a major intrinsic protein complex of the small intestinal brush border membrane (pro-sucrase–isomaltase). FEBS (Fed Eur Biochem Soc) Lett 136: 329-332

Walter P, Blobel G 1981 Translocation of proteins across the endoplasmic reticulum. III: Signal recognition protein (SRP) causes signal sequence-dependent and site-specific arrest of chain elongation that is released by microsomal membranes. J Cell Biol 91: 557-561

Molecular architecture of the microvillus cytoskeleton

ANTHONY BRETSCHER

Section of Biochemistry, Molecular and Cell Biology, Wing Hall, Cornell University, Ithaca, New York 14853, USA

Abstract This study deals with the molecular organization and function of the components of filament core bundles in intestinal epithelial microvilli. The core, isolated in the absence of free Ca^{2+}, contains five major proteins: the actin (M_r 43 000) that makes up the filaments, the villin (M_r 95 000) and fimbrin (M_r 68 000) that cross-link the filaments together, and the 110 000 M_r polypeptide–calmodulin complex that makes up cross-filaments which project laterally from the core and link it to the inner surface of the microvillus membrane. A minor component of the isolated core, an 80 000 M_r polypeptide, has also been isolated, but its function is unknown. *In vitro* studies have revealed that villin fragments the actin filaments when the free Ca^{2+} concentration is increased above 10^{-6} M and, as a consequence, treatment of microvillus cores with Ca^{2+} leads to their partial disassembly. The effects of treating isolated microvilli with various agents, including Ca^{2+}, were therefore examined in terms of the cytoskeletal components that were solubilized and the morphological changes that were induced. Treatment of isolated microvilli with concentrations higher than 10^{-6} M free Ca^{2+} resulted in the appearance of regular constrictions of the microvillus membrane and the solubilization of several cytoskeletal components. It is tentatively suggested that this process may occur reversibly *in vivo* in the normal functioning of the microvillus.

1983 Brush border membranes. Pitman Books Ltd, London (Ciba Foundation symposium 95) p 164-179

We are studying the molecular arrangement of components that make up the cytoskeletal cores of microvilli which form part of the brush border on intestinal epithelial cells. The function of these structures must be understood if the role played by the microvillus cytoskeleton in the uptake of nutrients through the microvillus membrane from the intestinal lumen is to be revealed. As discussed in detail below, the isolated microvillus does not behave as a purely rigid structure when subjected to various treatments *in vitro*, which opens up the possibility that it may not be a completely static structure *in vivo*. A molecular understanding of the microvillus cytoskeleton will therefore expand our knowledge of nutrient uptake by intestinal epithelial cells as well as provide a model system for studying the organization of microfilaments in a defined structure, which may also have relevance to structural organizations in other cells.

Results and discussion

Isolation, ultrastructure and polypeptide composition of microvillus cores

Highly purified intact brush borders from the apical end of intestinal epithelial cells can be isolated in a matter of hours by methods originally described by Miller & Crane (1961) and subsequently modified by others (Mooseker 1976, Bretscher & Weber 1978, Glenney & Weber 1980). Isolated brush borders consist of about one thousand highly ordered microvilli whose cytoskeletal cores extend and attach to the underlying filaments in the region of the terminal web. Intact microvilli can be isolated from brush borders by shearing of the preparation, followed by a series of differential centrifugation steps to separate the microvilli from the remains of the terminal web (Bretscher & Weber 1978). The cytoskeletons of brush borders and microvilli are relatively stable, so they can be isolated after solubilization of the plasma membrane by Triton X-100, giving a preparation of intact structures. Thus, the isolated core retains all the known ultrastructural features described for microvillus cytoskeletons on intestinal epithelial cells, and an electron micrograph of a negatively stained microvillus core is shown in Fig. 1.

FIG. 1. Electron micrograph of a microvillus core negatively stained with phosphotungstic acid. The regular array of adhering cross-filaments is visible (arrow-heads). Scale bar represents 100 nm. (Reproduced from Bretscher & Weber 1979.)

Previous studies have shown that the 20–30 actin filaments of the core bundle all have the same polarity, as determined by decoration with the S_1 fragment of myosin (Mooseker & Tilney 1975). The orientation, with the arrowhead decoration pointing away from the tip, is similar to many other terminal attachments of microfilaments to membranes (see, for example, Begg et al

1978). This orientation means that the end of the filament favoured for assembly, as determined from *in vitro* studies, lies at the plasma membrane. The bundle of actin filaments in the core often appears to be highly organized when observed in transverse section, with the filaments cross-linked together by inter-filament bridges that can sometimes be seen in longitudinal section (Mooseker & Tilney 1975). The microvillus core is attached to the plasma membrane in two ways. End-on attachment of the filament bundle at the tip results in a densely staining structure when examined by electron microscopy of sectioned material. Lateral attachment is provided by a regular array of helically disposed cross-filaments, spaced every 33 nm down the length of the core, which links the core laterally to the inner side of the microvillus membrane. These cross-filaments are recovered as part of the isolated microvillus core from which the membrane has been removed (Fig.1).

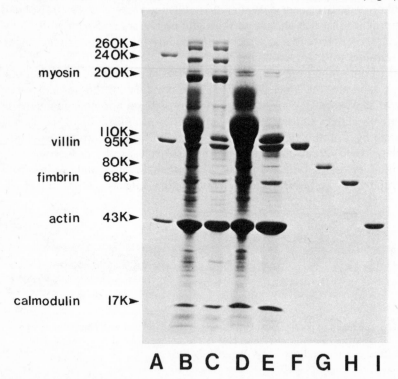

FIG. 2. 5–20% SDS polyacrylamide gel of the polypeptide components of brush borders, microvilli, their cytoskeletons and some of the purified microvillar proteins. (A) Molecular weight standards, filamin (250 K), α-actinin (100 K) and actin (43 K). (B–E): Polypeptide components of isolated brush borders (B), brush border cytoskeletons (C), microvilli (D), and microvillus cores (E). (F–I): Purified villin (F), the 80 K polypeptide (G), fimbrin (H) and actin (I).

The polypeptide compositions of brush-border and microvillus cyto-skeletons (Fig. 2) are remarkably simple, and a comparison between them reveals some additional major polypeptides in the brush border. These polypeptides must therefore be located in the terminal web region of the structure, and they include the heavy chains of myosin (M_r 200 000, or 200 K) and some high M_r polypeptides (260 K, 240 K). The isolated microvillus core contains five major proteins, the 110 K polypeptide, villin (95 K), fimbrin (68 K), actin (43 K), calmodulin (17 K) and some minor polypeptides. The use of highly specific antibodies to each of these major proteins, in indirect immunofluorescence microscopy, has shown that all the proteins are authentic components of the structure *in vivo*, since they are clearly present in the microvilli of cells fixed *in situ* (reviewed in Bretscher 1981b). However, some of the *in vivo* components of the core may be lost during isolation of microvilli, although most of the major ones must be recovered in the isolated structures since they appear intact as judged by electron microscopy. We are therefore trying to elucidate the role of each component in the core, in an effort to understand the entire structure at a molecular level.

Function of the major protein components of the microvillus core

The isolation and characterization of actin, villin, fimbrin and calmodulin from microvilli or brush borders has recently been described in work from this and other laboratories (Tilney & Mooseker 1971, Bretscher & Weber 1978, 1980a,b, Howe et al 1980, Mooseker et al 1980, Glenney et al 1980, 1981, Craig & Powell 1980, Bretscher 1981a, Matsudaira & Burgess 1982, and reviewed in Bretscher 1981b, 1982) and therefore only a summary will be included here.

The major cytoskeletal protein of microvilli is actin (Fig. 2) which is composed of both the β and γ cytoplasmic species in a ratio of about 40 : 60, respectively. The functional significance of the presence of both these closely related non-muscle actins in a defined cytoskeletal structure (the microvillus), or in any non-muscle cell, is currently not understood.

Villin has been purified to homogeneity (Fig. 2), either by traditional biochemical techniques or by making use of its ability to bind very tightly to monomeric actin in a Ca^{2+}-dependent manner. Isolated villin is a globular monomeric protein that has a tight binding site for Ca^{2+}, with a disassociation constant in the micromolar range. On binding Ca^{2+}, villin changes its properties from having little affinity for monomeric actin to binding 2–3 actin monomers very tightly. This Ca^{2+}-induced change is also reflected in the interaction of villin with F-actin. In the absence of Ca^{2+}, villin cross-links F-actin into bundles, whereas in the presence of Ca^{2+} it binds to the 'barbed' ends of actin filaments, thereby inhibiting end-to-end re-annealing of the filaments. Moreover, when it is added to preformed actin filaments in the presence of Ca^{2+}, it breaks them into short fragments. This Ca^{2+}-dependent activity of villin to sever F-actin is inducible by micromolar levels of free Ca^{2+} and can be used to partially disassemble the microvillus core *in vitro* by the addition of Ca^{2+}. Whether such a transformation occurs *in vivo* is discussed in more detail below.

Fimbrin can easily be purified from brush borders (Fig. 2) and is a globular monomeric protein in solution. It also cross-links F-actin *in vitro* to form filament bundles, although in a manner that is sensitive to the concentrations of KCl and divalent cations in the binding assay. Thus, optimal binding conditions are obtained in a buffer containing about 40 mM-KCl and 0.1 mM-Mg^{2+}, whereas the interaction is greatly reduced in the presence of more than 100 mM-KCl or millimolar Mg^{2+} or, in certain conditions, millimolar Ca^{2+}. Whether the sensitivities of the *in vitro* interaction play any physiological role *in vivo* is not known.

The microvillus core, therefore, contains two F-actin cross-linking proteins, villin and fimbrin. Electron microscopy of F-actin bundled by villin or fimbrin suggests that fimbrin, rather than villin, confers rigidity on the structure of the core. Biochemical studies show that the two proteins bind to different sites on F-actin and that the molar ratio of the cross-linking proteins to actin in the isolated core (actin : villin : fimbrin is about 10 : 1.2 : 0.65) is far below the maximum binding capacity of F-actin for these proteins (actin : villin : fimbrin maximum binding is about 10 : 5 : ~3). The significance of these findings will probably have to await a more detailed ultrastructural analysis of the core or a detailed localization of the individual proteins in the core.

Calmodulin is present in the core in a remarkably high amount and in a complex association. In the microvillus its concentration is about 0.2 mM, and since each calmodulin molecule has the ability to bind four Ca^{2+} ions, this represents a total Ca^{2+}-binding capacity of about 0.8 mM. Evidence for the complexity of the interaction comes from the finding that only about 50% of the calmodulin can be solubilized from the isolated core by treatment with the calmodulin-specific drug trifluoperazine, and that treatment with 10^{-5} M free Ca^{2+} partially disassembles the core and solubilizes about 30% of the calmodulin. Combined treatment with trifluoperazine and 10^{-6} M free Ca^{2+}—just below the concentration needed to disassemble the structure—solubilizes essentially all the calmodulin. Thus, some of the calmodulin appears to be bound in a Ca^{2+}-dependent manner, and some in a Ca^{2+}-independent manner. Work described by Glenney & Weber (1980) has shown that most, if not all, of the calmodulin is associated with the 110 K polypeptide.

The ultrastructural role of the 110 K polypeptide has been provided by the work of Matsudaira & Burgess (1979) in which they identified it as a component of the lateral cross-filaments that link the core laterally to the inner surface of the microvillus membrane. Their evidence came from the finding that isolated cores treated with ATP lost their cross-filaments, and biochemical analysis showed that the 110 K polypeptide had been solubilized (see also Fig. 3). Other evidence (reviewed in Bretscher 1982), although indirect, fully supports this assignment.

The above description has outlined current ideas about the ultrastructural location and function of the major proteins of the microvillus core. The isolated structure can simply be described as a bundle of unipolar actin filaments held together by the two F-actin cross-linking proteins villin and fimbrin, to which the 110 K polypeptide–calmodulin complex attaches to form the regularly spaced and laterally projecting cross-filaments. Although the major structural roles of these proteins are beginning to be understood, a number of questions follow naturally from these studies. Of these, we have chosen to try to understand why the core is built the way it is, and to investigate the minor components of the isolated core.

Minor protein components of the microvillus core

We have recently begun attempts to identify, purify and elucidate the function of minor components of the isolated microvillus core. So far we have studied an 80 K polypeptide that appears consistently to copurify with microvillus cores (Fig. 2). As discussed below, treatment of microvillus cores, or brush borders, with millimolar concentrations of Ca^{2+} results in the partial disassembly of the core and the solubilization of much of the villin, fimbrin, 80 K polypeptide, and about half the actin and one-third of the calmodulin. We have used such extracts to develop a rapid procedure for the simultaneous purification of villin, fimbrin and the 80 K polypeptide, incorporating the methods for the purification of villin and fimbrin previously described (Bretscher 1981b). The outline of the method is as follows. Brush borders are isolated from the small intestines of chickens and then treated with 5 mM-$CaCl_2$ to solubilize the components from the cytoskeletons. This extract is fractionated, by using ammonium sulphate, to give a soluble preparation containing villin, 80 K polypeptide, fimbrin, actin and calmodulin as major components. The preparation is dissolved in a Ca^{2+}-containing buffer and subjected to gel filtration on a Sephacryl S-300 column followed by passage through a Sepharose column to which pancreatic DNase I is covalently bound. This second column retains both the actin and the villin, since in these conditions actin binds very tightly to DNase I, and villin binds very tightly to the actin. Highly purified villin can then be selectively recovered from the

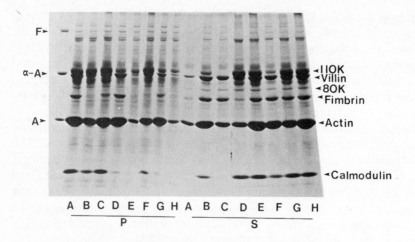

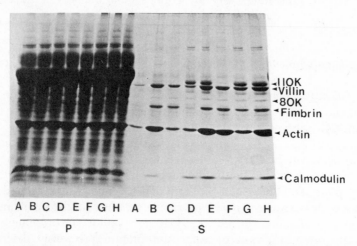

FIG. 3. 5–20% SDS polyacrylamide gel of the cytoskeletal components of microvillus cores (upper panel) and isolated microvilli (lower panel), solubilized by various treatments. Samples were treated for 30 min at 4 °C, the insoluble fraction harvested by centrifugation at 30 000 × *g* for 30 min and the pellet (P) and supernatant (S) fractions prepared for gel electrophoresis. Equal portions of the pellet and supernatant fractions were loaded on the gels. The treatments were done in solution I (see Bretscher 1981a) with the following additions: (A) none; (B) 5 mM-CaCl$_a$; (C) 25 mM-MgCl$_2$; (D) 1 mM-ATP; (E) 5 mM-CaCl$_2$, 1 mM-ATP; (F) 5 mM-CaCl$_2$, 25 mM-MgCl$_2$; (G) 25 mM-MgCl$_2$, 1 mM-ATP; and (H) 5 mM-CaCl$_2$, 25 mM-MgCl$_2$, 1 mM-ATP. To the left of lane (A) in the upper panel are the following relative molecular mass markers: F, filamin (250 K); α-A, α-actinin (100 K); and A, actin (43 K).

DNase I column by elution with a Ca^{2+}-chelating buffer, since the interaction between villin and actin, but not that between actin and DNase I, requires Ca^{2+}. The material that elutes from this double column contains fractions enriched in either 80 K polypeptide or fimbrin. These fractions are pooled separately, dialysed, and each is subjected to ion-exchange chromatography on diethyl amino ethyl (DEAE) columns. This gives a highly purified preparation of fimbrin, and a partially purified preparation of the 80 K polypeptide. Final purification of the 80 K polypeptide is achieved by chromatography on a hydroxyapatite column.

Purified 80 K polypeptide (Fig. 2) is a slightly elongated monomeric protein since it has a sedimentation coefficient of 3.9 s and a Stokes radius of about 4.3 nm, estimated on a Sephacryl S300 column, calibrated with the globular proteins ovalbumin (M_r 43 K, Stokes radius 3.05 nm), bovine serum albumin (M_r 68 K, Stokes radius 3.55 nm), aldolase (M_r 158 K, Stokes radius 4.8 nm) and ferritin (M_r 440 K, Stokes radius 6.1 nm). Antibodies raised in rabbits to the 80 K polypeptide recognize only the 80 K polypeptide component of microvillus cores as analysed by gel-transfer experiments. The protein is therefore not a breakdown product of some higher M_r species. Attempts to reveal the function of the 80 K polypeptide have so far not met with success. In experiments where mixtures of pure villin, fimbrin and the 80 K polypeptide were sedimented on sucrose gradients, the three proteins sedimented independently, implying that the 80 K polypeptide does not bind tightly to either of the other proteins in these conditions. Attempts to bind and co-sediment the 80 K polypeptide with F-actin alone, or in the presence of villin and/or fimbrin, have so far also been unsuccessful. Further experiments are therefore needed to uncover the function of this polypeptide in the microvillus core. Although we have not yet rigorously proved that the 80 K polypeptide is an authentic component of the microvillus *in vivo*, we intend to continue trying to elucidate the function of this protein. The 80 K polypeptide in the isolated core, being about 0.7% the concentration of actin, is present (on average) at about two to three copies per actin filament. We therefore suspect that the protein may play some interesting regulatory role in the microvillus core.

Functional organization of the microvillus cytoskeleton

The findings that the microvillus core can be partially disassembled by micromolar concentrations of free Ca^{2+}, and that ATP leads to the solubilization of the 110 K polypeptide–calmodulin complex has led us to examine the role these phenomena may play in the functional organization of the microvillus. We have investigated the effects of treating isolated cores and isolated microvilli with 1 mM-ATP, $10^{-7}-5 \times 10^{-3}$ M free Ca^{2+} or 25 mM-Mg^{2+}, especially in terms of the morphological changes induced and the solubilization of cytoskeletal proteins. Previous reports have documented that treatment of cores with these agents induces specific proteins to be solubilized (Matsudaira & Burgess 1979, Glenney et al 1980, Glenney & Weber 1980). The results reported here confirm and extend these findings (Fig. 3). Thus, treatment with ATP leads to the solubilization of most of the 110 K polypeptide and calmodulin; treatment with 5 mM-Ca^{2+} solubilizes some of the villin and fimbrin but essentially none of the 110 K polypeptide or calmodulin. The combined effects of the treatments on isolated cores is additive in that the solubilized proteins are the sum of each agent alone. As a result, treatment with ATP and Ca^{2+}, or with ATP, Ca^{2+} and Mg^{2+}, solubilizes essentially all the major proteins. All treatments appeared to solubilize the 80 K polypeptide to an appreciable extent.

The components released from intact microvilli by these treatments were surprisingly similar to those solubilized from microvillus cores, and no additional major proteins were released (Fig. 3). The results therefore indicate that a substantial number of microvilli in the purified preparation are not resealed at their basal ends. Moreover, of particular interest is the unexpected finding that the 110 K polypeptide and some calmodulin can be solubilized by treatment with ATP. This protein has been suggested as a major component of the cross-filaments that link the core laterally to the inner side of the microvillus membrane. Furthermore, the interaction of this protein with the core bundle can be specifically broken in the presence of ATP (Matsudaira & Burgess 1979). We therefore anticipated that it would remain associated with the microvillus membrane when intact microvilli were treated with ATP. The result thus suggests that both ends of the polypeptide, assuming it is the cross-filament protein, are released by 1 mM-ATP and, in addition, shows that the 110 K polypeptide cannot be an integral membrane protein.

We have examined the morphological changes induced by treating intact isolated microvilli with these agents, and the results will be reported in detail elsewhere (K. Verner & A. Bretscher, unpublished results). However, two observations are of interest when considering the function of the microvillus. First, treatment with ATP does not appear to alter the overall rigid, finger-like general appearance of isolated microvilli, although much of the 110 K polypeptide is solubilized, and electron microscopy of sectioned material shows that the cross-filaments are no longer visible. Second, treatment with concentrations higher than 10^{-5} M free Ca^{2+} induces constrictions in the microvillus membrane, resulting in a regular 'beading' appearance, with each bead being about 300 nm in length (Fig. 4). This beading is clearly far larger than the 33 nm-repeat of the cross-filaments; it is presumably not a result of their regularity but reflects some other, as yet undetected, regularity of the microvillus structure. The beading effect is enhanced by simultaneous treatment with Ca^{2+} and ATP, giving rise to many free vesicles.

As a result of these studies, the question arises of whether such induced transformations occur reversibly *in vivo* as part of the natural functioning of the microvillus. So far we have been unable to reverse the Ca^{2+}-induced beading *in vitro*, but this is hardly surprising since cytoskeletal components are lost from the structure during disassembly. We believe there are two

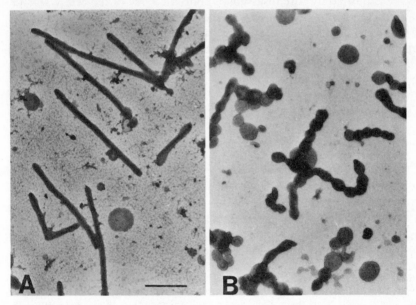

FIG. 4. Electron micrographs of microvilli after treatment in solution I with either no added calcium (A) or 5 mM-CaCl$_2$ (B). Similar structures to those shown in panel B were observed in samples treated with concentrations of free $Ca^{2+} \geqslant 10^{-6}$M. Specimens were adsorbed to Formvar coated electron microscope grids and stained with 1% aqueous uranyl acetate. Scale bar represents 1 μm.

pieces of circumstantial evidence that the organization of the microvillus core is regulated *in vivo* by the free Ca^{2+} level. The first is the presence of villin, a protein that disassembles the rigid structure of the core in the presence of more than 10^{-6} M free Ca^{2+}. It seems highly unlikely that Nature would have included within the microvillus—which is specially designed for the uptake of nutrients including Ca^{2+}—a protein like villin which can destroy the structure itself when free Ca^{2+} is raised above micromolar levels. The second piece of evidence is the abundance of calmodulin and its complex, Ca^{2+}-regulated association with the core. This again suggests some form of Ca^{2+} regulation in the microvillus, probably not by calmodulin regulating the activity of an enzyme, but rather by its acting as a regulator of the free level of Ca^{2+}. Perhaps in the normal functioning of the microvillus, the core undergoes disassembly/assembly cycles in a Ca^{2+}-regulated way, with the free Ca^{2+} level being carefully controlled by calmodulin. One could envisage a cyclical process to regulate free Ca^{2+} whereby increasing levels lead to the disassociation of some of the calmodulin (with bound Ca^{2+}) from the core, which then moves, or is flushed by core disassembly, into the body of the cell to release its Ca^{2+} and returns to reassociate with the microvillus core. The speculation, which is intended to be provocative, is presented as one possible model for the functioning of the microvillus, in an attempt to explain the Ca^{2+}-regulated proteins that are major components of the microvillus core *in vivo*.

Acknowledgement

This work was supported in part by National Institutes of Health grant GM30603.

REFERENCES

Begg DA, Rodewald R, Rebhun LI 1978 Visualization of actin filament polarity in thin sections. Evidence for the uniform polarity of membrane-associated filaments. J Cell Biol 79:846-852
Bretscher A 1981a Fimbrin is a cytoskeletal protein that cross-links F-actin *in vitro*. Proc Natl Acad Sci USA 78:6849-6853
Bretscher A 1981b Characterization and ultrastructural role of the major components of the intestinal microvillus cytoskeleton. Cold Spring Harbor Symp Quant Biol 46:871-880
Bretscher A 1982 Microfilament organization in the cytoskeleton of the intestinal brush border. In: Dowben RM, Shay JW (eds) Cell and muscle motility. Plenum, New York, vol 4, in press
Bretscher A, Weber K 1978 Purification of microvilli and an analysis of the protein components of the microfilament core bundle. Exp Cell Res 116:397-407
Bretscher A, Weber K 1979 Villin: the major microfilament-associated protein of the intestinal microvillus. Proc Natl Acad Sci USA 76:2321-2325
Bretscher A, Weber K 1980a Villin is a major protein of the microvillus cytoskeleton which binds both G and F actin in a calcium-dependent manner. Cell 20:839-847
Bretscher A, Weber K 1980b Fimbrin, a new microfilament-associated protein present in microvilli and other cell surface structures. J Cell Biol 86:335-340
Craig SW, Powell LD 1980 Regulation of actin polymerization by villin, a 95,000 dalton cytoskeletal component of intestinal brush borders. Cell 22:739-746
Glenney J, Bretscher A, Weber K 1980 Calcium control of the intestinal microvillus cytoskeleton: its implications for the regulation of microfilament organizations. Proc Natl Acad Sci USA 77:6458-6462
Glenney JR, Kaulfus P, Matsudaira P, Weber K 1981 F-actin binding and bundling properties of fimbrin, a major cytoskeletal protein of microvillus core filaments. J Biol Chem 256:9283-9288

Glenney JR, Weber K 1980 Calmodulin-binding proteins of the microfilaments present in isolated brush borders and microvilli of intestinal epithelial cells. J Biol Chem 255:10551-10554

Howe CL, Mooseker MS, Graves TA 1980 Brush border calmodulin. A major component of the isolated microvillus core. J Cell Biol 85:916-923

Matsudaira PT, Burgess DR 1979 Identification and organization of the components in the isolated microvillus cytoskeleton. J Cell Biol 83:667-673

Matsudaira PT, Burgess DR 1982 Partial reconstitution of the microvillus core bundle: characterization of villin as a Ca^{2+}-dependent, actin-bundling/depolymerizing protein. J Cell Biol 92:648-656

Miller D, Crane RK 1961 The digestive function of the epithelium of the small intestine. II: Localization of disaccharide hydrolysis in the isolated brush border portion of intestinal epithelial cells. Biochim Biophys Acta 52:293-298

Mooseker MS 1976 Brush border motility. Microvillar contraction in Triton-treated brush borders isolated from intestinal epithelium. J Cell Biol 71:417-433

Mooseker MS, Graves TA, Wharton KA, Falco N, Howe CL 1980 Regulation of microvillus structure: calcium-dependent solation and cross-linking of actin filaments in the microvilli of intestinal epithelial cells. J Cell Biol 87:809-822

Mooseker MS, Tilney LG 1975 Organization of an actin filament–membrane complex. Filament polarity and membrane attachment in the microvilli of intestinal epithelial cells. J Cell Biol 67:725-743

Tilney LG, Mooseker M 1971 Actin in the brush border of epithelial cells of the chicken intestine. Proc Natl Acad Sci USA 68:2611-2615

DISCUSSION

Kenny: Some years ago Andrew Booth and I looked at something that we called vesiculation. Is this phenomenon the same thing?

Bretscher: Yes, I believe so.

Hermon-Taylor: Are the microvilli in the brush borders treated with 5 mM-Ca^{2+} shorter than the untreated ones?

Bretscher: Isolated microvilli tend to break up when they are treated with calcium, so it is difficult to know if they have shortened.

Hermon-Taylor: If the microvillus core contracts and the peripheral envelope doesn't, it could account for the shape that the brush border assumes on exposure to 5mM-Ca^{2+}.

Mooseker: Burgess & Prum (1982) have done a quantitative study on the effects of calcium on microvilli length. They have shown that at high calcium concentrations (mM) one can obtain a microvillus that is vesiculated over its entire length, down to the terminal web. The old notion of retraction of cores to allow that is incorrect. At high calcium concentrations the core filaments are cut by MV-95K (villin), and because the core is not present to keep the membrane cylindrical the membrane assumes the more 'natural' spherical shape.

Schmitz: Calcium does not take out the actin from the microvilli because when one purifies the microvillous membrane by the calcium precipitation method (Schmitz et al 1973) the pelleted membranes are still full of microfilaments and core proteins, one of which migrates on SDS–PAGE as actin (Maestracci et al 1973).

Mooseker: But those microfilaments are very short.

Matsudaira: That is probably due to the trapping of actin in membrane vesicles.

Bretscher: If you treat microvillus cores with 5 mM-calcium you solubilize only about half the actin.

Alpers: The vitamin D-inducible calcium-binding protein (Ca^{2+}-BP) was originally shown to be localized to the brush border but has subsequently been suggested in other places. Does it interact with the brush border and, if so, does it play a role in the effects of a high calcium concentration?

Bretscher: I don't think enough is known about that to link it to the model.

Alpers: There is a lot of this protein in the intestine but I'm not sure whether it is on the brush border or just near it.

Louvard: Marche et al (1980) have localized the Ca^{2+}-BP by immuno-fluorescent techniques and they found it strictly in the terminal web.

Quaroni: But the problem with defining the distribution of the calcium-binding protein is how you fix the cell: for example, the protein was found in goblet cells purely because of an artifact in the fixation technique (Taylor & Wasserman 1970).

Mooseker: We have collaborated with R.H. Wasserman's group and have found, immunologically, that the isolated brush border does not contain Ca^{2+}-BP. But others have recently observed a highly specific localization in the terminal web. I agree about the problems with fixation. We are probably looking at a skeleton of a skeleton when we isolate the brush border.

Alpers: I am concerned about Dr Bretscher's interpretation of that point because decreased staining by immunofluorescence does not necessarily mean that one is losing a lot. In my experience there is little correlation between intensity of immunofluorescence and the actual amount of material. It depends on the availability of the antigen.

Bretscher: I quite agree.

Booth: Does anybody know if the ATP concentration in an enterocyte is of the order of 1 mM? And, if so, what bearing does that have on the severing of cross-bridges?

Jørgensen: The concentration is more like 2–3 mM.

Booth: So the ATP concentration may affect the ultrastructure, or at least have some bearing on it.

Louvard: But one doesn't know the real concentrations in the microvilli.

Mooseker: It will be important to know the bound:free concentration ratio as well.

Smith: Does anybody know what sticks the actin filament to the top, and how that relates to assembly?

Matsudaira: Nobody knows, but that is why Dr Bretscher is focusing on the proteins that bind to actin at very low molar ratios. With a bundle composed of 15 filaments, any protein that functions as a capping protein will be present in small amounts. Some of these minor ones appear to have major functions.

Kenny: A transverse section of a kidney microvillus has a predictably symmetrical array of one actin filament surrounded by a circle of six more filaments. In the intestine, however, there are 30 or so filaments arranged around the central one rather asymmetrically.

Bretscher: Villin is also present in kidney microvilli, as determined by immunofluorescence microscopy with villin antibody. Its presence there was originally suggested by the work of Booth & Kenny (1976) who showed that isolated kidney microvilli contain a cytoskeletal protein of M_r about 95 K. Therefore, any model that attempts to explain the presence of villin in intestinal microvilli must also apply to kidney microvilli.

Hauri: I gather that villin and fimbrin are localized at more or less the same place in the microvillus; what do you think is their function?

Bretscher: On a biochemical level they bind to different sites on F-actin as they do not compete for F-actin *in vitro*. It is not clear *exactly* where they are in the microvillus core. Electron microscopy has shown that they are both found along the entire length of the microvillus core.

Louvard: One must remember that even with the ferritin technique, which provides about 30 nm resolution, the amount of detail is not enough because the diameter of a microvillus is about 0.1 μm (100 nm).

Quaroni: What about the colloidal gold technique?

Louvard: That has similar problems.

Bretscher: The antibodies are too big; even Fab fragments are a little too big!

Rodewald: How many of these microvillar components are really specific for gut as opposed to kidney or other cell types that have less differentiated microvilli?

Bretscher: We have used immunofluorescence microscopy with antibodies to some of the components of the microvillus core on a wide variety of cells and tissues. We have found villin in the microvilli of intestinal epithelial cells, of the cells lining the kidney proximal tubule and of gall bladder epithelial cells. However, we have been unable to detect villin in any cultured cell type (see Bretscher et al 1981). By contrast, we have found fimbrin in every ordered microfilament bundle that we have looked at, with the exception of stress fibres of cultured cells (Bretscher & Weber 1980). Of particular interest is the presence of fimbrin in the stereocilium of the inner ear. This structure, which has a central core bundle of about one thousand actin filaments, contains fimbrin but none of the other known F-actin cross-linking proteins (A. Flock &

A. Bretscher, unpublished results). We currently believe that fimbrin is a general F-actin cross-linking protein for highly organized F-actin bundles. The 80 K polypeptide I discussed earlier, which we have just started working on, appears to be present not only in microvilli of intestinal epithelial brush borders but also in microvilli of cultured cells, such as fibroblasts.

Booth: How easily is it released?

Bretscher: As I discussed in my paper, many different treatments will release fimbrin *in vitro* from microvillus cores.

Mooseker: We are comparing cytoskeletal proteins from mammals (rat and rabbit) with those from the chicken. Although villin is present in the isolated brush border fraction, as assayed by Ca^{2+}-dependent solation of microvillus cores, the relative molecular masses are different. There may be some rather important differences in other cytoskeletal proteins—e.g. 110 K, calmodulin, myosin, etc.—in chickens, which are widely studied, and mammals. The organization of the terminal web is rather different too. Observations on brush border cytoskeletal proteins should therefore be extended beyond those on the chicken.

Schmitz: This problem struck us 10 years ago when we wanted to adapt for human beings a method devised for the hamster (Welsh et al 1972). The hamster behaves very differently from the rat, and the rat from the human. At that time we could only guess that these variations were due to differences in the organization of the microfilaments.

Kenny: I suppose there is not a more trivial explanation for these problems— e.g. in terms of mucus?

Schmitz: No.

Alpers: The view that these proteins are different may be important also because calcium absorption in the chick takes on quite a different importance than in mammals; these calcium interactions could be quite different in the two species.

REFERENCES

Booth AG, Kenny AJ 1976 Proteins of the kidney microvillus membrane. Identification of subunits after sodium dodecyl sulphate/polyacrylamide gel electrophoresis. Biochem J 159: 395-407

Bretscher A, Weber K 1980 Fimbrin, a new microfilament-associated protein present in microvilli and other cell surface structures. J Cell Biol 86: 335-340

Bretscher A, Osborn M, Wehland J, Weber K 1981 Villin associates with specific microfilamentous structures as seen by immunofluorescence microscopy on tissue sections and cells microinjected with villin. Exp Cell Res 135: 213-219

Burgess DR, Prum BE 1982 A re-evaluation of brush border motility: calcium induces core filament solation and microvillar vesiculation. J Cell Biol 94: 97-107

Maestracci D, Schmitz J, Preiser H, Crane RK 1973 Proteins and glycoproteins of the human intestinal brush border membrane. Biochim Biophys Acta 323: 113-124

Marche P, Cassier P, Mathieu H 1980 Intestinal calcium-binding protein. A protein indicator of enterocyte maturation associated with the terminal web. Cell Tissue Res 212: 63-72

Schmitz J, Preiser H, Maestracci D, Ghosh BK, Cerda JJ, Crane RK 1973 Purification of the human intestinal brush border membrane. Biochim Biophys Acta 323: 98-112

Taylor AN, Wasserman RH 1970 Immunofluorescent localization of vitamin D-dependent calcium-binding protein. J Histochem Cytochem 18: 107

Welsh JD, Preiser H, Woodley JF, Crane RK 1972 An enriched microvillus membrane preparation from frozen specimens of human small intestine. Gastroenterology 62: 572-582

Structure of human placental microvilli

A. G. BOOTH and O. A. VANDERPUYE

Department of Biochemistry, University of Leeds, Leeds LS2 9JT, UK

Abstract Cytoskeletons have been prepared from microvilli isolated from the human placental syncytiotrophoblast. They contain actin and a protein similar to fimbrin. In addition, they contain calmodulin and a protein of relative molecular mass (M_r) 105 000, both of which can be released from the cytoskeletons by treatment with Ca^{2+}. In this respect the 105 000 M_r protein is more similar to non-muscle α-actinin than to the intestinal microvillar protein with an M_r of 110 000. Human placental actin displays the anomalous properties of binding to phenyl-Sepharose and wheatgerm agglutinin-Sepharose, suggesting that one or more membrane glycoproteins is associated with the actin. Transferrin, presumably receptor-bound, has been identified in preparations of extensively washed placental microvillar cytoskeletons. These findings are discussed in terms of the earliest events in endocytosis and materno-fetal transfer.

1983 Brush border membranes. Pitman Books Ltd, London (Ciba Foundation symposium 95) p 180-194

Considerable progress has recently been made in identifying the proteins that form the underlying cytoskeleton of the microvillus and which are therefore responsible for its characteristic shape. Most of the information has come from microvilli isolated from a single source—the intestinal brush border. However, it is not clear how far the results from these studies can be extended to studies of microvilli from other sources. Indeed, at least two reports show that the cytoskeletons of microvilli from transformed cells contain different proteins from their counterparts in intestinal microvilli (Hiller et al 1979, Carraway et al 1980). We have therefore isolated microvilli from yet another source—the human placenta—and we have studied their cytoskeletal proteins in an attempt to broaden the information available on microvillar structure.

These microvilli border the placental syncytiotrophoblast and are bathed in maternal plasma. The syncytiotrophoblast is a true syncytium; the brush border membrane is completely separate from the basal membrane and there are no lateral membranes. Therefore no cell junctions are close to the brush border, and the terminal web region is much less apparent than that of enterocytes.

When small pieces of placental villus tissue are incubated in cold iso-osmolar saline, the microvilli are shed into the medium, from which they can be recovered by centrifugation and purified by treating the preparation with divalent cations (Booth et al 1980). Electron micrographs of tissue samples fixed during the incubation in cold saline show that when the microvilli are shed, they also entrap some of the terminal web material (A. G. Booth and D. Kershaw, unpublished results). Hence these preparations are referred to as 'microvilli', although some proteins of the terminal web may be expected to be present.

General characteristics of placental microvilli

Electron micrographs of our placental microvillus preparations show them to contain vesicles of various sizes which, judged by their content of fibrillar material, are mainly 'right-side-out'. Like microvillus vesicles prepared from

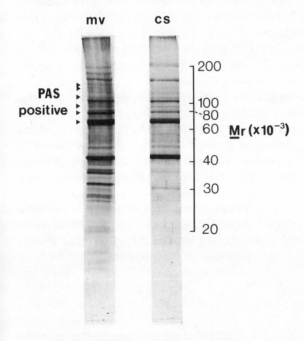

FIG. 1. Proteins of whole placental microvilli (mv) and their cytoskeletons (cs) separated by electrophoresis on sodium dodecyl sulphate (SDS) in 7–17% (w/v) polyacrylamide gradient gels, using the buffer system of Laemmli (1970). The gels were stained with Coomassie blue R250. The positions of bands that stained with Schiff's reagent after oxidation with periodic acid (PAS) are indicated.

other tissues, these appear to be sealed, and similar vesicles have been used by other workers for studies of glucose and amino acid transport (e.g. Montgomery & Young 1982). Compared to the initial homogenate these preparations are enriched 20–30 fold in 5'-nucleotidase and the heat-stable placental isoenzyme of alkaline phosphatase. They are almost devoid of the peptidase and disaccharidase activities so characteristic of intestinal and kidney microvilli. This is reflected in the pattern of bands seen when samples of placental microvilli are subjected to electrophoresis in polyacrylamide gradient gels in the presence of sodium dodecyl sulphate (SDS). The high relative molecular mass (M_r) glycoprotein subunits corresponding to sucrase, isomaltase, maltase, aminopeptidase N etc. are missing (Fig. 1). The major glycoprotein of the membrane $(M_r\ 68\ 000)$ corresponds to the major antigen and has been identified as alkaline phosphatase. Other protein bands which stain with Schiff's reagent after periodate oxidation are present at $M_r\ 77\ 000$, $M_r\ 95\ 000$, $M_r\ 120\ 000$, $M_r\ 140\ 000$ and $M_r\ 160\ 000$, although the last three usually stain very faintly.

We have used the two-dimensional electrophoretic system of Ames & Nikaido (1976) to resolve further the protein subunits of SDS-solubilized microvilli and their cytoskeletons. In this technique, the proteins are first resolved by isoelectric focusing (gradient pH 4.5–7.0) and then further resolved by electrophoresis in SDS on 7–17% (w/v) polyacrylamide gradient gels.

This showed (Fig. 2) that in the case of the total microvillar proteins, some of the bands visible after one-dimensional electrophoresis contained several protein subunits of identical M_r. Most noticeable was the band corresponding to $M_r\ 68\ 000$. After two-dimensional electrophoresis, this was shown to contain a protein identical to plasma albumin, a polymorphic glycoprotein probably identical with the membrane-bound enzyme alkaline phosphatase, a dimorphic cytoskeletal protein and some other proteins present in much smaller quantities. The major protein subunit present in the microvillus preparations is actin $(M_r\ 42\ 000$, dimorphic). Transferrin $(M_r\ 77\ 000$, polymorphic) and its membrane-bound receptor protein $(M_r\ 95\ 000)$ can also be identified after either one- or two-dimensional electrophoresis.

The microvillar cytoskeleton

Microvillar cytoskeletons were prepared by suspending microvillus preparations (5 mg protein/ml) in 75 mM-NaCl, 5 mM-MgCl$_2$, 1 mM-EGTA, 1 mM-dithiothreitol, 1 mM-phenylmethylsulphonyl fluoride, 2% (v/v) Emulphogene BC 720, 10 mM-imidazole, at pH 7.4. After standing at 20 °C for 15 min, the suspension was centrifuged at 20 000 g for 15 min in a microfuge and

Whole Microvilli

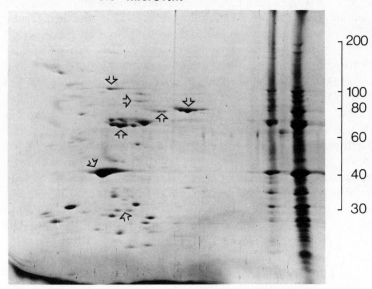

Cytoskeletons

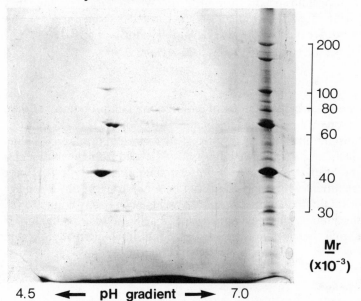

Mr
(x10⁻³)

4.5 ⟵ pH gradient ⟶ 7.0

FIG. 2. Two-dimensional electrophoresis of whole microvilli and their cytoskeletons. Electrophoresis of SDS-solubilized proteins was done as described by Ames & Nikaido (1976). The positions of spots common to both gels are indicated by arrows.

the pellet was washed with the same buffer once and then six more times with the buffer, containing 0.1% (v/v) Emulphogene BC 720. Identical results were obtained when the Emulphogene BC 720 was replaced by Triton X-100 or Nonidet P-40.

In addition to actin, proteins with the following M_r were present in the cytoskeletons: 20 000, 30 000 dimorphic, 36 000, 68 000 dimorphic, 77 000 polymorphic, 90 000 dimorphic, 105 000, 180 000 and 200 000. Additionally, traces of proteins of M_r 47 000 and 95 000 were usually observed. The protein of M_r 180 000 had identical electrophoretic properties to those of placental clathrin, while the solubility properties of the protein of M_r 200 000 have enabled us to identify it tentatively as the heavy chain of myosin. Although these proteins are always present in our preparations, by analogy with other brush borders, it is likely that they derive from the inter-microvillus plasma membrane and the terminal web respectively (see e.g. Mooseker et al 1978).

Other than actin, the major protein of the intestinal microvillar cyto-skeleton is villin (Bretscher & Weber 1980a). This protein (M_r 95 000) is a Ca^{2+}-dependent protein that severs actin filaments. In the presence of Ca^{2+}, villin is solubilized from the microvillar cytoskeleton. Although placental microvillar cytoskeletons contain small quantities of a protein of similar M_r, this protein is not released by Ca^{2+}. In fact, as described below, it is likely that this is the receptor protein specific for transferrin. We therefore conclude that the microvilli from human placentae differ markedly from those of the intestinal brush border in that they are devoid of villin.

Fimbrin

In placental microvillar cytoskeletons, the most abundant protein other than actin is one of M_r 68 000. Two-dimensional electrophoresis showed that this protein is dimorphic and can be distinguished from albumin and alkaline phosphatase which have a similar M_r. It is not solubilized from the microvillar cytoskeletons by brief treatment with buffers containing Ca^{2+} or ATP nor even by brief treatment with 0.6 M-KI. It can be solubilized only by extensive disruption of the actin filaments. It therefore seems to be firmly bound to the microvillar actin bundles and may be involved in actin–actin cross-linking. It seems probable that this protein is similar to the intestinal microvillar protein that Bretscher & Weber (1980b) have named 'fimbrin'.

Heat-stable proteins

Howe et al (1980) have demonstrated that calmodulin is a component of the intestinal microvillar cytoskeleton. We believe that this is also true for the

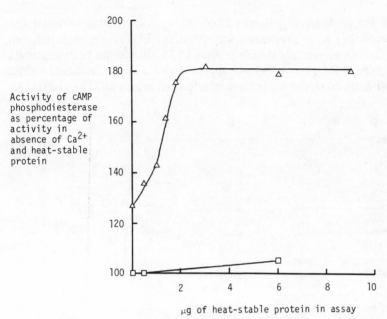

FIG. 3. Calcium-dependent activation of the c-AMP phosphodiesterase activity of *Candida albicans* strain CA2 by a preparation of heat-stable proteins obtained from placental microvillar cytoskeletons. Samples of the heat-stable protein preparations were mixed with a cell-free extract of *C. albicans*, incubated at 37 °C for 10 min, and then $50\,\mu$l aliquots were assayed for activity by the method of Lees et al (1974). The triangles denote the activity in the presence of $0.1\,\text{mM-CaCl}_2$ and $1.0\,\text{mM-MgCl}_2$. The squares denote the activity in the presence of $0.1\,\text{mM-CaCl}_2$, $1.0\,\text{mM-MgCl}_2$ and $1.0\,\text{mM-EGTA}$.

placental microvillar cytoskeleton. When cytoskeletons were boiled and then centrifuged, three protein subunits (M_r 20 000, M_r 30 000 and M_r 47 000) were found in the supernatant. The identity of the protein of M_r 47 000 is unknown. A protein of M_r 30 000 was also observed by Howe et al (1980) and was tentatively identified as tropomyosin. The protein of M_r 20 000 is almost certainly calmodulin since samples of the supernatants from boiled cytoskeletons activated a preparation of $3',5'$-cyclic AMP phosphodiesterase from *Candida albicans* in a Ca^{2+}-dependent manner (Fig. 3). It should be noted, however, that the bulk of placental microvillar calmodulin is associated with the membrane since much more calmodulin is obtained after boiling microvilli than after boiling cytoskeletons.

Other proteins of the placental microvillar cytoskeleton

After the protein of M_r 68 000, the next most prominent protein subunit of the cytoskeleton is one of M_r 105 000. This protein could be solubilized from the cytoskeletons by treating them with a buffer similar in composition to the one in which they were prepared except that the EGTA was replaced with 1 mM-CaCl$_2$. An apparently similar protein of M_r 110 000 has been described by Matsudaira & Burgess (1979) and appears to be a strong candidate for the membrane–actin cross-linking protein in intestinal microvilli. The 110 000 M_r

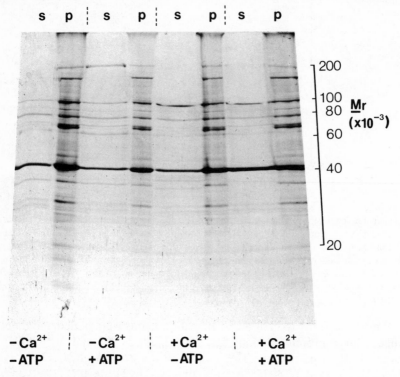

FIG. 4. The effect of Ca^{2+} and ATP on the cytoskeletons of human placental microvilli. Samples of cytoskeletons were incubated at 0 °C for 45 min in 75 mM-NaCl, 5 mM-MgCl$_2$, 1 mM-dithiothreitol, 1 mM-phenylmethylsulphonyl fluoride, 0.1% (v/v) Emulphogene BC720, 10 mM-imidazole at pH 7.4, containing either 1 mM-EGTA (−Ca^{2+}) or 1 mM-CaCl$_2$ (+Ca^{2+}), and with or without 1 mM-ATP. After centrifugation at 20 000 g for 15 min, the supernatants (s) and pellets (p) were examined by electrophoresis in SDS on 7–17% (w/v) polyacrylamide gels.

protein was released from the cytoskeleton by ATP. We found that for short incubations, i.e. 45 min at 0 °C, Ca^{2+} is much more effective than ATP in solubilizing the 105 000 M_r protein (Fig. 4) although they are equally effective when used in buffers against which the cytoskeleton preparations are extensively dialysed.

Calmodulin is also released from the cytoskeletons by brief incubation in the presence of Ca^{2+}. A similar finding has been reported for the intestinal microvillar cytoskeleton by Glenney & Weber (1980) who obtained evidence that the 110 000 M_r protein can bind calmodulin even after denaturation with SDS.

At the moment we do not know the relationship, if any, between the placental protein of M_r 105 000 and the intestinal protein of M_r 110 000. They are very different in their susceptibility to solubilization by Ca^{2+}. Microvilli from other sources have been shown to contain a protein of similar M_r, which has been identified as α-actinin (Hiller et al 1979, Carraway et al 1980). Particularly significant is the finding that human non-muscle α-actinin can be released from cytoskeletal structures by Ca^{2+} (Burridge & Feramisco 1981). We hope to establish whether the placental protein binds antibody raised to α-actinin from HeLa cells.

Placental microvillar cytoskeletons also contain a protein of M_r 77 000. This was initially confused with transferrin which is also present in the cytoskeleton preparations. However, the reduced and non-reduced forms of transferrin have markedly different electrophoretic mobilities on polyacrylamide gels in the presence of SDS. This is not so for the 77 000 M_r protein, and the two can be distinguished on this basis. The identity and function of this protein remains unknown.

'Anomalous' behaviour of placental microvillar actin

In the preparation of microvillar cytoskeletons, considerable amounts of actin are found in the supernatant after the treatment with non-ionic detergent. When the detergent concentration of such supernatants was decreased to 0.1% (v/v) and the preparation was applied to columns of phenyl-Sepharose CL-4B, more than 95% of the actin was retained by the column. The bound actin could be eluted by buffers containing 1% (v/v) Emulphogene BC 720. After identical treatment, samples of pig cardiac actin were not retained by the hydrophobic matrix of the column. When we repeated the experiments, using actin solubilized from cytoskeletons by dialysis against either the Ca^{2+}-containing buffer or the actin-depolymerizing buffer described by Spudich & Watt (1971), approximately 50% of the actin was retained by the column of phenyl-Sepharose.

We take these results to indicate that, in the placental microvilli, amphiphilic material is associated with the actin filaments, albeit probably indirectly. We believe that one or more membrane glycoproteins comprise this material since significant quantities of actin could be removed from a preparation of detergent-solubilized microvillar proteins by passage through a column of wheatgerm agglutinin–Sepharose 6B. The bound actin together with several glycoproteins could be specifically eluted by 0.2 M-N-acetylglucosamine.

So far, the only membrane glycoprotein that we have reproducibly identified in our preparations of microvillar cytoskeletons is transferrin.

Placental microvillar transferrin

During pregnancy, the fetus receives iron that has been transferred across the placenta from the maternal circulation. The source of this iron is the maternal plasma glycoprotein transferrin (Morgan 1974). The initial event in the placental transfer of iron is the binding of transferrin to a specific receptor protein on the microvillar membrane of the syncytiotrophoblast. The receptor is a dimeric intrinsic membrane glycoprotein of M_r 94 000 (Wada et al 1979, Enns & Sussman 1981) present in quantities of about 35 μg per mg of membrane protein (Enns et al 1981). It is found in the microvillar membrane throughout pregnancy (Booth & Booth 1982).

The transferrin–receptor complex is internalized into coated vesicles and is probably transported to lysosomes where the iron is removed before being transmitted to the fetal circulation. The iron-depleted transferrin is probably returned to the maternal circulation (Booth & Wilson 1981). The distribution of transferrin receptors on the plasma membrane is initially random (Galbraith et al 1980) and so the transferrin–receptor complexes must be moved to the sites of coated vesicle formation. Although this may be achieved solely by diffusion, the cytoskeleton might have some role to play.

As described above, preparations of placental microvillar cytoskeletons contain a protein whose electrophoretic properties are identical to those of authentic transferrin. The identity of this protein has been confirmed by overlaying gels with anti-transferrin antibody and radio-iodinated protein A (Fig. 5). The transferrin is present in quantities significantly greater than can be accounted for by contamination of our cytoskeleton preparations by coated vesicles. It is tightly bound to the cytoskeletons, probably via its receptor, since a protein with similar electrophoretic properties to the transferrin receptor can be identified in the cytoskeleton preparations after two-dimensional electrophoresis. We hope to confirm the presence of the receptor by 'western' blot techniques (Towbin et al 1979) using monoclonal antibodies raised to the transferrin receptor. Transferrin will dissociate from its receptor under the conditions used for immunoelectrophoresis (Booth & Booth 1982). This has allowed us to confirm the identification of the cytoskeleton-bound transferrin.

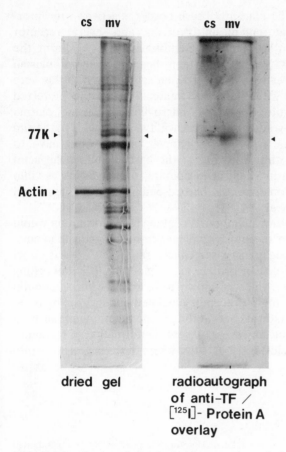

FIG. 5. Identification of transferrin in preparations of placental microvillar cytoskeletons. A polyacrylamide gel, containing the separated proteins of SDS-solubilized whole microvilli (mv) and cytoskeletons (cs), was soaked in 0.5 M-NaCl, 0.1% (w/v) NaN$_3$, 50 mM-Tris/HCl, at pH 7.5, for 18 h. It was then soaked in the same buffer, this time containing rabbit anti-human transferrin immunoglobulin G and 0.1% bovine serum albumin for 24 h. After extensive washing with the protein-free buffer, the procedure was repeated with ^{125}I-labelled Protein A, and the gel was lightly stained and radioautographed.

Discussion

Human placental microvilli are clearly different from their intestinal counterparts, most obviously in the lack of villin and in the presence of a protein whose properties are more similar to those of α-actinin than to the intestinal 110 000 M_r protein. These differences may reflect differences in the functions of the two brush borders. The placental brush border is active in receptor-mediated endocytosis of maternal plasma proteins, and several receptor proteins have been identified in its plasma membrane. Perhaps, during the initial stages of endocytosis, receptor proteins bearing maternal plasma proteins bind directly or indirectly to the microvillar cytoskeleton. If this were to be a dynamic structure, with the actin 'treadmilling' in the preferred direction—i.e. away from the tip of the microvillus—then the plasma protein–receptor complexes would be swept 'down' the microvillus to the site of coated vesicle formation. For this to happen, actin would have to polymerize in the preferred direction, i.e. at the barbed end of the actin filament. Clearly, for such a mechanism to operate, proteins such as villin must be absent since they would cap the barbed end of actin filaments and inhibit treadmilling (Glenney et al 1981).

At the inter-microvillar plasma membrane, coated vesicle formation would depend on the release of the receptor complexes from the actin filaments. This might be caused by a locally increased concentration of Ca^{2+}, its effect being transmitted to the $105\,000\,M_r$ protein via calmodulin. It is interesting that the drug trifluoperazine, which is known to interfere with calmodulin function, has been shown to inhibit receptor-mediated endocytosis by preventing the formation of the clathrin coats at the plasma membrane (Salisbury et al 1980). The drug does not, however, prevent the formation of receptor–ligand complexes or their clustering at sites where coated vesicle would otherwise form.

Acknowledgements

We are grateful to the staff of the labour ward, Leeds Maternity Hospital, for their cooperation in providing fresh placentae, to Mr W. J. O'Reilly for the phosphodiesterase assays, to Dr N. Graham for the cardiac actin, to Mr R. O. Olaniyan and Ms H. C. Edwards for their technical assistance and to the Medical Research Council for financial support.

REFERENCES

Ames GF-L, Nikaido K 1976 Two dimensional electrophoresis of membrane proteins. Biochemistry 15:616-623

Booth CM, Booth AG 1982 Immunoelectrophoretic evidence that the human syncytiotrophoblast transferrin receptor is identical to a major plasma membrane antigen present throughout pregnancy. Placenta 3:57-66

Booth AG, Wilson MJ 1981 Human placental coated vesicles contain receptor-bound transferrin. Biochem J 196:355-362

Booth AG, Olaniyan RO, Vanderpuye OA 1980 An improved method for the preparation of human placental syncytiotrophoblast microvilli. Placenta 1:327-336

Bretscher A, Weber K 1980a Villin is a major protein of the microvillus which binds both G and F actin in a calcium-dependent manner. Cell 20:839-847

Bretscher A, Weber K 1980b Fimbrin, a new microfilament-associated protein present in microvilli and other cell surface structures. J Cell Biol 86:335-340

Burridge K, Feramisco JR 1981 Non-muscle α-actinins are calcium-sensitive actin-binding proteins. Nature (Lond) 294:565-567

Carraway KL, Huggins JW, Cerra RF, Yeltman DR, Carothers Carraway CA 1980 α-Actinin-containing branched microvilli isolated from an ascites adenocarcinoma. Nature (Lond) 285:508-510

Enns CA, Sussman HH 1981 Physical characterization of the transferrin receptor in human placentae. J Biol Chem 256:9820-9823

Enns CA, Shindelman JE, Tonik SE, Sussman HH 1981 Radioimmunochemical measurement of the transferrin receptor in human trophoblast and reticulocyte membranes with a specific anti-receptor antibody. Proc Natl Acad Sci USA 78:4222-4225

Galbraith GMP, Galbraith RM, Faulk WP 1980 Immunological studies of transferrin receptors of human placental trophoblast. Placenta 1:33-46

Glenney JR, Weber K 1980 Calmodulin-binding proteins of the microfilaments present in isolated brush borders and microvilli of intestinal epithelial cells. J Biol Chem 255:10551-10554

Glenney JR, Kaulfus P, Weber K 1981 F actin assembly modulated by villin: Ca^{2+}-dependent nucleation and capping of the barbed end. Cell 24:471-480

Hiller G, Weber K, Schneider L, Parajsz C, Jungwirth C 1979 Interaction of assembled progeny pox viruses with the cellular cytoskeleton. Virology 98:142-153

Howe CL, Mooseker MS, Graves TA 1980 Brush border calmodulin. A major component of the isolated microvillus core. J Cell Biol 85:916-923

Laemmli UK 1970 Cleavage of structural proteins during the assembly of the head of bacteriophage T4. Nature (Lond) 227:680-685

Lees MB, Sandler SW, Eichberg J 1974 Effect of detergents on 2',3'-cyclic nucleotide 3'-phosphodiesterase activity in myelin and erythrocyte ghosts. Neurobiology 4:407-413

Matsudaira PT, Burgess DR 1979 Identification and organization of the components in the isolated microvillus cytoskeleton. J Cell Biol 83:667-673

Montgomery D, Young M 1982 The uptake of naturally occurring amino acids by the plasma membrane of the human placenta. Placenta 3:13-20

Mooseker MS, Pollard TD, Fujiwara K 1978 Characterization and localization of myosin in the brush border of intestinal epithial cells. J Cell Biol 79:444-453

Morgan EH 1974 Transferrin and transferrin iron. In: Jacobs A, Worwood M (eds) Iron in biochemistry and medicine. Academic Press, London, p 29-71

Salisbury JL, Condeelis JS, Satir P 1980 Evidence for the involvement of calmodulin in endocytosis. Ann N Y Acad Sci 356:429-432

Spudich JA, Watt S 1971 The regulation of rabbit skeletal muscle contraction. I: Biochemical studies of the interaction of the tropomyosin–troponin complex with actin and the proteolytic fragments of myosin. J Biol Chem 246:4866-4871

Towbin H, Staehelin T, Gordon J 1979 Electrophoretic transfer of proteins from polyacrylamide gels to nitrocellulose sheets: procedure and some applications. Proc Natl Acad Sci USA 76:4350-4354

Wada HG, Hass PE, Sussman HH 1979 Transferrin receptor in human placental brush border membranes. Studies on the binding of transferrin to placental membrane vesicles and the identification of a placental brush border glycoprotein with high affinity for transferrin. J Biol Chem 254:12629-12635

DISCUSSION

Smith: What is the evidence that you originally had an even distribution of receptors for transferrin on microvillous membranes?

Booth: When we prepare our microvilli they always contain non-latent receptor-bound transferrin. We always have a slight contamination by coated vesicles but one cannot correlate the content of transferrin with the content of coated vesicles. The receptor, and the transferrin that is bound to it, is always on the microvillus.

Smith: But it need not therefore be a uniform distribution, surely?

Booth: No, but I am convinced that the receptor is microvillar. King (1976) has evidence that the receptor is localized in the intermicrovillus space, but those results might depend on the way that the material was prepared.

Alpers: You were staining your two-dimensional gels with Coomassie blue but you might get a better resolution with silver.

Booth: I'm sure we would, and we are just beginning to use silver.

Mooseker: What do the cytoskeletons look like when you treat them with detergent?

Booth: We have looked at them under electron microscopy to see whether any cross-bridges radiating from them are visible but we have seen only tightly bundled filaments and no cross-bridges. It may be a problem with the stain.

Rees: What is the possibility of a non-specific association of actin with proteins during the solubilization process? For example, Fc binds strongly to actin, and so does DNase. Some proteins might bind and complicate the interpretation of your phenyl-Sepharose results.

Booth: I agree. We must look into that by identifying those membrane proteins that interact with the cytoskeleton, and by examining the nature of the interaction.

Boyd: Do you have any information on the number of actin filaments in each microvillus in the placenta as compared to the kidney and intestine, which we discussed after Dr Bretscher's paper (p 175–179).

Booth: The number is low, and closer to that in the kidney than in the intestine. Electron microscopy of the placenta, however, does not reveal the relatively ordered hexagonal structures seen in the kidney and intestine. I am not sure whether that is a fixation problem or a genuine difference.

Boyd: Have you any information on the nature of the branching that one sees clearly in some microvilli on the syncytiotrophoblast?

Booth: A slight problem with the placenta is to obtain fresh specimens. One cannot obtain placental tissue as fresh as that from the intestine or the kidney, and one is always examining specimens at least 15 min after removal. One always wonders whether the branched microvilli in these conditions are genuine or artifactual.

Kenny: What are the differences from a placenta obtained by Caesarian section?

Booth: We have not yet looked at Caesarian specimens under electron microscopy, but it is worth doing.

Boyd: One certainly does see branched microvilli on placentas from Caesarian specimens (Boyd et al 1968).

Quaroni: Have you studied placentas from other animals, e.g. from the rat?

Booth: The problem here is that there is no good model for the human placenta. The placenta can be considered as the crowning achievement of evolution, and the human placenta is certainly one of the latest evolutionary developments. Rat, cat and dog placentas are very different from human ones. Even the guinea-pig placenta, allegedly a good model for the human, has a different structure.

Bretscher: When you run the two-dimensional gels, are β- and γ-actin present?

Booth: Yes. They do not appear very clearly on the two-dimensional gel because it is overloaded, but on the first-dimension gel both are present in relatively even amounts.

Louvard: Are you confident that you have membrane protein on your two-dimensional gel? This can be a problem with that technique.

Booth: We had a lot of trouble with two-dimensional gels at first. We tried the conventional techniques of using urea and non-ionic detergents, and we had trouble getting protein into the first-dimension gel. We eventually solved this problem, as I described, by using the system of Ames & Nikaido (1976), where the initial solubilization is done with SDS. I was surprised this worked, because I had the feeling that SDS bound to a protein would not come off and, being negatively charged, it might affect the isoelectric point. But during the isoelectric focusing the SDS does come off, and mixed micelles form further down the gel. This method gives good results because one has control of the solubilization at the start, which is critical.

Alpers: We have used that technique on the intestine and it works (G.P. Young & D.H. Alpers, unpublished work). I understand that the structure of calmodulin is well preserved through different phylla. Is it possible that antibodies to calmodulin from non-human animal species would cross-react with human calmodulin, and could you identify it that way?

Booth: Probably, but we have not yet tried it.

Bretscher: For most cytoskeletal proteins there is more tissue specificity than species specificity, so calmodulin antibody from an animal would be likely to cross-react with human calmodulin.

Hauri: Your speculation on how the transferrin receptor reaches the coated pit would conflict with what happens in the intestine. You proposed that the absence of villin would facilitate endocytosis. In the intestine, however, villin is present but endocytosis via coated vesicles does take place (see Rodewald et al, this volume).

Mooseker: 'Treadmilling' of actin is an interesting concept. An actin filament, like a pencil or a pen, has a head and a tail. The critical concentration for assembly when you polymerize a filament in the test tube is higher at the pointed (slow) end than at the barbed (fast-growing) end. This means that with a pure actin filament, at steady state, when everything has assembled, there will be a net polymerization at the barbed end and a depolymerization at the pointed end, so the net effect is that subunits treadmill through the filament from the barbed to the pointed end.

Hauri: Can you inhibit that by adding villin?

Mooseker: Yes. Villin inhibits monomer exchange between actin filaments at Ca^{2+} concentrations greater than about 5 μM. However, this is an *in vitro* experiment using pure actin. We still have no idea if treadmilling occurs *in vivo*.

REFERENCES

Ames GF-L, Nikaido K 1976 Two-dimensional electrophoresis of membrane proteins. Biochemistry 15: 616-623

Boyd JD, Hamilton WJ, Boyd CAR 1968 The surface of the syncytium of the human chorionic villus. J Anat 102: 553-563

King BF 1976 Localization of transferrin on the surface of the human placenta by electron microscopic immunocytochemistry. Anat Rec 186: 151-160

Regulation of cytoskeletal structure and contractility in the brush border

MARK S. MOOSEKER, THOMAS C. S. KELLER III and NOBUTAKA HIROKAWA*

*Department of Biology, Yale University, New Haven, Connecticut 06511, and *Department of Physiology and Biophysics, Washington University Medical School, St. Louis, Missouri 63110, USA*

Abstract Calcium plays a vital part in the regulation of cytoskeletal structure and contractility in the brush border of intestinal epithelial cells. An increased Ca^{2+} concentration causes a rapid but reversible solation of microvillar core filaments, which is mediated by an actin-'severing' protein of the core ($M_r = 95\,000$), referred to as MV-95 K or villin. Results of recent experiments on the Ca^{2+}-dependent interaction of MV-95 K with actin are summarized, and various functions for this actin-severing protein in the intestinal epithelial cell are discussed. Calcium also regulates contractility in the brush border, as shown by studies of isolated brush borders *in vitro* from chicken intestine. In the presence of Ca^{2+} (> 1 µM) and ATP (at 37 °C) isolated brush borders dramatically contract, over 1–4 min, via an isometric contraction of the terminal web region, similar to that observed by R. Rodewald on neonatal rat brush borders. This contraction is mediated, at least in part, by contraction of the circumferential bundle of actin filaments that are associated with the zonula adherens and may also involve myosin-mediated contractions between adjacent microvillar rootlets. Analysis of Ca^{2+}-dependent phosphorylation of brush border proteins during terminal web contraction demonstrates a simultaneous phosphorylation of the regulatory light chain of brush border myosin. Like contraction, the brush border myosin kinase is activated by free Ca^{2+} (> 1 µM) and is inhibited by trifluoperazine, an inhibitor of calmodulin function. These results demonstrate that the machinery required for both production and regulation of force are integral components of the brush border cytostructure.

1983 Brush border membranes. Pitman Books Ltd, London (Ciba Foundation symposium 95) p 195-215

The cytoskeletal apparatus associated with the brush border surface of intestinal epithelial cells is among the most highly ordered arrays of actin and associated proteins found in a non-muscle cell. In the brush border are at least two structurally and perhaps functionally distinct cytoskeletal domains—the microvillus and the terminal web. Within each of the 1000–2000 microvilli on the surface of an intestinal epithelial cell is a bundle of 20–30 actin-containing filaments that are connected to and presumably responsible for supporting the microvillus membrane. The basal end of this bundle (the microvillus *core rootlet*) descends below the membrane for a further 0.5–1.0 μm into the apical cytoplasm of the cell. This region is called the terminal web because it contains a complicated meshwork of filamentous material which interdigitates between the core rootlets. This region contains large amounts of myosin (Mooseker et al 1978) between the core rootlets (Drenckhahn & Gröschel-Stewart 1980, Hirokawa et al 1982, Herman & Pollard 1981) and also at the lateral, junctional margins of the cell (Bretscher & Weber 1978). The presence of myosin in the terminal web region of the brush border raises the possibility that the cytoskeletal apparatus has 'active' motile functions in addition to its obvious architectural role in supporting the brush border membrane (see Mooseker & Howe 1982 for a review, and references on brush border cytoskeletal organization and chemistry).

Because of its exquisite structural organization, and the fact that preparations of isolated brush borders can be isolated *en masse* for biochemical studies, the brush border has become a popular, and highly useful 'model' system for analysis of cytoskeletal protein structure, chemistry and function. Despite this interest and intense study, we know almost nothing about the part played by the cytoskeletal apparatus in the function of the intestinal epithelial cell. We can only speculate, from *in vitro* observations, about the functions of the brush border cytoskeletal apparatus *in vivo*. We present here some of our recent results on the Ca^{2+}-dependent regulation of cytoskeletal structure and contractility in the brush border. These results allow us at least to raise some interesting and, in some instances, testable hypotheses about the role(s) this remarkable array of contractile proteins may play in the absorptive functions of the intestinal epithelial cell.

Materials and methods

All the experiments described here were conducted on brush borders isolated from the upper third of small intestines from chickens. Methods of brush border and microvillus isolation, and techniques of electron microscopy, are discussed in detail elsewhere (Mooseker & Howe 1982). The micrographs of brush borders that had been quick-frozen, deep-etched and rotary-replicated with platinum–carbon, were made by Dr Hirokawa, in the laboratory of Dr John Heuser, using techniques already described (Heuser & Salpeter 1979, Hirokawa & Heuser 1981). The phosphorylation experiments were conducted by Dr Keller, using techniques described elsewhere (Keller & Mooseker 1982).

Results and discussion

Ca²⁺-dependent regulation of microvillus structure

Ca^{2+}-dependent regulation of microvillus structure

One function of the cytoskeletal apparatus is obvious—the microvillus cores support the brush border membrane, whose absorptive function is presumably facilitated by the vast increase in surface area provided by the microvilli rather than by a smooth surface. The bundle of filaments underneath the microvillar membrane may, however, be more active in brush border function. Using preparations of isolated microvillus cores we observed that the structural integrity of both the bundle and the filaments that comprise the bundle is regulated by Ca^{2+} (Howe et al 1980, Mooseker et al 1980). At concentrations of free Ca^{2+} above 5–10 μM, there is a dramatic disruption of both bundles and core filaments which we have termed *core solation*. This Ca^{2+}-dependent solation results from the rapid 'chopping up' of core filaments into short fragments. This cutting is mediated by one of the major proteins of the microvillus core, a protein of relative molecular mass (M_r) 95 000, and variously referred to as villin (Bretscher & Weber 1980) or MV-95 K (Mooseker et al 1980; see Craig & Pollard 1982 for a summary of the various investigations on this protein). MV-95 K is one of a 'growing' family of Ca^{2+}-sensitive actin-binding proteins, recently identified in a wide variety of cell types (see Craig & Pollard 1982) which regulate actin filament length by 'shortening' the filaments, but only in the presence of Ca^{2+}.

It is a mystery that the microvillus should contain a protein with the potential to 'dissolve' the supporting core of the microvillus itself at increased Ca^{2+} concentrations. When membrane-intact microvilli, rather than demembranated cores, are treated with Ca^{2+}-containing solutions (Fig. 1a), the 95 K-dependent solation of the underlying core induces the formation of regular-sized vesicles along the long axis of the microvillus membrane. These results indicate that the core is, indeed, responsible for maintaining the cylindrical form of the microvillus membrane. That vesiculation is not simply a direct effect of Ca^{2+} on the microvillar membrane is indicated by results of similar experiments in which phalloidin-treated microvilli are exposed to Ca^{2+}. Phalloidin stabilizes the underlying core filaments and prevents the 95 K-dependent cutting of the filament (Mooseker et al 1980). In such preparations, no Ca^{2+}-dependent vesiculation of the membrane is observed, presumably because the underlying core maintains the form of the membrane.

Such Ca^{2+}-dependent vesiculation of the membrane may be a normal feature of the brush border *in vivo*. Recently, Misch et al (1980) studied extensively the changes in brush border structure in fasted and in fed animals. Feeding markedly increased the microvillar vesiculation in previously fasted animals. Perhaps the release of microvillar vesicles raises the activities of membrane-bound enzymes in the lumen, thus facilitating hydrolysis of luminal contents (see Matsudaira, this volume, for discussion on the correlation between microvillar vesiculation and several diseases of the small intestine).

Although the function of MV-95 K may be to regulate vesiculation of the microvillus membrane, several recent studies on the interaction of MV-95 K with actin suggest that this actin-binding protein may have other functions in intestinal absorption and in regulating changes in microvillus length *in vivo* (for discussion, see Mooseker et al 1981, 1982). The interaction of MV-95 K with

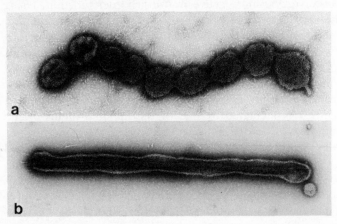

FIG. 1. Effects of Ca^{2+} on microvillus structure. (a) A negatively stained microvillus treated with buffer containing 100 μM-Ca^{2+}. MV-95 K-mediated solation of the underlying core has occurred (note short fragments of core filaments in background) which results in vesiculation of the microvillus membrane. (b) A microvillus treated as in (a) except that the underlying core filaments have been stabilized with phalloidin before Ca^{2+} treatment. This drug binds to the core filaments and prevents the Ca^{2+}-dependent solation of the core. The surrounding membrane retains its cylindrical form, indicating that vesiculation is a passive effect of core solation rather than a direct effect of Ca^{2+} on the microvillus membrane.

actin has been analysed in relation to its effects on actin polymerization and on the structure of pre-formed actin filaments. The effects of this protein on actin assembly *in vitro* are summarized below. At Ca^{2+} concentrations above about 1 μM, MV-95 K acts as a potent nucleus for actin assembly, as analysed by viscometry or changes in absorbance at 232 nm (see Craig & Pollard 1982 for references). However, the filaments formed are much shorter than in control preparations. This is probably due to the 'capping' of the 'barbed' or fast-assembly end of the filaments by MV-95 K (see Pollard & Craig 1982 for a review of actin assembly) because, in the presence of this protein, growth from the barbed end of filaments is prevented (Bonder & Mooseker 1981, Glenney et al 1981). Finally, we have recently demonstrated (A. Weber, E. Bonder and

M. Mooseker, unpublished results) that MV-95 K raises the critical concentration of actin assembly from 0.2 μM to about 1 μM in the presence, but not the absence, of Ca^{2+}. We did this by using a fluorescent derivative of actin, NBD-actin (Detmers et al 1981), which undergoes a change in fluorescence upon assembly. This increase in critical concentration of actin in the presence of MV-95 K presumably reflects the difference in critical concentrations between the barbed end (which is capped by MV-95 K) and the pointed end of the actin filament. Given these dramatic effects of MV-95 K on actin assembly, particularly on capping at the 'fast' assembly-end of a growing filament, it is plausible that MV-95 K itself, together with an intracellular Ca^{2+} control system, may function in regulating both the assembly of microvillar core filaments and the changes in microvillus length (for further discussion on regulation of microvillus assembly see Mooseker et al 1981, 1982).

MV-95 K also has a profound effect on pre-assembled filaments. Its addition to a solution of F-actin rapidly reduces the viscosity, primarily because of an MV-95 K-catalysed shortening of filaments. (However, some depolymerization also occurs because of the effect of MV-95 K on the critical concentration; but this effect is negligible at high concentrations of F-actin.) Filament length is inversely proportional to the amount of 95 K added (see Craig & Pollard 1982). This shortening of filaments is probably due to direct severing by an MV-95 K-catalysed disruption of monomer–monomer interactions along the length of the actin filament (Bonder & Mooseker 1981, Mooseker et al 1981, Glenney et al 1981).

One important difference between the Ca^{2+}-dependent effects of MV-95 K on the cutting of pre-formed filaments and the 'capping' effects on actin polymerization is that 'cutting' requires somewhat higher levels of Ca^{2+} than 'capping' does (10–20 μM for cutting compared with 1–5 μM for capping; Mooseker et al 1980, and A. Weber, M. Mooseker & E. Bonder, unpublished results). Thus, in the cell, the effects of MV-95 K on assembly and on severing of filaments could be regulated by control over the intracellular $[Ca^{2+}]$. For example, we originally observed that at 'threshold' levels of Ca^{2+} (in the 1–10 μM range) complete 'solation' of microvillus cores did not take place. Rather, unbundling and partial fragmentation of core filaments was observed. *In vivo*, such 'threshold' effects of MV-95 K on core structure could result in a partial 'softening' of the microvillus core, reducing substantially the cytoplasmic viscosity within the microvillus without causing complete solation which would result in destruction of the microvillus through membrane vesiculation. It is important to note here that the viscosity of microvillus cytoplasm should be extremely high, given the presence of over 100 mg/ml F-actin. Consequently, MV-95 K-induced reduction in this viscosity might well facilitate absorption by increasing diffusion rates of molecules that are transported across the microvillus membrane down into the interior of the cell.

Ca²⁺-dependent regulation of brush border contractility

The simplest explanation for large amounts of myosin in the terminal web region is that myosin is involved, via interaction with the core rootlets, in the generation of some form of microvillar motility. Movement of microvilli could facilitate absorption by stirring the extracellular space surrounding the microvilli. Alternatively, an up-and-down or rotational movement of the core bundle inside the microvillus might increase rates of diffusion of absorbed molecules from the microvillus cytoplasm towards the cell interior. Despite early reports of microvillar movement in intact epithelial cells, either from mucosal scrapings (Thuneberg & Rostgaard 1969) or in organ culture (Sandström 1971), belief in microvillar movements has faltered, primarily because these observations have not been successfully repeated in a wide variety of epithelial cell preparations (e.g. personal communication from S. Ito, P. Matsudaira & D. Burgess, and unpublished observations by M. Mooseker & C. Howe).

Despite the possibility that microvilli may not move *in vivo*, the terminal web does contain 'massive' amounts of myosin, compared to most non-muscle cells, and presumably the myosin is doing *something* active for the cell, via interaction with actin. That the brush border cytoskeletal apparatus has potential for motility has been convincingly demonstrated by studies on isolated brush borders *in vitro* treated with solutions that contain ATP and promote contraction. Rodewald et al (1976) observed that addition of ATP to brush borders isolated from neonatal rats results in a pronounced isometric contraction of the terminal web region. Furthermore, Mooseker (1976) reported that addition of ATP, in the presence of Ca²⁺, to brush borders that were demembranated with Triton X-100 induced a rapid retraction of microvillus cores into the terminal web region. However, later observations (Howe et al 1980) on the Ca²⁺-dependent solation of microvillus cores caused us to have serious doubts about our earlier contraction studies (Mooseker 1976). Consequently, we have reinvestigated this phenomenon using video-enhanced light microscopy at much higher magnifications. As a result, we now know that our earlier interpretation of contractility was incorrect and that what actually occurs is a partial tip-to-base solation of microvillus cores coupled with a lateral contraction of the terminal web region, similar to that observed by Rodewald et al (1976) in neonatal rat brush borders. We have recently conducted an extensive morphological and biochemical study on terminal web contractility in brush borders isolated from chicken intestine (Keller & Mooseker 1982). These results, summarized below, yield important insights into possible functions for myosin in the terminal web and also provide evidence about the molecular basis for regulation of contractility.

Light and electron microscopic studies on terminal web contractions. To investigate the nature of terminal web contractility at the light microscope level of resolution, we gently homogenized preparations of epithelial cell sheets to yield clusters of 10–30 brush borders that were still attached to one another by intercellular junctions (see Fig. 2). In the presence of ATP and Ca^{2+} (about 1 µM) the terminal webs of brush borders in such clusters dramatically contract (Fig. 2) in a temperature-dependent manner, with an optimum of 37 °C, and taking place over 1–4 min. Contraction of terminal webs in these sheets of interconnected brush borders causes an extensive rounding of individual brush borders. This rounding fans out each brush border's array of microvilli, thereby changing the apical surface of the sheet to give a scalloped appearance.

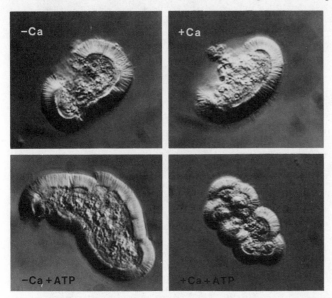

FIG. 2. Light microscopy of terminal web contraction in isolated brush borders. Sheets of 5–10 brush borders, interconnected by junctional complexes, were suspended in buffers containing (i) less than 10 nM Ca^{2+} and no ATP (marked '-Ca'); (ii) 1 µM Ca^{2+}, no ATP ('+Ca') (iii) 10 nM Ca^{2+}, 2 mM ATP ('-Ca + ATP'); (iv) 1 µM Ca^{2+}, 2mM ATP ('+ Ca + ATP'). In the presence of a higher Ca^{2+} concentration and ATP, contraction of the terminal web regions causes extensive rounding of the individual brush borders within the sheet. Slight contraction in the terminal web region occurs in the presence of ATP and a relative absence of Ca^{2+}. No contraction is detectable in the absence of ATP.

In preparations treated with ATP in the absence of any added Ca^{2+}, only slight contraction of the terminal web is observed (Fig. 2). However, the level of Ca^{2+}-sensitivity shown in Fig. 2 was observed in only about half our preparations. Some preparations exhibited little, if any, detectable Ca^{2+}-sensitivity (as originally reported by Rodewald et al 1976), and the extent of contraction in both presence and absence of added Ca^{2+} was as dramatic as depicted in Fig. 2

FIG. 3. Electron microscopy (EM) of terminal web contraction. (a) Thin-section EM of a junctional region between two brush borders in a sheet similar to that in Fig. 2. These brush borders were incubated at 37 °C in the presence of 1 μM-Ca^{2+} without ATP. Note that at this concentration of Ca^{2+}, no solation of the microvillus cores occurs. In the brush border on the left, the circumferential bundle of actin filaments (arrow) has become detached from the zonula adherens. In these uncontracted brush borders, there is a uniform distribution of filamentous material interdigitating with the core rootlets along their full lengths in the terminal web. (Original magnification ×54 000.) (b) Low-magnification (×6300) EM of a cluster of three contracted brush borders that

('+Ca, +ATP'). Although dependence of terminal web contraction on Ca^{2+} is somewhat variable (for a possible explanation, see below), ATP is an absolute requirement. For example, non-hydrolysable analogues such as adenylylimidodiphosphate (AMP-PNP) and adenosine-5'-O-(3-thiotriphosphate) (ATP-γ-S) failed to induce contraction. Finally, we observed that the drug trifluoperazine, an inhibitor of calmodulin function, blocks the Ca^{2+}-dependent contraction of the terminal web.

Examination of these preparations by electron microscopy (Fig. 3) confirms the overall morphological changes that accompany terminal web contraction observed by light microscopy. Examination of brush borders incubated at 37 °C in control solutions containing 1 µM-Ca^{2+} but no ATP demonstrates that neither the temperature nor 1 µM Ca^{2+} has much effect either on the general organization of the terminal web (Fig. 3a), which has been well established in previous studies (see Mooseker & Howe 1982, for refs), or as compared to control preparations treated with solutions containing neither Ca^{2+} nor ATP (results not shown). In addition, at 1 µM Ca^{2+}, no detectable solation of microvillus cores is observed, and the junctional complexes between adjacent brush borders remain intact (although some material appears to have been extracted from the complexes during brush border isolation; Fig. 3a).

In the presence of ATP and Ca^{2+}, the dramatic 'rounding' of the brush borders observed by light microscopy is also quite apparent at the electron microscopic level (Fig. 3b). The constriction of the terminal web region causes a complete disruption of junctions between brush borders (Fig. 3b). The organization of the terminal web region in contracted brush borders is dramatically changed. Most obviously, the lateral margins of the terminal web constrict at the level of the zonula adherens, probably because of an active contraction of the circumferential bundle of actin filaments attached to the lateral membrane of the cell at the level of the zonula adherens (Hull & Staehelin 1979, and see Fig. 3). This bundle of filaments, which may be structurally analogous to the stress factors observed in cultured cells, is characteristic of epithelium, and its 'contractile ring'-like properties were first demonstrated by Owaribe et al (1981) on glycerinated corneal tissue.

Although contraction of the zonula adherens ring may be solely responsible for the terminal web contraction, we cannot rule out isometric contractions

---

(*contd*)
were connected to one another by junctions before contraction. Although the brush borders are still associated, the extensive contraction of their terminal webs has greatly disrupted the junctional connections between them. (c) Terminal web region of a contracted brush border. The lateral margins of the brush border appear to be 'pinched in' at the level of the zonula adherens. Note the clear zone directly beneath the plasma membrane which is relatively free of interdigitating filaments between the core rootlets. (Original magnification, ×34 000.)

between rootlets throughout the terminal web, mediated by myosin. In contracted brush borders, there is considerable 'bunching up' of the rootlets, which could be due either to 'active' inter-rootlet contractions or (passively) to the zonula adherens contractile 'ring.' Another important change in morphology of the terminal web is the presence of a 'clear zone' immediately below the brush border membrane. In control preparations without ATP (Fig. 3a) there is a uniform distribution of filamentous material interdigitating along the full length of the core rootlets. In contracted brush borders, the density of interdigitating filaments apparently increases between the basal ends of the rootlets and decreases in the apical region of the web, directly underneath the membrane. This clear zone could be generated by a redistribution of terminal web material towards the basal ends of the rootlets. Alternatively, a pulling of microvillus cores downwards or a lifting up of the membrane, thus exposing regions of microvillus cores formerly surrounded by membrane, could produce the morphological change. Either of these latter alternatives seems most likely because the microvillus rootlets appear to be considerably longer than in control preparations. (This is a qualitative impression which has not yet been confirmed by detailed measurements.)

We have examined the structural rearrangements of the terminal web that accompany Ca^{2+}-dependent contraction also by using the technique of quick-freeze, deep-etch rotary replication (QFDERR, see Heuser & Salpeter 1979). The main advantage of this technique for structural analysis of the terminal web (see Hirokawa & Heuser 1981, Hirokawa et al 1982) is that the etching process allows visualization of a much thinner 'section' through the terminal web than is possible with conventional plastic sections in which super-positioning of material makes it difficult to 'untangle' the complicated structural organization of the web.

The images of brush borders obtained by the QFDERR technique (Figs. 4,5) tell the same story as revealed by analysis of thin-sectioned material: the same clustering of the rootlets at their basal ends and the same 'clear zone' underneath the apical membrane is seen during contractions. However, the density of interdigitating filaments in this zone is not appreciably less than that in control preparations. Moreover, except for the decreased distance between rootlets, the density of interdigitating filaments (some of which have been identified as myosin—see Hirokawa et al 1982) between the basal ends of rootlets does not appear to be substantially greater than in uncontracted brush borders. There is, nevertheless, considerable distortion and some unbundling of rootlets in this region. Perhaps this partial 'pulling apart' of rootlets is mediated by the myosin localized between rootlets, but the distortion could also be due to the contraction of the zonula adherens ring (seen in cross section in Fig. 4b). Another striking structural change associated with terminal web contraction in the replicas, and in thin-sectioned material, is the marked

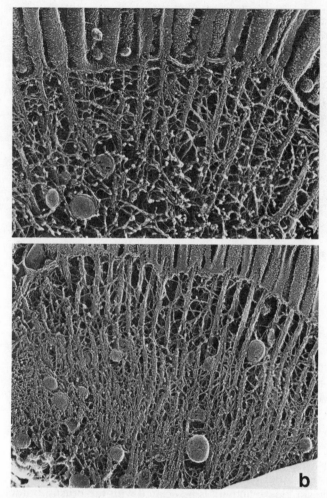

FIG. 4. Analysis of terminal web contraction using the QFDERR technique. (a) Terminal web region of a brush border in an uncontracted, control preparation. Note the uniform distribution of interdigitating filaments along the length of the core rootlets. (b) Terminal web region of a contracted brush border. The zonula adherens ring is seen in cross section at the left margin of the terminal web. Note that the core rootlets are somewhat distorted, and are more closely spaced at their basal ends than in control preparations.

increase in the number of smooth-surfaced vesicles tightly associated with the core rootlets (the possible significance of this finding is discussed below).

Role of myosin phosphorylation in brush border contractility. The studies outlined above convincingly demonstrate that Ca^{2+} is involved in the regula-

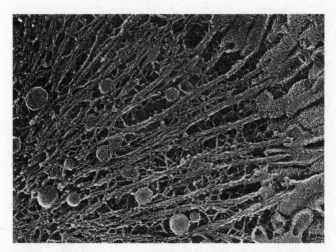

FIG. 5. QFDERR of a terminal web region in a brush border contracted in the presence of ATP and Ca^{2+}. Note the numerous smooth-surfaced vesicles associated with the core rootlets along their lengths.

tion of brush border contractility *in vitro*. Presumably, Ca^{2+} is also responsible for regulating whatever contractile events occur *in vivo*. To investigate the molecular basis for the Ca^{2+}-dependent regulation of contractility, we have analysed the possible role of myosin phosphorylation in the contraction of the terminal web *in vitro*. In vertebrate smooth muscle, and in a number of non-muscle systems, Ca^{2+}-dependent activation of actin–myosin interaction is mediated by a Ca^{2+}–calmodulin-activated kinase which phosphorylates the regulatory light chains of myosin. Once phosphorylated, the Mg-ATPase activity of myosin can be activated by actin, and presumably force production and movement can result (see Adelstein & Eisenberg 1980 for review).

To test whether myosin kinase activity is associated with the brush border cytoskeletal apparatus, we incubated preparations of brush borders and de-membranated·brush borders for various times in solutions containing [γ-^{32}P]ATP, both in the presence and in the absence of Ca^{2+}. Samples were then analysed by autoradiography of sodium dodecyl sulphate (SDS) polyacrylamide gels. Results of such experiments, presented in detail elsewhere (Keller & Mooseker 1982, Mooseker et al 1981, Keller et al 1981, Howe et al 1982), provide graphic evidence for the presence of a cytoskeletal-associated, Ca^{2+}–calmodulin-dependent, myosin light-chain kinase. In both the presence and the relative absence of Ca^{2+} ($< 10^{-8}$ M), numerous cytoskeletal proteins of the brush border are rapidly phosphorylated (see Fig. 6), but at concentrations of Ca^{2+} greater than about 1 µM there is a dramatic increase in the phosphoryla-

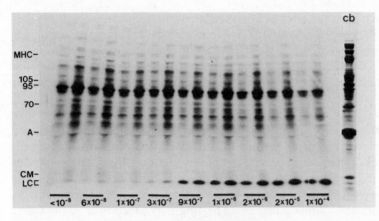

FIG. 6. Ca^{2+}-dependent phosphorylation of brush border myosin. Demembranated brush borders were suspended in buffers containing 0.1 mM $[\gamma-^{32}P]ATP$ in the presence of nine different $[Ca^{2+}]$ ranging from $> 10^{-8}M$ to 0.1 mM. Gel samples were made after 30 and 60 s and were then electrophoresed on a 5–15% polyacrylamide gradient gel containing SDS. Shown is the autoradiograph and one lane (cb) of the Coomassie blue-stained gel. Numerous brush border cytoskeletal proteins become rapidly phsophorylated at all $[Ca^{2+}]$ tested. However, at a $[Ca^{2+}]$ of $>$ about 1 µM there is a marked increase in the phosphorylation of a 19 K subunit identified as the regulatory light chain of brush border myosin. The migration of certain brush border proteins is marked, including myosin heavy chain (MHC), the 105 K, 95 K, and 70 K core proteins, actin (A), calmodulin (CM) and the two myosin light chains (LC).

tion of a subunit with M_r of 19 000 (Fig. 6), which we have identified as the regulatory light chain of brush border myosin. When terminal web contraction takes place (i.e. at 37 °C), there is a rapid Ca^{2+}-dependent phosphorylation of brush border myosin, with the maximum loading (up to 0.6 moles phosphate per mole of myosin) having a time course exactly correlated with the onset of contractility. Furthermore, in preparations that contracted both in the presence and relative absence of Ca^{2+}, high levels of myosin phosphorylation were also observed. The most likely explanation for these results is that in these preparations limited proteolysis of the myosin kinase had occurred. Such proteolysis generates an enzyme that no longer requires interaction with Ca^{2+}–calmodulin for its activation (see Adelstein & Eisenberg 1980, for refs).

Finally, we have shown that the Ca^{2+}-sensitive phosphorylation of myosin is blocked by trifluoperazine, which implicates calmodulin in the Ca^{2+}-dependent activation of myosin light-chain kinase in the brush border. Interestingly, although the brush border cytoskeletal apparatus contains large amounts of calmodulin (Howe et al 1980), this is primarily, if not exclusively, localized in the microvillus core in association with the 110 K subunit of the core (Howe et al 1982, Glenney & Weber 1980). The calmodulin is therefore localized away from the sites of contractility in the terminal web. However, treatment of microvillus cores with Ca^{2+} causes a large portion of this calmodulin to dissociate from the core (Howe et al 1980). Thus, under Ca^{2+} concentrations that activate contractility, calmodulin may be free to diffuse down from the microvillus to activate the myosin kinase which is presumably localized in the terminal web.

Possible functions for brush border myosin in vivo. We have already discussed the possible involvement of myosin in the generation of microvillar movements. The results presented here on terminal web contractility *in vitro* allow us to suggest additional modes of action for myosin in the brush border. Most obvious is the participation of myosin in the contraction of the ring of filaments associated with the zonula adherens. The ring may function in maintaining tension between cells in the epithelial sheet. Alternatively, it may function in migration of epithelial cells from the crypt to the tip of the villus. Another possibility is that the ring mediates transient opening of the cell's tight junctions, thus regulating trans-epithelial permeability. To address this last possibility, we hope to conduct experiments *in vivo* in which the levels of myosin phosphorylation are monitored in parallel with the physiological measurements of epithelial sheet permeability.

One final speculation is that myosin is involved in the translocation of vesicles from the smooth endoplasmic reticulum (SER), up the core rootlets, to fusion sites on the plasma membrane. This suggestion is based on the marked increase observed in the number of vesicles associated with the core rootlets after Ca^{2+}- and ATP-induced contraction of the terminal web (see Figs. 3–5). These vesicles presumably arise from the large number of SER vesicles that lie beneath the terminal web in the intact cell as well as in the isolated brush borders used for these studies. The increased number of vesicles on core rootlets after addition of Ca^{2+} and ATP may be because the vesicles have been passively squeezed up into the terminal web during contraction. Or perhaps the core rootlets act as 'railroad tracks' for the upward, myosin-mediated movement of vesicles from the endoplasmic reticulum to the brush border membrane. Given the polarity of the actin filaments within the rootlets (with heavy meromyosin arrowheads pointing downwards), the best model for upward movement of a vesicle by an acto–myosin mechanism is for the 'tail' ends of myosin molecules to be attached to the vesicles. Such a vesicle, with myosin heads protruding from its cytoplasmic surface could 'walk up' the rootlet to the membrane. Ultrastructural examination of the rootlet-associated vesicles, by the QFDERR technique, reveals thin bridges connecting the vesicles to the rootlets (see Figs. 4b, 5). However, it is impossible, without further study using antibody localization techniques, to determine if these bridges are formed from myosin, and more evidence is needed before we can take the above speculation seriously. Nevertheless, this model does provide a simple, efficient mechanism for the movement of newly synthesized microvillar membrane proteins from the endoplasmic reticulum to the brush border membrane.

Acknowledgements

We would like to thank Mr Douglas Fishkind for his excellent technical assistance. We also thank Hector Alicea, Ed Bonder, Chris Howe and Mirilee Pearl for valuable discussions. This work was supported by National Institutes of Health Grant no. AM 25387 to M.S. Mooseker, a Basil O'Connor Starter Grant from the March of Dimes Foundation to M.S. Mooseker, a grant from the Muscular Dystrophy Association (MDA) to N. Hirokawa and a postdoctoral fellowship from the MDA to T.C.S. Keller.

REFERENCES

Adelstein RS, Eisenberg E 1980 Regulation and kinetics of actin myosin–ATP interactions. Annu Rev Biochem 49:921-956

Bonder EM, Mooseker MS 1981 The acrosomal process: a new tool in studying actin assembly and structure. J Cell Biol 91:306a

Bretscher A, Weber K 1978 Localization of actin and microfilament associated proteins in the microvilli and terminal web of the intestinal brush border by immunofluorescence microscopy. J Cell Biol 79:839-845

Bretscher A, Weber K 1980 Villin is a major protein of the microvillus cytoskeleton which binds both G and F actin in a calcium-dependent manner. Cell 20:839-847

Craig SW, Pollard TD 1982 Actin binding proteins. Trends Biochem Sci 7:88-91

Detmers P, Weber A, Elzinga M, Stephens RE 1981 7-Chloro- 4-nitrobenzeno-2-oxa-1,3-diazole actin as a probe for actin polymerization. J Biol Chem 256:99-105

Drenckhahn D, Gröschel-Stewart U 1980 Localization of myosin, actin, and tropomyosin in rat intestinal epithelium: immunohistochemical studies at the light and electron microscope levels. J Cell Biol 86:475-482

Glenney JR Jr, Weber K 1980 Calmodulin-binding proteins of the microfilaments present in isolated brush borders and microvilli of intestinal epithelial cells. J Biol Chem 255:10551-10554

Glenney JR, Kaulfus P, Weber K 1981 F-actin assembly modulated by villin: Ca^{2+}-dependent nucleation and capping of the barbed end. Cell 24:471-480

Herman I, Pollard TD 1981 Electron microscopic localization of cytoplasmic myosin with ferritin-labeled antibodies. J Cell Biol 88:346-351

Heuser JE, Salpeter SR 1979 Organization of acetylcholine receptors in quick-frozen, deep-etched and rotary-replicated torpedo post-synaptic membrane. J Cell Biol 82:150-173

Hirokawa N, Heuser J 1981 Quick-freeze, deep-etch visualization of the cytoskeleton beneath surface differentiations of intestinal epithelial cells. J Cell Biol 91:399-409

Hirokawa N, Tilney LG, Fujiwara K, Heuser JE 1982 Organization of actin, myosin, and inter-mediate filaments in the brush border of intestinal epithelial cells. J Cell Biol 94:425-443

Howe CL, Mooseker MS, Graves TA 1980 Brush border calmodulin. A major component of the isolated microvillus core. J Cell Biol 85:916-923

Howe CL, Keller TCS III, Mooseker MS, Wasserman RH 1982 Analysis of cytoskeletal proteins and Ca^{2+}-dependent regulation of structure in intestinal brush borders from rachitic chicks. Proc Natl Acad Sci USA 79:1134-1138

Hull BE, Staehelen LA 1979 The terminal web. A re-evaluation of its structure and function. J Cell Biol 81:67-82

Keller TCS III, Mooseker MS 1982 Ca^{2+}-calmodulin-dependent phosphorylation of myosin and its role in brush border contraction in vitro. J Cell Biol 95:943-959

Keller TCS III, Howe CL, Mooseker MS 1981 Ca^{2+}-dependent phosphorylation of myosin in situ in brush border isolated from intestinal epithelium. J Cell Biol 91:309a

Misch DW, Giebel PE, Faust RG 1980 Intestinal microvilli: responses to feeding and fasting. Eur J Cell Biol 21:269-279

Mooseker MS 1976 Brush border motility. Microvillar contraction in Triton-treated brush borders isolated from intestinal epithelium. J Cell Biol 71:417-432

Mooseker MS, Howe CL 1982 The brush border of intestinal epithelium: a model system for analysis of cell-surface architecture and motility. Methods Cell Biol 25:144-175

Mooseker MS, Pollard TD, Fujiwara K 1978 Characterization and localization of myosin in the brush border of intestinal epithelial cells. J Cell Biol 79:444-453

Mooseker MS, Graves TA, Wharton KA, Falco N, Howe CL 1980 Regulation of microvillus structure: calcium-dependent solation and cross-linking of actin filaments in the microvilli of intestinal epithelial cells. J Cell Biol 87:809-822

Mooseker MS, Bonder EM, Grimwade BG et al 1981 Regulation of contractility, cytoskeletal structure, and filament assembly in the brush border of intestinal epithelial cells. Cold Spring Harbor Symp Quant Biol 46:855-870

Mooseker MS, Pollard TD, Wharton KA 1982 Nucleated polymerization of actin from the membrane-associated ends of microvillar filaments in the intestinal brush border. J Cell Biol 95:223-233

Owaribe K, Kodama R, Eguchi G 1981 Demonstration of contractility of circumferential actin bundles and its morphogenetic significance in pigmented epithelium in vitro and in vivo. J Cell Biol 90:507-514

Pollard TD, Craig SW 1982 Mechanism of actin polymerization. Trends Biochem Sci 7:55-58

Rodewald R, Newman SB, Karnovsky MJ 1976 Contraction of isolated brush borders from the intestinal epithelium. J Cell Biol 70:541-554

Sandström B 1971 A contribution to the concept of brush border function. Observations in intestinal epithelium in tissue culture. Cytobiologie 3:293-297

Thuneberg L, Rostgaard J 1969 Motility of microvilli: a film demonstration. J Ultrastruct Res 29:578a

DISCUSSION

Kenny: Thuneberg & Rostgaard (1969) made a phase-contrast, time-lapse cine film of renal proximal tubular cells in which the microvilli appeared to move in waves.

Mooseker: Unfortunately, more details of those results have not been published. Microvilli can be encouraged to move, in ways that appear to be active, but induced calcium-dependent solations of the underlying core filaments by villin probably make the microvilli subjectable to Brownian motion.

Alpers: When you added calcium in the presence of trifluoperazine (Stelazine) did you see changes other than simply in the light chains?

Mooseker: Yes: we saw a general suppression of phosphorylation. We have to use 0.2 mM-trifluoperazine because there is so much calmodulin in these preparations.

Alpers: But at that concentration trifluoperazine can produce many non-specific changes. Your results on phosphorylation showed only a two-fold difference, which is less than I would have guessed from your results on gels. Have you done a similar experiment, but with another protein from that gel, to test whether you simply obtained two-fold changes in *all* the proteins?

Mooseker: That is not happening. The general, non-specific effects of trifluoperazine reduce the phosphorylation of other Ca^{2+}-independent phosphoproteins by only about 10–30%, depending on the preparation. The inhibition of Ca^{2+}-dependent phosphorylation of myosin light chain is substantially greater, and is invariably similar to that observed in the absence of Ca^{2+} and the drug. One other point should be made. The non-specific effects of trifluoperazine are much greater at 37 °C than at 25 °C. The results of phosphorylation experiments at the lower temperature show even greater Ca^{2+}-sensitivity (4–5 fold activation), and the trifluoperazine inhibition of Ca^{2+}-sensitive light chain phosphorylation is complete.

Bretscher: Your data imply that the myosin light chain kinase is part of the brush border cytoskeleton. Have you identified it? Secondly, you see an activation of the myosin light chain kinase at about 1μM free calcium. Since this enzyme requires calmodulin for activation, is it possible that the effect occurs because calmodulin bound to the microvillus cores is released by 1μM free calcium and is then available to activate the kinase?

Mooseker: It could, and we have tried the effect of exogenous bovine brain calmodulin to check for that, and we saw the same activity. Of course chicken calmodulin may not be the same as bovine calmodulin.

Matsudaira: When myosin is phosphorylated it is believed to assemble into filaments, suggesting that in the absence of calcium there might not be filaments. I have never seen thick filaments in the terminal web. Little is known about the state of myosin in non-muscle cells.

Semenza: What is the new electron microscopy technique that you used?

Mooseker: This was developed by John Heuser and Tom Reese and is called the 'freeze slam' technique. Fixed or unfixed preparations are placed on a plunger and slammed into a copper block that is cooled to liquid helium temperature. The sample is then removed and put in a Baltzers freeze-fracture apparatus and fractured. Because it is so cold when frozen, large ice crystals do not form, so deep etching of the sample is unhindered. The key to the technique is a rotary shadowing at a fairly low angle to prevent 'puddles' of metal appearing to pile up on one side of the structure. The technique allows distinction between an actin filament and a 10-nm filament on the basis of distinctive surface profiles.

Smith: How thick is the myosin?

Mooseker: The myosin filaments visualized by this 'quick-freeze, deep-etch rotary replication' (QFDERR) technique are about the size of a dimer (see Hirokawa et al 1982).

Smith: Is there any correlation between the presence or absence of myosin and the regularity of brush border membrane structure? If one were just to put a pencil through a thin sheet it would not stay straight. Could not the force of contraction exerted by myosin in the terminal web be responsible for regularity of microvillus structure?

Mooseker: That's a good idea. Matsudaira & Burgess (1981) have a formalized model that is similar to that. One can examine the myosin in a core in cross-section in the terminal web. For example, Drenckhahn & Gröschel-Stewart (1980) have localized myosin well; they have shown that it is wrapped radially around the core. The myosin could be purely structural and concerned with keeping the microvilli erect. But a passive structural protein like spectrin might be more suitable for such a role

Matsudaira: The myosin could be activated when it needs to be, and it need not be contracting all the time. If myosin is a dimer and you expect it to be involved in force production, you would have to suggest a myosin-binding site, or some such, on the rootlet. Presumably the myosin would have to be localized at certain areas in the terminal web?

Mooseker: Yes. One must ask what keeps myosin where it is. A glib answer to that is tropomyosin. Myosin may bind preferentially to the core rootlet filaments that have tropomyosin on them. It would be interesting to do a self-assembly study with pure actin versus tropomyosin–actin to see if myosin interacts cooperatively with the filaments containing tropomyosin.

Rodewald: What are the differences between the actin filaments within the core of the microvillus and those within the terminal web?

Mooseker: The filaments of the core are continuous from tip to base, but different proteins are associated with that region of the bundle within the microvillus than with the terminal web. For example, only the 'rootlet' end of the core contains tropomyosin. Conversely, only the microvillus end of the core contains the 110 K—the presumed filament–membrane linking protein. The composition of the filaments in the zonula adherens has not been determined.

Rodewald: What do you mean by 'rootlets'?

Mooseker: The term has been loosely applied to the portion of the core that is not in the microvillus but is in the terminal web.

Rees: I wish to comment on vesicle movement. If you postulate a myosin-binding site on the surface of these vesicles then, presumably, after fusion this surface will end up on the cytoplasmic side of the membrane, and that is precisely where you don't see any myosin associated. So why doesn't the myosin bind at the cytoplasmic side of the microvillar membrane?

Mooseker: It's not clear that it doesn't. Myosin binding, to actin, for example, depends on its state of phosphorylation and the presence of ATP. Consequently, there may be other myosin binding sites, on the membrane for example, which depend on the ATP concentration or the phosphorylation state of the myosin.

Jørgensen: What is the time-course of the contraction? For example, at a low plasma concentration of ATP, is contraction continuous or is there some kind of a feedback into the cascade that would interrupt the contraction?

Mooseker: I don't know. *In vitro*, contraction stops after a few minutes, and addition of extra substrate or extra ATP has no effect. Again, one could postulate a coupling with phosphorylation of myosin *in vivo* but I have no information about the kinetics of phosphorylation of myosin in intact cells. *In vitro* addition of extra substrate leads to more phosphorylation as long as calcium is present and as long as the kinase is not proteolysed. Thus a phosphatase may be part of the contraction cycle.

Jørgensen: From a transport point of view the usefulness of this contractile system could be to alter the area of luminal membrane exposed to the medium. Given an even distribution of sodium-coupled carriers for amino acids and glucose in the brush border membrane, the palisade arrangement is not effective for transport because it presents a diffusion barrier. The type of contraction you have described could give a sudden increase in surface area and, presumably, a rapid increase in the rate of influx of nutrients in company with sodium ions. An increase in the cytoplasmic $[Na^+]$ could, in turn, increase the cytoplasmic calcium if the $[Ca^{2+}]$ depends on sodium/calcium exchange. That would give rise to a negative feedback if the effect of calcium through the cascade is not stopped, and this could result in a continuous contraction.

Mooseker: That is true, and the system may never be 'off'.

Jørgensen: The contraction would thus lead to an increase in flux of sodium in such a way that the contraction could be maintained as long as substrate for the sodium-coupled carriers is available from the luminal surface.

Mooseker: That's right. Another model of regulation is based on the activating protein, calmodulin, not being present in the terminal web *in vitro*. One way to regulate the whole system, is that a rise in intracellular calcium, which may be coupled to general transport, could loosen the structure of the core by the calcium-dependent severing of the 95 K protein, which, in turn, would reduce the viscosity of the cytoplasm. The core contains 100 mg/ml of actin, which makes it very viscous. Chopping the core filaments may facilitate transport just by increasing the diffusion rates of absorbed nutrients. On the other hand, when calcium is added to the core, some of the calmodulin is dissociable, and thus is free to diffuse down into the terminal web to activate the kinase, which in turn will activate contractility. During cessation of calcium transport, the calmodulin competes in the resting state with the calcium in the cytoplasm which is reduced again, presumably by some mitochondrial function or unidentified sarcoplasmic reticulum-like fraction. The calmodulin then goes back up into the microvillus where it binds to the 110 K, which is the only protein identified in the system as binding calmodulin in the absence of calcium. So a cycle of movement of both calcium and calmodulin from the core in turn activates the contractile functions in the terminal web, and could also facilitate transport. The 'on' and 'off' control for this process is unknown.

Hauri: I would question a physiological role for this mechanism. You deal with isolated brush borders, but what happens if you expose an intact epithelium to calcium and ATP? Can you see the same contraction?

Mooseker: No. With intact epithelium one can even add Ca^{2+}- ionophore and not see very much.

Matsudaira: With epithelial cell sheets (extensive arrays) that have been permeabilized by glycerination, ATP induces contraction only in cells on the periphery of the sheet but not in those in the middle (Burgess & Prum 1982). We proposed (Matsudaira & Burgess 1981) that the contraction effects are artifactual when one is looking at isolated cells or fragments of cells such as brush borders.

Booth: Could the contraction have something to do with the movement of *cells* along the villus?

Mooseker: Yes. The cells have to move by some mechanism from the crypt to the tip. This problem is general for epithelial sheets required to maintain their integrity.

Smith: Is the idea that cells move together with their basement membrane no longer accepted?

Quaroni: I don't think there is any evidence for movement of the basement membrane.

Mooseker: I know of no convincing observations of cell movement in the crypt.

Rodewald: Does this terminal web band play any part in the extrusion of cells at the tip of the villus?

Mooseker: I could postulate that the *zonula adherens* ring functions to extrude the cells by a purse-string contraction, or they could close up the gap, as in a wound.

Hauri: In addition, the contact of the enterocytes with the underlying basement membrane appears to be important for the extrusion process. This adhesion diminishes along the crypt–villus axis.

Mooseker: One would have to break junctions too. A possible physiological function for this mechanism would be in regulating junctional permeability— the paracellular route—or the leakiness of tight junctions. There is a vast array of contractile proteins at the lateral margin which might open or close the junctions.

Alpers: Do you think they open up the junctions? In the gall bladder, transport of fluid and electrolytes has been studied, and during periods of intensive transport, the intracellular space swells as if the junction *hadn't* opened up (Fromter & Diamond 1972). So paracellular transport is viewed as *across* the luminal membrane and then out through the *lateral* margin without any necessary opening up of the junction.

Mooseker: I agree. There is no evidence in the intestine for changes at the junctional margins where paracellular flow has actually been measured.

Semenza: Even if microvilli move *in vivo* there *is* a huge unstirred layer between the surface of the brush border and the bulk of the lumen, as shown by Gray & Ingelfinger (1965) for sucrase. *In vivo* this layer is at least one order of magnitude larger than *in vitro*, as they demonstrated by perfusion experiments compared with *in vitro* assay. Sodium leaks out through the paracellular pathways, and the unstirred layer, which acts as a diffusion barrier, prevents the sodium from diffusing freely into the lumen. This can be favourable because the Na^+ builds up at the luminal surface of the brush border membrane thus providing an electrochemical gradient of sodium sufficient to drive glucose and amino acids in through the membrane. One more question: many of us prepare vesicles with calcium. Does magnesium also cause vesiculation?

Bretscher: Vesiculation doesn't take place in the presence of micromolar quantities of magnesium. Dr Mooseker uses 5mM-magnesium in the buffer in which he routinely studies brush borders, and as we have seen they are beautifully intact. At higher concentrations of magnesium vesiculation eventually takes place, but this is probably simply a salt effect.

REFERENCES

Burgess DR, Prum BE 1982 A re-evaluation of brush border motility: calcium induces core filament solation and microvillar vesiculation. J Cell Biol 94: 97-107

Drenckhahn D, Gröschel-Stewart U 1980 Localization of myosin, actin and tropomyosin in rat intestinal epithelium: immunohistochemical studies at the light and electron microscope levels. J Cell Biol 86: 475-482

Fromter E, Diamond J 1972 Route of passive ion permeation in epithelia. Nature (Lond) 235: 9-13

Gray GM, Ingelfinger FJ 1965 Intestinal absorption of sucrose in man: the site of hydrolysis and absorption. J Clin Invest 44: 390-398

Hirokawa N, Tilney LG, Fujiwara K, Heuser JE 1982 Organization of actin, myosin, and intermediate filaments in the brush border of intestinal epithelial cells. J Cell Biol 94:425-443

Matsudaira PT, Burgess DR 1981 Structure and function of the brush-border cytoskeleton. Cold Spring Harbor Symp Quant Biol 46: 845-854

Thuneberg L, Rostgaard J 1969 Motility of microvilli: a film demonstration. J Ultrastruct Res 29: 578a

Characterization of membrane glycoproteins involved in attachment of microfilaments to the microvillar membrane

EVELYNE COUDRIER, HUBERT REGGIO and DANIEL LOUVARD

European Molecular Biology Laboratory, Postfach 102209, Meyerhofstrasse 1, 6900 Heidelberg, Federal Republic of Germany

Abstract We have characterized a novel integral membrane glycoprotein, from intestinal microvilli, with a relative molecular mass (M_r) of 140 000 as measured by sodium dodecyl sulphate–polyacrylamide gel electrophoresis (SDS–PAGE). This glycoprotein has been purified to homogeneity, and specific antibodies have been prepared to localize it immunocytochemically and to determine its topological organization with respect to the membrane bilayer. This protein's major features are: (1) in contrast to other major glycoproteins of the microvillus membrane it cannot be quantitatively extracted by detergents; (2) treatment of the core residue (an insoluble fraction which remains after Triton X-100 treatment of purified microvilli) with low-ionic-strength buffer in the presence of chelating agents promotes partial solubilization of the *amphipathic* glycoprotein; (3) controlled proteolysis with papain, using right-side-out sealed vesicles derived from microvilli, results in solubilization of the protein. Once solubilized by papain, the protein co-migrates (on SDS–PAGE) with the protein obtained by dialysis but, unlike the low-ionic-strength form, it does not bind detergents or exhibit *hydrophilic* properties. These observations are consistent with the protein having a small hydrophobic domain that anchors it to the microvillar membrane. Most of these features were reported some years ago for aminopeptidase, but this newly described protein has a distinct behaviour with respect to its association with microfilaments. We have demonstrated that the 110 K protein, a major cytoskeletal protein of the lateral bridges, will bind to the glycoprotein *in vitro*. These observations suggest that this 140 K polypeptide is a transmembrane protein and may provide attachment sites *in vivo* for cytoskeletal proteins.

1983 Brush border membranes. Pitman Books Ltd, London (Ciba Foundation symposium 95) p 216-232

The apical brush border of intestinal cells is highly organized. This organelle-like structure formed during terminal differentiation of enterocytes provides a useful model for study of membrane–cytoskeleton interaction in non-muscle nucleated cells. Understanding of the interaction between microfilaments and

216

membrane has been hampered by difficulties in isolation of subcellular fractions in which such interactions are preserved for morphological and biochemical analysis. In contrast to the erythrocytes, for which a detailed molecular analysis has led to the biochemical characterization of membrane and cytoskeletal proteins (see review by Branton et al 1981) little is known about similar interactions in nucleated cells.

The microvilli from intestinal cells provide a suitable model system for the following reasons.

(1) Each microvillus contains a bundle of axial microfilaments anchored at its tip. In addition, short filaments connect each bundle to the membrane in an orientation perpendicular to the long axis of the bundle (Mooseker & Tilney 1975). These sorts of microfilament–membrane association have been suggested to occur in other cell types including erythrocytes (Bennett & Stenbuck 1980), fibroblasts in culture, and in the protozoon *Dictyostelium discoideium* (Luna et al 1981).

(2) Large amounts of microvilli can be prepared by using several subcellular fractionation procedures, which yield preparations of intact microvilli (Bretscher & Weber 1978a, Howe et al 1980) or small sealed vesicles oriented right-side-out (Louvard et al 1973). Both types of preparation are composed of microvillar membranes still associated with microfilaments.

(3) Biochemical analysis of insoluble material obtained after extraction of microvilli preparations with non-ionic detergents has demonstrated the relative simplicity of the material's polypeptide composition. Five major polypeptides associated with the microfilaments have been identified. None of the actin-binding proteins of non-muscle cells has been found in intestinal microvilli (Bretscher & Weber 1978b, Geiger et al 1979), but a specific set of previously undescribed actin-binding proteins has been identified (see this volume, papers by Bretscher and Matsudaira). Associated with the axial actin bundles are: *villin* (95 K), an actin-binding protein exclusively linked with intestinal and renal (proximal tubular) microvilli (Bretscher et al 1981) and regulated by Ca^{2+} ions (Bretscher & Weber 1980a); and *fimbrin* ($M_r = 68$ K), another actin-binding protein found in several other cell types (Bretscher & Weber 1980b). Associated with the lateral bridges connecting the axial actin bundles to the membrane are: a *110 K protein* whose association with the actin bundles may be controlled *in vitro* by ATP (Matsudaira & Burgess 1979, Coudrier et al 1981a); and *calmodulin*, an abundant polypeptide in purified brush borders (Howe et al 1980).

We recently reported the presence of another polypeptide ($M_r = 140$ K) associated with the core residue of intestinal microvilli. This polypeptide is presumably glycosylated since it binds specifically to concanavalin A Ultrogel (Coudrier et al 1981b). We report in this paper the further characterization of this *140 K polypeptide*, its organization in the membrane bilayer and its binding to detergent micelles. Furthermore, we have demonstrated that this protein binds to the 110 K polypeptide *in vitro*, indicating that it may be a transmembrane glycoprotein that provides an attachment site *in vivo* for the lateral bridges which connect the axial actin-bundle microfilaments to their surrounding microvillar membranes.

Results and discussion

The core residue prepared from intestinal microvilli contains a glycosylated polypeptide of high M_r (140 000)

We have recently reported the presence of this novel polypeptide in microvilli extracted in Triton X-100. Its apparent molecular weight is 140 K, as measured by polyacrylamide sodium dodecyl sulphate gel electrophoresis (SDS–PAGE), and it is particularly abundant in microvilli preparations derived from intestinal mucosa that has been homogenized in the presence of calcium ions (Coudrier et al 1981b). Fig. 1 shows that the core residue (P_1) contains the well described cytoskeletal polypeptides (see above) as well as a 140 K species. The major hydrolases (e.g. aminopeptidase and disacchar-idases) have the same range of M_r, but are quantitatively extracted by non-ionic detergent (S_1) (Louvard et al 1975). Careful enzymic analysis of the core residue revealed extremely low amounts of the well characterized enzymes associated with intestinal microvilli, such as aminopeptidase, alka-line phosphatase, disaccharidases and γ-glutamyltransferase.

Further extraction of the core residue with various non-ionic or ionic detergents or with chaotropic or denaturing agents proved to be inefficient for quantitative recovery of this polypeptide in a non-sedimentable form (100 000 g for 45 min).

Using a quantitative immunological technique (Howe & Hershey 1981) and specific antibodies raised against this protein (see below) we observed that 50–70% of the protein is extracted by Triton X-100. Its presence in the first supernatant (S_1) can be assessed only by using a specific reagent (such as antibody) since it co-migrates with other high M_r polypeptides (mainly aminopeptidase and disaccharidases). These data indicate that two forms of the antigen (co-migrating on SDS–PAGE) exist in our preparations of microvilli. The reason for the weak association of approximately 50–70% of the 140 K proteins with a core residue remains to be explained.

We have already reported that this 140 K polypeptide behaves as glycosy-lated species, which binds to immobilized concanavalin A and specifically elutes with α-D-methylmannopyranoside (0.2 M) (Coudrier et al 1981b). These observations prompted us to investigate further the structure of the glycosylated protein and the significance of its association with the core residue that contains cytoskeletal polypeptides.

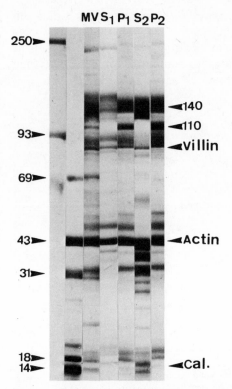

FIG. 1. Microvilli of pig intestinal mucosa and extracted fractions analysed by SDS–PAGE on a gradient gel of 6.5%–17.5% acrylamide. MV, total microvillar protein from right-side-out vesicles derived from microvilli (Louvard et al 1973); S_1, Triton X-100 extract of the microvilli preparation; P_1, core residue obtained after Triton X-100 extraction of the microvilli preparation; S_2, supernatant obtained after treatment of P_1 with a low ionic strength buffer (see text); P_2, pellet obtained after treatment with the low ionic strength buffer. Molecular weight markers: filamin (250 K); phosphorylase b (93 K); bovine serum abumin (69 K); actin (43 K); pancreatic DNase (31 K); soybean trypsin inhibitor (18 K); and lysozyme (14 K). The positions of the major identified microvillar proteins are also indicated; cal, calmodulin.

Dissociation procedures used to release the 140 K polypeptide in a non-sedimentable form

(a) Trypsin treatment and low-ionic-strength extraction. Early attempts to extract the 140 K protein from the insoluble pellet involved a mild proteolysis with trypsin at 4 °C. This procedure leads to the solubilization (up to 30%) of a polypeptide that co-migrates with the protein band in the core residue. With supernatants of this limited proteolysis, a purification procedure using ion exchange chromatography (DEAE cellulose) and gel filtration (Ac22 Ultrogel) yielded an essentially pure fraction of the 140 K polypeptide

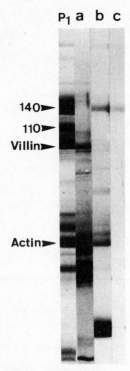

FIG. 2. Protein composition of fractions used for isolation of the 140 K protein. Fractions were analysed by SDS–PAGE on a gradient gel of 6.5%–17% acrylamide. P_1, core residue (same as Fig. 1); a, pellet after papain treatment; b, supernatant after papain treatment (0.5 mg/ml, 15 min, 37 °C); c, protein peak eluted from DEAE Trisacryl, previously equilibrated in potassium phosphate buffer (10 mM, pH 6.0) by a linear NaCl gradient.

(Coudrier et al 1981b). We shall refer later to the 140 K protein prepared by this procedure as the *trypsin form*.

Recently, we have attempted to avoid using protease treatment. Further extraction of the core residue in very low ionic strength buffer, containing chelating agents (2.5 mM EDTA) and 0.1% Triton X-100, allows an incomplete solubilization (up to 30%) of the 140 K polypeptide (Fig. 1, S_2). However, subsequent purification of the 140 K polypeptide from this extract (by conventional chromatography procedures) proved difficult and irreproducible, possibly because the extract contained large amounts of cytoskeletal proteins, particularly villin and actin. We shall refer later to the 140 K protein prepared by this procedure as the *low ionic strength form*.

(b) Preparation of a 'papain form' of the 140K polypeptide. A limited digestion of the core residue by papain (Fig. 2, P_1) proved efficient for

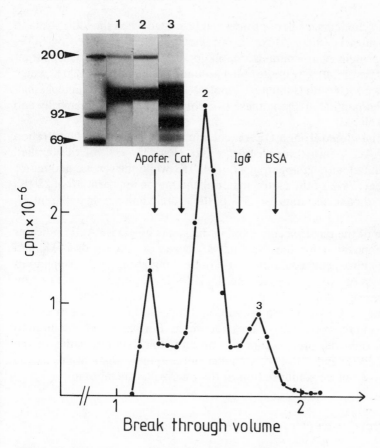

FIG. 3. Elution profile on Ac22 Ultrogel of material obtained in the peak from DEAE Trisacryl. The protein had been iodinated with the Bolton Hunter reagent before the chromatography was done. Insert shows the analysis on SDS–PAGE of the protein peaks labelled 1, 2, and 3. Molecular mass (M_r) markers for Ultrogel filtration were apoferritin (Apofer., 430 K) catalase (Cat., 250 K), rabbit immunoglobulin G (IgG, 150 K) and bovine serum albumin (BSA, 69 K). The column was 100 × 2.5 cm, equilibrated in 50 mM-potassium phosphate, pH 7.8, and run at 6 ml/h. Units on abscissa: break-through volumes. M_r markers for PAGE were myosin heavy chain from rabbit skeletal muscle (200 K), phosphorylase b (92 K) and bovine serum albumin (69 K).

quantitative solubilization of the 140 K protein (Fig. 2b). As demonstrated later (p 227) the papain-solubilized 140 K protein lacks the hydrophobic domain that is present in the trypsin form. This proteolytically cleaved protein can be purified to homogeneity in relatively large quantities by chromatography on DEAE Trisacryl resin, which fully absorbs the solubilized protein extract when the resin is equilibrated in 10 mM-phosphate buffer at pH

6.0. A single symmetric peak of protein can be eluted when the ionic strength is increased linearly (0–0.2 M-NaCl, not shown). When analysed on SDS–PAGE this protein peak contains one major polypeptide with an apparent molecular mass of 140 K (Fig. 2c) plus a minor polypeptide of 200 K which usually stains poorly with Coomassie blue. As shown later by immunochemical analysis and peptide mapping these two polypeptides are antigenically and structurally related.

The material eluted from a DEAE column can be separated, by filtration on Ultrogel Ac22, into three distinct peaks (Fig. 3). 13% of the applied material is eluted with an apparent M_r of 480 K, while the second and major peak represents 74% of the eluted material and has an apparent M_r of 220 K. The last eluted peak accounts for 13% of the protein and has an apparent M_r of 90 K.

Separation of the material contained in the peaks by SDS–PAGE indicates a similar composition for the two high M_r peaks (a mixture of 140 K and 200 K). The third peak contains polypeptides migrating with an apparent molecular mass of 140 K and 90 K, and the latter is presumably a degradation product generated during the preparation. These results indicate an oligomeric structure for the native protein, and suggest the presence of dimers and tetramers in the conditions of the experiment. Further work is required to establish not only the precise composition and stoichiometric ratios of the oligomers of 140 K and 200 K polypeptides but also their relationships to one another *in vivo* before solubilization of the microvillar membrane.

Antibodies raised against the purified 140 K polypeptide

The products of several purification procedures that yielded homogeneous preparations of the 140 K protein were used to raise antibodies against the protein. Material obtained by mild trypsin digestion (Coudrier et al 1981b) and material prepared by electroelution of a preparative SDS–PAGE (Coudrier et al 1981a) were each injected into several rabbits. To assay the specificity of our antibodies we have used immunoprecipitation procedures and western blotting (Burnette 1981) with microvillar proteins separated on SDS–PAGE.

Antibodies raised against products of the two procedures gave essentially identical results. Fig. 4a shows that the sera specifically recognized two polypeptides, with M_r values of 140 K and 200 K. Quantitative immunoblotting (Howe & Hershey 1981) has shown that the 140 K antigen is twice as abundant in microvilli as the 200 K antigen.

Antibodies were affinity-purified by using excised strips of nitrocellulose to which the 140 K or 200 K polypeptide had been transferred according to the procedure described by Olmsted (1981). These antibodies allowed us to demonstrate that the polypeptides share common antigenic sites (Fig. 4b). In addition, peptide mapping by the procedure of Cleveland et al (1977) demonstrated a striking homology for the two species (E. Coudrier et al, unpublished results). The 140 K polypeptide presumably derives from the 200 K one by proteolytic cleavage. Further work should elucidate whether this modification occurs during intracellular transport or after the protein has

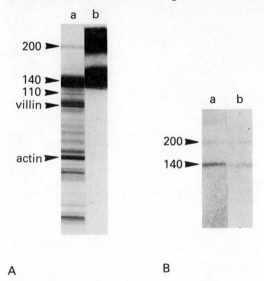

A   B

FIG. 4. (A, *left*) Characterization of the antibody raised against the 140 K protein. (a) total polypeptides from microvilli stained with Coomassie blue; (b) microvillar protein transferred to nitrocellulose sheets that were reacted with specific sera and [125I]protein A. The 200 K and 140 K bands can be seen. (B, *right*) Evidence for antigenic homology between the 140 K and 200 K polypeptides. Total microvillar protein transferred to nitrocellulose as described in (A) was then incubated with antibody affinity-purified (according to the procedure described by Olmsted 1981) (a) against the 140 K protein; and (b) against the 200 K protein. Note that the antibodies affinity-purified for each polypeptide still bind to both antigens.

been inserted into the plasma membrane and exposed to pancreatic proteases in the intestinal lumen, as shown for the sucrase–isomaltase complex and aminopeptidase (Hauri et al 1979, Sjöström et al 1978).

Immunolocalization in intestinal mucosa

Thin frozen sections were prepared and processed according to the technique of Tokuyasu (1973) to localize the 140 K polypeptide and its related antigen

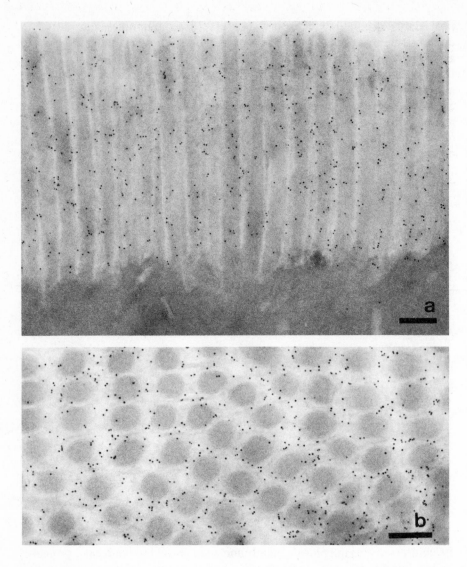

FIG. 5. Electron micrograph of thin frozen sections from rat intestinal mucosa labelled with an antibody raised against the 140 K protein and with protein A–gold. Average diameter of gold particles, 12 nm. a, longitudinal section: the 140 K protein is associated with the microvilli and the terminal web region is not labelled; bar indicates 0·2 μm. b, cross section; the 140 K protein is detected primarily outside the microvillar membrane; bar indicates 0.2 μm.

(200 K) in tissues. The results of light and electron microscopic studies have already been reported (Coudrier et al 1981b), and Fig. 5 shows a longitudinal and a cross section of intestinal mucosa labelled with antibody specific for the 140 K protein. In the longitudinal section the staining is restricted to the microvilli. No labelling is observed in the terminal web. The cross section reveals a preferential distribution of gold particles at the periphery of the microvilli, indicating that most antigenic sites are exposed to the outside. In mature enterocytes, the reaction is exclusively associated with the brush border area (Coudrier et al 1981b).

Topological organization in the microvillar membrane

(a) External accessibility. The preparation of sealed right-side-out vesicles (Louvard et al 1975) allowed us to do topological studies. We used papain and elastase treatments to establish the external accessibility of the 140 K protein and its related 200 K antigen to proteases, which are known to promote quantitative solubilization of intestinal hydrolases (Louvard et al 1975, Maestracci 1976).

Fig. 6 shows that quantitative release of the 140 K and 200 K proteins can be obtained on treatment of microvilli vesicles with papain or elastase.

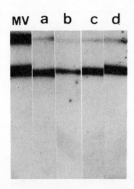

FIG. 6. Proteolytic cleavage and solubilization of the 140 K and the 200 K proteins. Proteins of each fraction were separated on SDS gels, transferred to nitrocellulose paper and reacted with specific antisera plus [^{125}I]protein A. MV, total microvillar protein; a, pellet separated after treatment of microvillar vesicles with papain (0.5 mg/ml, 10 min, 37 °C); b, the corresponding papain supernatant; c, pellet separated after treatment of microvillar vesicles with elastase (140 U/ml, 25 min, 37 °C); d, the corresponding elastase supernatant.

Analysis of solubilized products on SDS–PAGE and staining with Coomassie blue demonstrated the absence from the supernatant of cytoskeletal proteins such as villin, 110 K or actin (not shown). In these experiments no significant changes in the M_r values of the 140 K and 200 K antigens were noticeable since the solubilized antigens co-migrated with the corresponding membrane-bound antigens (Fig. 7).

(b) Amphipathic nature of the 140 K polypeptide. The properties of the 140 K protein resemble those previously described for another protein of microvilli, aminopeptidase. Both are glycosylated and can be released by a mild proteolysis without noticeable change in their M_r values. We showed several years ago that aminopeptidase is an integral transmembrane glycoprotein anchored by a short hydrophobic domain which spans the membrane bilayer (Maroux & Louvard 1976, Louvard et al 1976).

To assess the presence of a hydrophobic domain in the 140 K protein we investigated its binding to detergent micelles, using a simple assay recently reported by Bordier (1981). Briefly, the non-ionic detergent Triton X-114 has a cloud point of 30 °C, and at this temperature a detergent-rich phase can be separated from an aqueous phase by centrifugation through a sucrose barrier.

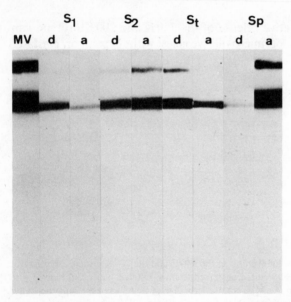

FIG. 7. Binding of the 140 K and the 200 K proteins to detergent micelles. Proteins of each fraction were separated on SDS gels, transferred to nitrocellulose and reacted with the anti-140 K antisera plus [^{125}I]protein A. The protein fractions shown are: S1, S2 (see Fig. 1); S_t, supernatant obtained after treatment of the core residue P_2 with trypsin ($30\,\mu g/ml$, 1 h, 4 °C); and Sp, supernatant obtained after treatment of microvillar vesicles or the core residue with papain (0.5 mg/ml, 15 min, 37 °C). Each supernatant was processed as described by Bordier (1981) to separate the detergent-rich phase (d) from the aqueous phase (a).

In these conditions, proteins containing hydrophobic domain are able to interact with detergent micelles and are recovered selectively in the detergent phase while hydrophilic proteins stay within the aqueous phase. The results of such an experiment are illustrated in Fig. 7. The following conclusions can be drawn.

(1) The papain-solubilized antigens S_p (from intestinal microvilli or from core residue) are hydrophilic.

(2) The low ionic strength forms (S_2) or trypsin forms (S_t) contain hydrophobic domains, which are presumably responsible for the associations of these forms with the detergent micelles.

(3) All the antigenic forms derived from the 140 K and 200 K proteins, including those found in the first detergent extract (S_1) have a similar M_r.

These data together suggest that the 140 K protein is an amphipathic protein anchored to the membrane bilayer by a short hydrophobic polypeptide region. The bulk of the protein is hydrophilic, exposed to the outside, and can be released quantitatively by papain or elastase.

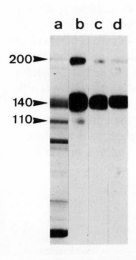

FIG. 8. Binding of the 140 K to the 110 K cytoskeletal protein. a, Polypeptide composition of the core residue (P_2) seen after protein transfer to nitrocellulose and staining with Coomassie blue. b, Polypeptides revealed by antisera against the 140 K protein after incubation with the core residue proteins (P_2) blotted to nitrocellulose sheets. Before immunological staining the blot had been incubated with the detergent-rich phase derived from the low ionic strength extract (S_2). c, Same as in (b) but the blot had been incubated with the aqueous phase derived from the low ionic strength extract (S_2). d, The nitrocellulose paper was processed directly without preincubation for identification of the 140 K and 200 K antigens. Arrows point at 200 K, 140 K and 110 K polypeptides.

Binding of the 140 K polypeptide to the major component of the cytoskeletal bridges (110 K)

As a working hypothesis we assumed that a portion of the 140 K molecule was exposed on the cytoplasmic face of the membrane and provided an anchor for a polypeptide associated with microfilaments. This proposal implied that the 140 K protein found in the Triton X-100 detergent phase would contain a binding site for a cytoskeletal protein. In contrast the hydrophilic form of the 140 K protein, recovered in the aqueous phase, would lack such activity and provide a control for the experiment.

Polypeptides from the core residue were first separated on SDS–PAGE and transferred onto nitrocellulose sheets. Blots were incubated with protein extracts containing either the amphipathic or the hydrophilic forms of the 140 K polypeptide, which was then visualized by using its antibody and [^{125}I]-protein A. For both conditions, the nitrocellulose blots showed ^{125}I-labelled bands at 200 K and 140 K, as expected. However, the blot incubated with an extract containing the amphipathic form of the 140 K protein showed an additional band co-migrating with the 110 K polypeptide (Fig. 8). This band was never observed when we used a protein extract containing equivalent amounts of the *hydrophilic* form of the 140 K protein. Binding of the amphipathic form of the 140 K protein to one of the major polypeptides of the lateral bridges (110 K) can thus be demonstrated *in vitro*. Since the extract used in this experiment contains proteins other than the 140 K species, such as actin, villin and calmodulin, we cannot yet tell if the interaction between the 110 K and the 140 K proteins is direct or involves other cytoskeletal proteins. Purification of the uncleaved form of the 140 K protein should allow us to answer this question. Knowledge of the molecular mechanisms involved in this interaction may help us to understand the association between the cytoskeleton and the plasma membrane.

Acknowledgements

We are grateful to B. D'Arcy, P. Webster and Ch. Sahuquillo for skilful technical assistance, to K. Soderberg for criticism and discussion of the manuscript, and to A. Steiner for diligent secretarial assistance.

REFERENCES

Bennett V, Stenbuck PJ 1980 Association between ankyrin and the cytoplasmic domain of band 3 isolated from the human erythrocyte membrane. J Biol Chem 225:6424-6432

Bordier C 1981 Phase separation of integral membrane proteins in Triton X-114 solution. J Biol Chem 256:1604-1607

Branton D, Cohen CM, Tyler J 1981 Interaction of cytoskeletal proteins on the human erythrocyte membrane. Cell 24:24-32

Bretscher AP, Weber K 1978a Purification of microvilli and analysis of the protein components of the microfilament core bundle. Exp Cell Res 116:397-407

Bretscher AP, Weber K 1978b Localization of actin and microfilament-associated proteins in the microvilli and terminal web of the intestinal brush-border by immunofluorescence microscopy. J Cell Biol 79:839-845

Bretscher A, Weber K 1980a Villin is a major protein of the microvillus cytoskeleton which binds both G and F actin in a calcium-dependent manner. Cell 20:839

Bretscher A, Weber K 1980b Fimbrin, a new microfilament-associated protein present in microvilli and other cell surface structures. J Cell Biol 86:335-340

Bretscher A, Osborn M, Wehland J, Weber K 1981 Villin associates with specific microfilamentous structures as seen by immunofluorescence microscopy on tissue sections and cells micro-injected with villin. Exp Cell Res 135:213-219

Burnette WN 1981 'Western blotting': electrophoretic transfer of proteins from sodium dodecyl sulfate–polyacrylamide gels to unmodified nitrocellulose and radiographic detections with antibody and radioiodinated protein A. Anal Biochem 112:195-203

Cleveland DW, Fischer SG, Kirschner MW, Laemmli UK 1977 Peptide mapping by limited proteolysis in sodium dodecyl sulfate and analysis by gel electrophoresis. J Biol Chem 252:1102-1106

Coudrier E, Reggio H, Louvard D 1981a Immunolocalization of the 110,000 molecular weight cytoskeletal protein of intestinal microvilli. J Mol Biol 152:49-66

Coudrier E, Reggio H, Louvard D 1981b The cytoskeleton of intestinal microvilli contains two polypeptides immunologically related to proteins of striated muscle. Cold Spring Harbor Symp Quant Biol 46:881-892

Geiger B, Tokuyasu KT, Singer J 1979 Immunocytochemical localization of α-actinin in intestinal epithelial cells. Proc Natl Acad Sci USA 76:2833-2837

Hauri H-P, Quaroni A, Isselbacher J 1979 Biogenesis of intestinal plasma membrane: posttranslational route and cleavage of sucrase–isomaltase. Proc Natl Acad Sci USA 76:5183-5186

Howe CL, Mooseker MS, Gray TA 1980 Brush-border calmodulin. J Cell Biol 85:916-923

Howe JG, Hershey JWB 1981 A sensitive immunoblotting method for measuring protein synthesis initiation factor levels in lysates of Escherichia coli. J Biol Chem 256:12836-12839

Louvard D, Maroux S, Baratti J, Desnuelle P, Mutaftschiev S 1973 On the preparation and some properties of closed membrane vesicles from hog duodenal and jejunal brush-border. Biochim Biophys Acta 291:747-763

Louvard D, Maroux S, Vannier C, Desnuelle P 1975 Topological studies on the hydrolases bound to the intestinal brush-border membrane. I: Solubilization by papain and Triton X-100. Biochim Biophys Acta 375:236-248

Louvard D, Semeriva M, Maroux S 1976 The brush-border intestinal aminopeptidase a transmembrane protein as probed by macromolecular photolabelling. J Mol Biol 106:1023

Luna EJ, Fowler VM, Swanson J, Branton D, Taylor DL 1981 A membrane cytoskeleton from Dictyostelium discoideium. I: Identification and partial chararacterization of an actin-binding activity. J Cell Biol 88:396-409

Maestracci D 1976 Enzymic solubilization of the human intestinal brush-border membrane enzymes. Biochim Biophys Acta 433:469-481

Maroux S, Louvard D 1976 On the hydrophobic part of aminopeptidase and maltases which bind the enzyme to the intestinal brush-border membrane. Biochim Biophys Acta 419:189-195

Matsudaira PT, Burgess DR 1979 Identification and organization of the components in the isolated microvillus cytoskeleton. J Cell Biol 83:667

Mooseker MS, Tilney LG 1975 Organization of an actin filament membrane complex. Filament polarity and membrane attachment in the microvilli of intestinal epithelial cells. J Cell Biol 67:725-743

Olmsted JB 1981 Affinity purification of antibodies from diazotized paper blots of heterogeneous protein samples. J Biol Chem 256:11955-11957

Sjöström H, Norén O, Jeppesen L et al 1978 Purification of different amphiphilic forms of a microvillus aminopeptidase from pig small intestine using immunoadsorbent chromatography. Eur J Biochem 88:503-511

Tokuyasu KT 1973 A technique for ultracryotomy of cell suspensions and tissues. J Cell Biol 57:551-565

DISCUSSION

Kenny: No doubt you would love to find out if the 140 K protein has any of the known enzyme activities of microvilli. How far have you explored this question?

Louvard: The fact that we have not identified an enzymic activity doesn't mean that it is not an enzyme. But it is not one that anyone here has been studying!

Norén: Phosphodiesterase I (EC 3.1.4.1) could be a possible candidate.

Louvard: Don't forget that protein accounts for about 10% of the protein in our vesicle preparation, and we don't see it because it doesn't stain well either with Coomassie blue or silver techniques.

Semenza: Certainly. You made your point very beautifully and I am convinced that it is a kind of anchoring or structural protein.

Louvard: Cross reacting antigens with the 140 K and 200 K polypeptides are found in striated muscle, where a membrane–microfilament interaction is also needed between the cytoplasmic reticulum and the actomyosin filaments forming the myofibrils. We have used the western blot technique to identify the cross-reacting polypeptide(s). With a crude preparation of microsomes derived from rat skeletal muscle, containing a large amount of sarcoplasmic reticulum, we observed a 100 K protein cross-reacting with the antibodies directed against the intestinal 140 K polypeptide. A preparation of Ca^{2+}-ATPase (100 K), which Dr G. Warren provided in pure form, also cross-reacts. In addition we found that the cross-reacting antigen in muscle (Ca^{2+}-ATPase) has only a specific domain in common with the 140 K protein. Several proteolytic procedures have been described to cleave Ca^{2+}-ATPase into various peptides. The cross-reacting domain between the 140 K protein of intestine and the calcium ATPase corresponds to the 24 K polypeptide (A2) described by Green et al (1980). That domain is precisely the one exposed to the cytoplasmic face in muscle cells and able to interact with actomyosin filaments. We don't think that this 140 K protein is the Ca^{2+}-ATPase since we didn't find any activity (when we assayed in the conditions used for Ca^{2+}-ATPase from muscle), although we cannot exclude the possibility of having lost the activity during our purification procedure. Perhaps we have a family of proteins with a well conserved domain operating as an anchoring site. In muscle the Ca^{2+}-ATPase may be directly responsible for the observed association of the sarcoplasmic reticulum with the actomyosin filaments. Dr Mooseker proposed (1976) that the microvillar system contracts in analogy with muscle, although he has just suggested here that it doesn't contract (p 195–215). However, membranes are linked to microfilaments in both systems, so maybe that is where the analogy stands. We have looked for the 140 K protein, or its equivalent antigen, in other epithelia and found it only in the intestine and kidney epithelia, where there are highly organized brush borders.

Kenny: Is the stoichiometry very much out of line between the 110 K protein and the 140 K protein, which is 10% of the membrane protein?

Louvard: There is more of the 140 K than the 110 K protein but we can extract about 50–60% of the 140 K during the first treatment with Triton X-100. So there is some subtle difference between what can be extracted, which does not interact strongly with the cytoskeleton, and what seems to interact more tightly.

Booth: You have also described a protein 'X', from fibroblasts (Ash et al 1977). Do your antibodies to X cross-react with this protein?

Louvard: No.

Hauri: Your conclusion that this membrane protein specifically interacts with the cytoskeleton was drawn from a single type of experiment (western blotting). There is no question that you are dealing with a membrane protein, but we know that membrane proteins aggregate with each other via the hydrophobic anchor. Did you do any control experiments by, for instance, blotting aminopeptidase and overlaying it with, say, sucrase–isomaltase? Would you get any labelling in those conditions?

Louvard: We have not done this with sucrase–isomaltase because we do not have the antibody, but we did do a control with aminopeptidase and obtained no labelling.

Hauri: Do you have any other evidence which would substantiate the idea that this protein specifically interacts with the cytoskeleton?

Louvard: I must emphasize that it may interact directly or indirectly, and other components may be involved in the interaction. We have two types of control: (1) if we clip the domain it does not bind, but that may not be fair because it is also the most sticky portion of the molecule; and (2) if we incubate the nitrocellulose paper, blotted with the core residue, with a detergent extract containing aminopeptidase, the aminopeptidase does not interact at all in that assay. I have no other evidence. But if you can suggest another assay for the study of membrane cytoskeletal interaction I would be happy to try it!

Norén: But isn't it strange that you have these specific membrane protein–cytoskeletal interactions, because you would expect to destroy the specific interaction domains on both types of protein during the electrophoretic pretreatment?

Louvard: No. The 110 K protein may be denatured but the 140 K protein was used in its native form in solution. Glenney & Weber (1980) have shown that the 110 K protein interacts specifically with calmodulin in the same type of assay. I believe that there is some re-naturation on the nitrocellulose paper. Providing one has a sensitive technique there are always enough active molecules for the study of specific interactions. It is not a quantitative technique, and we are far from the beautiful work done by Branton et al (1981) when they studied spectrin–ankyrin–band 3 interactions in erythrocytes.

Jørgensen: In your analogy with the 24 K fragment of the Ca^{2+}-ATPase, to which part of the molecule do you refer? The 24 K fragment, I believe, has at least two transmembrane segments, and yet you seem to have only one transmembrane segment in your protein.

Louvard: Yes, but that doesn't matter; We are looking at common antigenic site(s). The common domain may be rather small, however functionally important it is.

Booth: If your protein interacts with the 110 K protein, then should it not be released in the same conditions which release *that* protein? So if you take cytoskeletons and treat them with ATP, or possibly even trifluoperazine, the 110 K and the 140 K proteins should come off. Does that happen?

Louvard: We have little success with ATP treatment, especially with our sealed vesicle preparation, so I cannot answer this question.

Matsudaira: When I used this treatment I started with isolated cores, which makes quite a difference.

REFERENCES

Ash JF, Louvard D, Singer SJ 1977 Antibody-induced linkages of plasma membrane proteins to intracellular actomyosin-containing filaments in cultured fibroblasts. Proc Natl Acad Sci USA 74: 5584-5588

Branton D, Cohen CM, Tyler J 1981 Interaction of cytoskeletal proteins on the human erythrocyte membrane. Cell 24: 24-32

Glenney JR Jr, Weber K 1980 Calmodulin-binding proteins of the microfilaments present in isolated brush borders and microvilli of intestinal epithelial cells. J Biol Chem 255: 10551-10554

Green NM, Allen G, Hebdon GM 1980 Structural relationship between the calcium- and magnesium-transporting ATPase of sarcoplasmic reticulum and the membrane. Ann NY Acad Sci 358: 149-158

Mooseker MS 1976 Brush border motility. Microvillar contraction in Triton-treated brush borders isolated from intestinal epithelium. J Cell Biol 71: 417-432

Structural and functional relationship between the membrane and the cytoskeleton in brush border microvilli

PAUL T. MATSUDAIRA

MRC Laboratory of Molecular Biology, Hills Road, Cambridge CB2 2QH, UK

Abstract Electron microscopic and biochemical studies have described the organization and composition of microvilli from chicken intestinal brush borders. An actin-based cytoskeleton, composed of a paracrystalline core of bundled microfilaments, maintains the finger-like shape of the membrane through a helical array of membrane–microfilament linkages. Two proteins, fimbrin and villin, are components of the core bundle *in situ* and can independently bundle the actin filaments *in vitro*. Structural studies comparing microvillar core bundles with villin bundles and fimbrin bundles suggest that fimbrin, and not villin, is the major actin-filament-bundling protein in the microvillus core. These points, together with the capability of villin to sever actin filaments when activated by Ca^{2+}, raise questions about villin's function in the microvillus. One possible explanation is that villin induces vesiculation of the membrane by disassembling the underlying cytoskeleton.

1983 Brush border membranes. Pitman Books Ltd, London (Ciba Foundation symposium 95) p 233-244

The intestine is responsible for the uptake of nutrients into the body. To increase the efficiency of this process each absorptive epithelial cell that lines the lumen of the intestine has organized its membrane into a densely packed array of finger-like projections called microvilli. Each microvillus is simply organized and contains a central core of bundled actin filaments which is attached laterally to the surrounding membrane by membrane–microfilament linkages. Microvilli and their underlying support structures—the terminal web—comprise the apical specialization of absorptive cells called the brush border. Recent biochemical and ultrastructural studies suggest that the integrity of the cytoskeleton is necessary for the maintenance of the microvillus shape. In this paper I shall discuss how a possible understanding of the biochemistry and structure of the microvillus cytoskeleton can provide additional insight into the physiological function of the microvillus.

Ultrastructural studies on microvillar structure

Over the past 30 years, from the time of the first micrographs demonstrating
the presence of microvilli (Granger & Baker 1950), electron microscopy has
provided much structural information on microvilli. These structures (Fig. 1)
are 1–2 μm long and 0.1 μm in diameter and consist of a hollow finger of
membrane surrounding a central core of filaments (Palay & Karlin 1959,

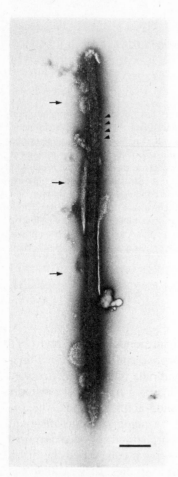

FIG. 1. The evenly spaced microfilament–membrane connections (arrow-heads) are revealed by
negative staining only after the membrane is partially removed by detergents. Because of their
tilt, the connections decorate the bundle in an arrow-head-like fashion and point away from the
membrane-capped microvillus tip. Individual filaments within the bundle are seen at intervals
along the length of the bundle (arrows). Bar = 0.2 μm.

Millington & Finean 1962, Mukherjee & Williams 1967). The core filaments, composed of actin filaments (Ishikawa et al 1969) that point unidirectionally from the membrane (Mooseker & Tilney 1975, Begg et al 1979), are bundled together along their length (Mukherjee & Williams 1967, Mukherjee & Staehelin 1971) and extend into the underlying terminal web (Palay & Karlin 1959, Brunser & Luft 1970). The centre-to-centre distance between filaments in intact, hydrated microvilli is 14 nm, as measured by X-ray diffraction (Matsudaira et al 1983). The core bundle is connected to the membrane laterally by short filaments or strands (Millington & Finean 1962, Mukherjee & Staehelin 1971) which are evenly spaced every 33 nm along the length of the bundle (Mooseker & Tilney 1975) and are helically distributed (Matsudaira & Burgess 1982b). The core bundle is directly connected to the cytoplasmic surface of the membrane at its distal end.

The membrane is coated on its extracellular surface by a thick carbohydrate coat, the glycocalyx (Ito 1965), while the cytoplasmic surface is lined by a thickened layer that is seen in micrographs as an electron-opaque zone (Sjostrand 1963). This peripheral layer is distributed in patches which, in isolated microvilli, seem associated with the laterally projecting microfilament–membrane linkages (Matsudaira & Burgess 1982b).

Biochemical studies on the cytoskeleton

Biochemical studies on the composition of the microvillus membrane and cytoskeleton were possible once methods were developed for the isolation of brush borders and microvilli (Miller & Crane 1961, Eichholtz & Crane 1965, Booth & Kenny 1976a, Mooseker & Tilney 1975, Bretscher & Weber 1978). The purification of actin from isolated brush borders (Tilney & Mooseker 1971) or isolated microvilli (Booth & Kenny 1976b) directly confirmed the previous observations of Ishikawa et al (1969) who used heavy meromyosin (HMM) decoration to identify actin filaments in microvilli. Analysis of sodium dodecyl sulphate (SDS) gels showed that demembranated brush borders also contained a polypeptide with a relative molecular mass (M_r) of 95 000. More detailed studies on this and other microvillar proteins were possible once a reliable microvillar isolation procedure was developed (Bretscher & Weber 1978).

As found in previous studies the 95 000 M_r polypeptide named villin was identified as a component of demembranated microvilli (Bretscher & Weber 1978). However, when the purification method was modified to avoid proteolysis several other polypeptides, with M_r values of 110 000, 68 000 and 16 500, were then identified (Matsudaira & Burgess 1979, Howe et al 1980, Bretscher & Weber 1980b). The structural locations of these proteins were suggested on the basis of selective extraction experiments. The results suggest that the 110 000 M_r protein is a component of the membrane–microfilament linkages while the 95 000 and 68 000 M_r polypeptides are components of the bundle (Matsudaira & Burgess 1979). Whether the 95 000, or the 68 000 M_r proteins, or both, functioned as bundling proteins could not be determined. The 16 500 M_r polypeptide, identified as calmodulin (Howe et al 1980, Glenney et al 1980), is thought to be a part of the membrane link because calmodulin binds the 110 K polypeptide *in vitro* (Glenney & Weber 1980).

Although the microvillus might be thought of as a static structure, the experiments of Howe and co-workers (1980) demonstrated that the integrity of the cytoskeleton is very sensitive to the concentration of Ca^{2+} in solution. Demembranated microvilli disassemble into non-sedimentable fragments when the free Ca^{2+} concentration is greater than micromolar (Howe et al 1980, Glenney et al 1980). This effect of calcium was understood once villin was purified and characterized (Bretscher & Weber 1980b, Mooseker et al 1980, Craig & Powell 1980, Glenney et al 1981a, Matsudaira & Burgess 1982b). Villin is a schizophrenic protein. When the free concentration of calcium is low (less than micromolar) villin aggregates actin filaments into bundles. However, when the free calcium concentration is higher than micromolar villin fragments the preformed actin filaments into short non-sedimentable pieces. With these dual properties villin can play a key role in regulating the integrity of the cytoskeleton. The other major protein in the core bundle, fimbrin, was also purified, and like villin it bundles actin filaments *in vitro* (Glenney et al 1981b, Bretscher 1981). However, the bundling properties of fimbrin are not affected by calcium in the way that villin's properties are affected.

Comparisons between fimbrin and villin bundles

The demonstration that either villin or fimbrin can bundle actin filaments *in vitro* is merely consistent with, but not proof that, either of the proteins performs that function *in vivo*. To make a functional distinction between the two proteins requires biochemical and structural studies which compare the two types of bundles with the microvillar core bundle. Fortunately much is known about the structure of actin bundles in general. From studies with other actin-bundling proteins such as fascin (DeRosier et al 1977, Bryan & Kane 1978), we know that in highly ordered bundles a bundling protein is restricted in its cross-linking of two actin filaments by the helical repeat in the twin-stranded actin filament. For fascin bundles, actin is saturated at a 1:5 molar ratio (Bryan & Kane 1978), and each cross-link is probably composed of one fimbrin molecule. The bundles assembled *in vitro* as well as those found *in vivo* display distinctive stripes which repeat every 11 nm along the length of the bundle (DeRosier et al 1977, Burgess & Schroeder 1977, Spudich & Amos 1979, DeRosier & Edds 1980). The stripes arise because the positions of fascin in the bundle are evenly distributed and because the actin filaments are in a lateral register.

In comparison, fimbrin saturates actin filaments at a 1:5 molar ratio while villin saturates actin filaments at a 1:2 to 1:3 molar ratio (P. Matsudaira, E. Mandelkow & K. Weber, unpublished results). Since villin saturates filaments at a 1:2 molar ratio then either a cross-link is composed of an oligomer of villin or there are villin molecules bound to the filament which do not participate directly in an actin–actin cross-link. In the latter case, villin would be an actin-binding protein which can also bundle filaments (HMM is another example). Two lines of evidence favour the second explanation. Biochemical studies have demonstrated that native villin is a monomer in solution (Bretscher & Weber 1980b). In addition, ultrastructural studies demonstrate that villin decorates the full length of actin filaments and is present where no cross-linking could occur—for instance in the periphery of bundles (P. Matsudaira, unpublished results). When visualized by negative staining, actin subunits can readily be seen when bundles are assembled at low villin:actin ratios (1:10), but as the molar ratio increases the subunits become rapidly obscured.

Villin bundles also differ from fimbrin bundles in their apparent order. When assembled at molar ratios of cross-linker:actin similar to the ratio found in the core bundle *in situ* (1:5 to 1:10), fimbrin bundles display distinct stripes, spaced evenly at 36 nm intervals along the length of the bundle, while villin bundles do not display any periodicity in a variety of conditions (Fig. 2) (P. Matsudaira, E. Mandelkow & K. Weber, unpublished results). In comparison, microvillar core bundles whose membrane connections are removed by ATP-treatment (Matsudaira & Burgess 1979) display a striping pattern that repeats every 36 nm, like that observed for fimbrin bundles (P. Matsudaira, E. Mandelkow & K. Weber, unpublished results). These observations suggest that fimbrin, and not villin, is responsible for the structural order of the filaments in the microvillar core bundle.

Villin's possible function

If fimbrin is the major bundling protein, then we are left with the problem of determining villin's function in the microvillus. One possibility incorporates villin's Ca^{2+}-dependent actin-severing capability. A recent study demonstrated that when native villin was micro-injected into living cells (Bretscher et al 1981) the organization of the cytoskeleton was not disrupted and the

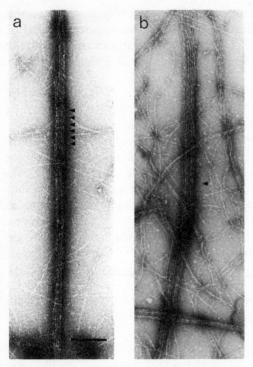

FIG. 2. Actin filaments can be reconstituted into bundles with either purified fimbrin (a) or villin (b). In fimbrin bundles, the actin filaments are in a lateral register, which gives rise to the periodically spaced stripes (arrow-heads). Villin bundles do not display any striping and the filaments appear twisted or distorted. This difference is reflected in the optical diffraction patterns of villin bundles by an absence of the first-layer line (not shown). Bar = 0.2 μm.

injected villin was localized along actin filaments (villin is not found in the cells used for injection). This result would be expected since at physiological levels of calcium (less than micromolar) villin would act as a bundling protein rather than as a severing protein. Consider, then, the effect of higher levels of calcium on villin and the microvillus. As described, the cytoskeleton disintegrates (Howe et al 1980) leaving the membrane without any supportive elements. Several studies have shown that disruption of the core bundle subsequently leads, as expected, to vesiculation of the membrane (Booth & Kenny 1976a, Hearn et al 1981, Matsudaira & Burgess 1982a).

A requirement for disassembly of microvilli *in vivo* is ideally fulfilled by villin's actin-bundling and actin-severing dual personality. There is, in the cytoplasm of other cells, an actin-severing protein, gelsolin, which is similar to villin in its M_r (90 000) and its actin-severing properties (Yin & Stossels

1979, 1980, Yin et al 1980). However, neither gelsolin nor the villin core (a 90 000 M_r proteolytic fragment of villin which retains only the Ca^{2+}-activated severing property; see Glenney & Weber 1981) binds to the sides of actin filaments in free calcium concentrations that are less than micromolar. Therefore under normal low-calcium conditions these proteins should not be bound to the actin filaments in microvilli. In contrast, in the same conditions villin would be situated not only with actin filaments but also, because of its bundling properties, mainly in the microvillar core bundle. Thus, it appears that villin is a specialized protein which may aid in the removal of membrane. This point is consistent with immunofluorescence studies showing that villin is localized only in the intestine and kidney (Bretscher & Weber 1978, Bretscher et al 1981) while fimbrin is found in many cells, generally with actin bundles (Bretscher & Weber 1980a) such as hair cell stereocilia (Flock et al 1977).

The question then arises of whether *in vitro*-induced vesiculation is physiologically relevant, since the cytoplasmic concentration of free calcium is less than micromolar, and vesiculation should therefore not occur. There are several cases in which epithelial cells shed their membrane through vesiculation. This process has been observed when organ cultures of embryonic intestine are exposed to cortical steroids (Black et al 1980), and during the very early stages of malabsorption diseases such as those induced by enterotoxins or glutens (Shiner 1981, Phillips 1981). The common factor in these examples is that the inducing agent for vesiculation, whether toxin, gluten or hormone, initially binds to the membrane. Although there is disagreement about whether some of these disorders (non-coeliac sprue in particular) result from a defect in the membrane or in the immune system, the above observations predict that one of the initial events involves an increase in free calcium concentration in the microvillus and the subsequent activation of villin.

Regulation of the free calcium concentration in the cytoplasm

The induction of vesiculation *in vivo* raises several interesting questions about the regulation of free calcium concentration in the microvillus. Since one of the functions of the intestine is absorption of dietary calcium, there must be a mechanism to protect the microvillus from disintegration during the high flux of calcium uptake. Calcium enters the cell by passive or facilitated diffusion, presumably across the microvillus membrane, and it is actively transported from the cell across the basolateral membrane. Not much is known about the route taken in transit through the cell nor how calcium is packaged in the cell. However, since microvilli do not vesiculate during dietary calcium uptake calcium buffers must be present in the cytoplasm. Preliminary observations suggest a strong buffering capacity, since epithelial cells incubated in the presence of millimolar calcium and the calcium ionophore A23187 do not shed their membranes. Two water-soluble proteins, calmodulin and the vitamin D-dependent calcium-binding protein, are present in high concentrations and might be calcium buffers (Glenney et al 1981a, Matsudaira & Burgess 1982a). Consistent with this proposal is the finding that filipin, a Ca^{2+} ionophore, induced microvillar disruption in rachitic chicks (Wong et al 1970).

Loss of regulation of calcium could occur by several different mechanisms. The free calcium in microvilli could increase through release of internal calcium stores, inhibition of the calcium pump in the basolateral membrane, or through prevention of calcium buffering. As found with the binding of cholera toxin to the membrane, binding of other agents could result in a secretion of ions from the cell. In these conditions it would be advantageous for the cell to shed its membrane (and the toxic agent bound to it) for two possible reasons. Binding to the membrane could lead to an ion imbalance in the microvillus through inhibition of transport systems or stimulation of ion effluxes. Many transport systems in the microvillar membrane are driven through electrochemical gradients which would be disrupted by such ion imbalances. Also, an ion efflux would cause water loss from the cell and would eventually lead to dehydration. The net result of vesiculation would be to provide temporary protection until the intestinal epithelium is renewed by the mitotic population in the basally located crypts.

Studies in the last three years have greatly increased our understanding of the microvillus cytoskeleton. In this paper I have used the biochemical and structural information available to speculate on possible explanations for villin's calcium-regulated properties. Whether these ideas are valid or not awaits more detailed studies of the physiology and biochemistry of calcium absorption.

Acknowledgements

I would like to thank Drs K. Weber, J. Glenney and L. Hesterberg for their discussions on villin and vesiculation, Drs E. Mandelkow, E. M. Mandelkow and L. Amos for introducing me to structural analysis, and Drs A. Weeds and H. Huxley for their help and discussions. Support is provided by a Muscular Dystrophy Association postdoctoral fellowship.

REFERENCES

Begg DA, Rodewald RA, Rebhun LI 1979 The visualization of actin filament polarity in thin sections. Evidence for the uniform polarity of membrane-associated filaments. J Cell Biol 79:846-852

Black BL, Yoneyama Y, Moog F 1980 Microvillus membrane vesicle accumulation in media during culture of intestine of chick embryo. Biochim Biophys Acta 601:343-348

Booth AG, Kenny AJ 1976a Morphometric and biochemical investigation of vesiculation of kidney microvilli. J Cell Sci 21:449-463

Booth AG, Kenny AJ 1976b Proteins of the kidney microvillus membrane. Identification of subunits after sodium dodecyl sulfate/polyacrylamide gel electrophoresis. Biochem J 159:395-407

Bretscher A 1981 Fimbrin is a cytoskeletal protein that crosslinks F-actin in vitro. Proc Natl Acad Sci USA 78:6849-6853

Bretscher A, Weber K 1978 Purification of microvilli and an analysis of the protein components of the microfilament core bundle. Exp Cell Res 116:397-407

Bretscher A, Weber K 1980a Fimbrin, a new microfilament-associated protein present in microvilli and other cell surface structures. J Cell Biol 86:335-340

Bretscher A, Weber K 1980b Villin is a major protein of the microvillus cytoskeleton which binds both G and F actin in a calcium-dependent manner. Cell 20:839-847

Bretscher A, Osborn M, Wehland J, Weber K 1981 Villin associates with specific microfilamentous structures as seen by immunofluorescence microscopy on tissue sections and cells microinjected with villin. Exp Cell Res 135:213-219

Brunser O, Luft J 1970 Fine structure of the apex of absorptive cells from rat small intestine. J Ultrastruct Res 31:291-311

Bryan J, Kane RE 1978 Separation and interaction of the major components of sea urchin actin gel. J Mol Biol 125:207-224

Burgess DR, Schroeder TE 1977 Polarized bundles of actin filaments within microvilli of fertilized sea urchin eggs. J Cell Biol 74:1032-1037

Craig S, Powell LL 1980 Regulation of actin polymerization by villin, a 95,000 dalton cytoskeletal component of intestinal brush borders. Cell 22:739-746

DeRosier D, Mandelkow E, Silliman A, Tilney L, Kane R 1977 Structure of actin containing filaments from two types of non-muscle cells. J Mol Biol 113:679-695

DeRosier D, Edds K 1980 Evidence for fascin crosslinks between the actin filaments in coelomocyte filopodia. Exp Cell Res 126:490-494

Eichholtz A, Crane RK 1965 Studies on the organization of the brush border in intestinal epithelial cells. I. Tris disruption of isolated hamster brush borders and density gradient separation of fractions. J Cell Biol 26:687-691

Flock A, Flock B, Murray E 1977 Studies on sensory hairs of receptor cells in inner ear. Acta Oto-laryngol 83:85-91

Glenney JR jr, Weber K 1980 Calmodulin-binding proteins of the microfilaments present in isolated brush borders and microvilli of intestinal epithelial cells. J Cell Biol 255:10551-10554

Glenney JR jr, Weber K 1981 Calcium control of microfilaments: uncoupling of the F-actin severing and -bundling activity of villin by limited proteolysis in vitro. Proc Natl Acad Sci USA 78:2810-2814

Glenney JR jr, Bretscher A, Weber K 1980 Calcium control of intestinal microvillus cytoskeleton: its implications for the regulation of microfilament organizations. Proc Natl Acad Sci USA 77:6458-6462

Glenney JR jr, Kaulfus P, Weber K 1981a F-actin assembly modulated by villin: Ca^{2+}-dependent nucleation and capping of the barbed end. Cell 14:471-480

Glenney JR jr, Kaulfus P, Matsudaira P, Weber K 1981b F-actin binding and bundling properties of fimbrin, a major cytoskeletal protein of microvillus core filaments. J Biol Chem 256:9283-9288

Granger B, Baker RF 1950 Electron microscope investigation of the striated border of intestinal epithelium. Anat Rec 107:423-436

Hearn PR, Russell RGG, Farmer J 1981 The formation and orientation of brush border vesicles from rat duodenal mucosa. J Cell Sci 47:227-236

Howe CL, Mooseker MS, Graves TA 1980 Brush border calmodulin. A major component of the isolated microvillus core. J Cell Biol 85:916-923

Ishikawa H, Bischoff R, Holtzer H 1969 Formation of arrowhead complexes with heavy meromyosin in a variety of cell types. J Cell Biol 43:312-328

Ito S 1965 The enteric surface coat on cat intestinal microvilli. J Cell Biol 27:475-491

Matsudaira PT, Burgess DR 1979 Identification and organization of the components in the isolated microvillus cytoskeleton. J Cell Biol 83:667-678

Matsudaira PT, Burgess DR 1982a Partial reconstruction of the microvillus core bundle: characterization of villin as a Ca^{2+}-dependent actin-bundling/depolymerizing protein. J Cell Biol 92:648-656

Matsudaira PT, Burgess DR 1982b Organization of cross-filaments in intestinal microvilli. J Cell Biol 92:657-664

Matsudaira PT, Mandelkow E, Renner W, Hesterberg LK, Weber K 1983 X-ray diffraction from isolated microvilli and reconstituted actin bundles. Nature (Lond), in press

Miller D, Crane RK 1961 A procedure for the isolation of the epithelial brush border membrane of hamster small intestine. Anal Biochem 2:284-286

Millington PF, Finean JB 1962 Electron microscope studies of the structure of microvilli in principal epithelial cells of rat jejunum after treatment with hypo- and hypertonic saline. J Cell Biol 14:125-139

Mooseker MS, Tilney LG 1975 Organization of an actin filament–membrane complex. Filament polarity and membrane attachment in the microvilli of intestinal epithelial cells. J Cell Biol 67:725-743

Mooseker MS, Graves TA, Wharton KA, Falco N, Howe CL 1980 Regulation of microvillus structure: calcium-dependent solation and crosslinking of actin filaments in the microvilli of intestinal epithelial cells. J Cell Biol 87:809-822

Mukherjee TM, Williams AW 1967 A comparative study of the ultrastructure of microvilli in the epithelium of small and large intestine of mice. J Cell Biol 34:447-461

Mukherjee TM, Staehelin LA 1971 The fine structural organization of the brush border of intestinal epithelial cells. J Cell Sci 8:573-599

Palay SL, Karlin LJ 1959 An electron microscopic study of the intestinal villus. I: The fasting animal. J Biophys Biochem Cytol 5:363-372

Phillips AD 1981 Small intestinal mucosa in childhood in health and disease. Scand J Gastroenterol 16:65-85

Shiner M 1981 Ultrastructural features of allergic manifestations in the small intestine of children. Scand J Gastroenterol 16:49-64

Sjostrand FS 1963 The ultrastructure of the plasma membrane of columnar epithelium cells of the mouse intestine. J Ultrastruct Res 8:517-541

Spudich JA, Amos LA 1979 Structure of actin filament bundles from microvilli of sea urchin eggs. J Mol Biol 129:319-331

Tilney LG, Mooseker MS 1971 Actin in the brush border of epithelial cells of the chicken intestine. Proc Natl Acad Sci USA 68:2611-2615

Wong RG, Adams TH, Roberts PA, Norman AW 1970 Studies on the mechanism of action of calciferol IV. Interaction of the polyene antibiotic, filipin, with intestinal mucosal membranes from vitamin D-treated and vitamin D-deficient chicks. Biochim Biophys Acta 219:61-72

Yin H, Stossels T 1979 Control of cytoplasmic actin gel–sol transformation by gelsolin, a calcium-dependent regulatory protein. Nature (Lond) 281:585-586

Yin H, Stossels T 1980 Purification and structural properties of gelsolin, a Ca^{2+}-activated regulatory protein of macrophages. J Biol Chem 255:9490-9493

Yin H, Zaner K, Stossels T 1980 Ca^{2+} control of actin gelation. Interaction of gelsolin with actin filaments and regulation of actin gelation. J Biol Chem 255:9490-9500

DISCUSSION

Rees: With regard to your helical model, do you see any evidence in the diffraction pattern for the helical repeat?

Matsudaira: Yes. In an optical diffraction pattern from bundles, if laser light is shone through an electron micrograph of bundled actin filaments, a spot of undiffracted light is obtained, together with spots corresponding to light diffracted by the filaments. In negatively stained microvilli, if the membrane connections are distributed around the core bundle in a 'barber's pole' arrangement, then one would expect to pick up contributions from the membrane connections on both sides (front and back) of the bundle. This would be seen as a criss-cross arrangement in the diffraction pattern. This is what I have found but it needs more analysis. Although the membrane connections are arranged every 37 nm along the sides of the bundle, the number of filaments in the bundle can vary, which means the width of the bundle can vary. Thus, the striping pattern of the membrane connections has to change its angle but not its spacing. That should be visible in the diffraction patterns.

Alpers: Your interpretation of the ionophore data makes me wonder what connection there is between your data *in vitro* and *in vivo*. Your explanation suggests that calcium is still important for that vesiculation but Levine et al (1981) have found in the intact animal that when the lumen is perfused with EDTA the microvilli shorten and vesiculation occurs. How does that fit with your interpretation of what calcium is doing?

Matsudaira: We don't know where the calcium is coming from in these experiments. The calcium doesn't necessarily have to have an inward flux across the membrane: a lot of calcium can be sequestered in cytoplasmic membrane stores, for example. Perfusion with EDTA will deplete extracellular calcium and magnesium, but how does that affect membrane proteins?

Alpers: We suspect that the surface is almost depleted of calcium and magnesium because when we perfuse in that way we remove intrinsic factor, which is bound to its receptor in a calcium- and magnesium-dependent binding (Hooper et al 1973). So when we perfuse, the intrinsic factor comes off but the price paid is the vesiculation. We don't yet know whether we can use that technique to study the physiological localization and recycling of the intrinsic factor to the membrane.

Matsudaira: I would like to know whether the EDTA is working on a membrane protein and causing some sort of damage to the membrane. Many pharmacological and physiological experiments are not done in conjunction with light or electron microscopy, but these should be attempted. Vesiculation is easily seen under the light microscope.

Smith: Calcium transport to me indicates a carrier-mediated transport and not diffusion. When people look by microprobe analysis they see sequestered calcium moving across the cell (Warner & Coleman 1979). So I don't really take your point that we should look at calcium in relation to its transport. Besides, not all enterocytes are transporting calcium: it is localized in certain parts of the intestine.

Matsudaira: As I understand it, there are two pathways for calcium transport: one through active transport and one through passive diffusion. The highest rate of calcium transport is in the part of the duodenum most proximal to the stomach, but the *bulk* of the calcium is absorbed farther down.

Smith: But when we talk about passive movement we often mean between cells and not *into* cells.

Semenza: There are various routes for calcium absorption.

Schmitz: Is it feasible to measure the calcium concentration in the apex of gigantic intestinal epithelial cells, like those of Necturus, by micropuncture?

Boyd: Nobody to my knowledge has used Ca^{2+}-sensitive microelectrodes to do this in the small intestine, but the technology is probably available.

Alpers: W. McD. Armstrong is setting about doing this at the moment, with an electrode that detects only free calcium. Calcium-binding protein is present in large amounts, however, so the total calcium flux may be grossly underestimated by those measurements, and only steady-state concentrations could be measured. Anything that enters quickly and binds to cytoskeletal structures may not be detected. It may also be more difficult when the cell is not easy to hit: the longer the microvilli, the harder it is to puncture the cell because it keeps floating away, I believe.

Hauri: You made an interesting suggestion on the pathophysiological role of this vesiculation process in coeliac disease. Is there more behind this suggestion? Research on coeliac disease has made little progress in the last 10 years. How could gluten disturb the calcium balance?

Matsudaira: The examples of vesiculation were with wheatgerm agglutinin, concanavalin A and antibodies against sucrase–isomaltase. I don't understand how those would increase calcium concentrations, unless there is perturbation of the membrane potential or of the movement of ions. So these are simply suggestions, without an experimental basis.

REFERENCES

Hooper DC, Alpers DH, Burger RL, Mehlman CS, Allen RH 1973 Characterization of ileal vitamin B_{12} binding using homogeneous human and hog intrinsic factors. J Clin Invest 56: 3074-3083

Levine JS, Nahane PK, Allen RH 1981 The immunoelectron-microscopic localization of intrinsic factor. Gastroenterology 80: 1210 (abstract)

Warner RR, Coleman JR 1979 Electron probe analysis of calcium transport by small intestine. J Cell Biol 64: 54-74

General Discussion II

A pathological condition due to congenital disorganization of the brush border

Schmitz: As a paediatrician I find our discussions most interesting when they are relevant to patients and to the understanding of diseases. In contrast, diseases may sometimes help us to understand physiological events. I should like to present such a case, which raises interesting questions about the synthesis and organization of the brush border membrane. A few hours after birth, the patient (C.Q.) began to have a profuse and watery diarrhoea, containing only electrolytes and mucus; it persisted, despite nothing being given by mouth, until her death at 7 months of age. An intestinal biopsy showed only a partial villous atrophy; enterocyte height was within normal limits; at first sight the brush border region appeared normal, on haematoxylin–eosin staining; in fact, disaccharidase and peptidase specific activities were normal. However, electron micrographs (done by J. Jos) revealed enterocytes with very abnormal microvilli and abnormal dense vesicular bodies in the cytoplasm just beneath the brush border. Each vesicle had a diameter similar to that of a microvillus. In some places inward budding of the whole brush border or of the lateral plasma membrane could be seen. The terminal web was completely disorganized. The degree of abnormality of the brush border varied, from cell to cell, from short and irregular microvilli to no microvilli at all (Fig. 1).

Returning to light microscopy, we found that PAS staining appeared extremely abnormal; instead of the neat, dense and regularly thick staining that usually lines the enterocyte luminal border, the PAS stain was of irregular density and thickness, making smears *inside* the cells (Fig. 2).

Using peroxidase-labelled anti-sucrase antibody N. Triadou found immunoperoxidase staining of irregular density and thickness on the brush border and in the apical cytoplasm in the region of the terminal web. In controls this staining was very regular and restricted to the brush border. This finding parallels what we found with PAS stains. The brush border membrane seems, therefore, to be completely disorganized. This condition could be explained by excessive endocytosis or by an abnormal building up of the brush border that might be secondary to defective glycosylation of membrane proteins or to abnormalities of its cytoskeleton.

Quaroni: You also seem to have heavy labelling of the basolateral membrane, which you didn't have in the normal cells.

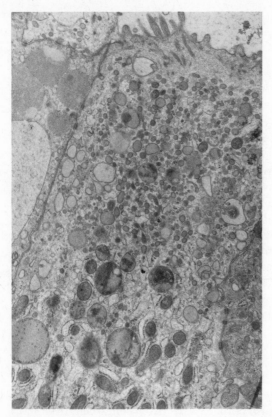

FIG. 1. (*Schmitz*) Electron micrograph of the apical portion of an enterocyte in a case of congenital microvillus atrophy. The brush border region (microvilli and terminal web) is completely disorganized. The apical cytoplasm is filled with dense vesicular bodies but also contains larger empty vacuoles. Magnification, × 8000.

Alpers: The amount of Golgi there also seems to be reduced.

Schmitz: The question arises of whether this condition is congenital or acquired. We cannot say with certainty that the enterocytes were like that at birth, but they were abnormal in the depths of the crypts. Furthermore, after 48 h in organ culture the PAS staining pattern was similar. The condition is thus likely to be congenital.

Rubino: I believe that another French group described two siblings with the same type of disease, which would suggest that it was a familial trait.

Schmitz: Yes. Davidson et al (1978) described the condition five years ago and found that it was associated with similar cases in the families concerned, which would suggest that it arises from a mutation.

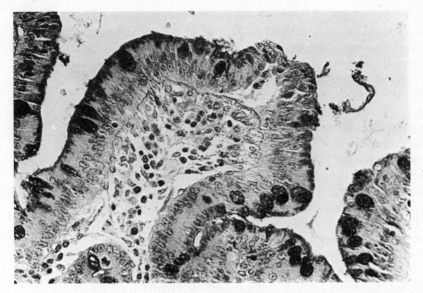

FIG. 2. (*Schmitz*) Light micrograph with PAS staining of a villus in the same patient as Fig. 1. Instead of being dense and regular, and lining the enterocyte luminal border, the PAS staining is irregular and makes smears inside the apical part of the cytoplasm where vesicular bodies were noted at the ultramicroscopic level. Goblet cells are stained normally. Magnification, × 25.

Jørgensen: You mentioned that the hydrolytic activities in the intestinal lumen were normal, but do you know anything about the transport of hexoses, phosphate or amino acids from the lumen to the blood?

Schmitz: Glucose was not absorbed at all when it was perfused through the jejunum. We did not test for other hexoses, or amino acids or phosphate. J.F. Desjeux did some electrophysiological studies *in vitro* and showed that the conductance of the tissue was normal. So we may say that the tight junctions were not more leaky than normal.

Jørgensen: If, in only part of the intestine, the sodium-coupled glucose or amino acid absorption were to fail, because the carriers were absent, the cells would end up secreting sodium and fluid. There would still be sodium transport across the basolateral membrane, and the diffusion of sodium from the intercellular space to the lumen would exceed the transport of sodium from lumen to cytoplasm. This would produce a secreting epithelium in the area of the intestine where there is no glucose or amino acid absorption, and this might explain the diarrhoea. The diarrhoea could thus be a symptom of the absence from the brush border of the transport molecule due to an inborn error of metabolism.

Schmitz: This is an interesting explanation for the diarrhoea. J.F. Desjeux measured the transmural short-circuit current in the presence and absence of glucose and, surprisingly, found that it was in the normal range.

Alpers: But your glucose absorption done *in vivo* was a *net* absorption, so what was the dilution factor for the non-absorbable marker that you used during the perfusion. Was it high?

Schmitz: Yes.

Alpers: So that might explain it. There could be unidirectional absorption to some extent but a much larger secretion *in vivo*.

Boyd: Did you test renal function or do a renal biopsy?

Schmitz: Renal function was normal, but we did not do a renal biopsy.

Booth: Was there anything strange about the pregnancy?

Schmitz: No; this is a good point. In congenital chloride diarrhoea, hydramnios is common. But in this case, as in the others (Davidson et al 1978, Goutet et al 1982) the diarrhoea started at birth, but not before, which is curious.

Booth: Did you get a chance to look at the placenta?

Schmitz: No.

Smith: Could the difference in the glucose effect be caused by an enhanced metabolism due to more rapid cell turnover? It would have been interesting to have looked at this with a non-metabolizable actively transported sugar.

Schmitz: You are right, but we didn't do this.

Jørgensen: You said that the glucose absorption was zero, and that the glucose-induced short-circuit current was normal, but that is difficult to understand. Did you measure the short-circuit current in the colon?

Schmitz: No; this was done in the jejunum, where the biopsy was taken.

Smith: I believe that the difference between absorption and secretion, in relation to Dr Jørgensen's earlier explanation just now, depends on a different enzyme, adenylate cyclase, and on a different ion, chloride. Activation of adenylate cyclase increases chloride permeability through the tight junction and across all membranes in the enterocytes, and this leads to secretion. But the simple removal of sugars and amino acids should not lead to large-scale secretion.

Boyd: I agree. The *converse* is that one sees normal absorption of sugars and amino acids in cholera.

Alpers: Some patients with an inborn error of metabolism have no carrier proteins for glucose and galactose but neither do they have diarrhoea in the absence of these sugars (Lindquist et al 1962).

Quaroni: This is not clear to me because the tight junctions would still be permeable to sodium, so the sodium could enter the intercellular space via the tight junctions and it could then enter the cells, regardless of the absence of carriers on the luminal side.

Jørgensen: I am assuming that the carrier has gone and that the cell has a 'tight' luminal membrane.

Quaroni: It seems to me that the permeability of the tight junction is as important as the location of the carriers.

Jørgensen: True. Assuming an unchanged permeability of the tight junction, and the absence of carriers from the brush border membrane one would see sodium secretion. But isolation of the carriers themselves is probably the most useful approach.

Louvard: There must be fewer carriers on the surface because Dr Schmitz showed that there was no brush border on some of these cells, but only a flat surface. If the basolateral membrane has as much ATPase as the normal cells any effect of the carriers cannot compensate for the transport of sodium by the Na^+,K^+-ATPase. I believe that the case described by Dr Schmitz is probably a more general disorder in the assembly of the membrane, which would result in fewer carriers on the surface.

Quaroni: On the other hand, sucrase–isomaltase is present on the basolateral membrane so there may also be a sodium-dependent carrier there, which would probably act on that side of the cells if glucose is there.

Alpers: Conversely, Na^+,K^+-ATPase might be on the surface in that patient.

Jørgensen: That would be a strange coincidence of two errors!

Alpers: It would be an assembly error. In glucose/galactose malabsorption the patients do not have diarrhoea.

Rubino: That is correct. Patients with glucose malabsorption have no problems if they do not receive glucose by mouth; they have no secretory diarrhoea.

Jørgensen: If cells like those in the proximal tubules of the kidney contain carriers for more than one molecule, such as phosphate, glucose and amino acids, then if there were a deficiency for one molecule, e.g. glucose, the flux of sodium accompanying the amino acids and phosphate could be sufficient to cancel out the leak. But in the case described by Dr Schmitz, the membrane seems to be depleted of carrier molecules. The measurements of tracer flux across the epithelium from the patient showed zero flux for glucose. Although addition of glucose to the medium apparently changed the potential across the epithelium, the tracer flux was zero.

Schmitz: But, as I mentioned, the fluxes for amino acids were not checked in this patient (C.Q.).

Norén: What is the M_r of sucrase–isomaltase in this case? Can one isolate sucrase–isomaltase from biopsies by use of a specific antibody and then determine the M_r by SDS-PAGE? Such an analysis could help discriminate between a defect in the biogenesis of the microvilli and a defect in the degradation of microvilli. In the former case one would expect to find single-chain, high M_r sucrase–isomaltase, as the enzyme has not been exposed to pancreatic proteases.

Schmitz: No; we have not tried this.

Matsudaira: What do you think is the material in the vesicles?

Schmitz: I think it is glycocalyx or brush border membrane-related material.

Inoue: There may be a defect in the mechanism that transfers newly synthesized membrane proteins and secretory proteins into the luminal portion. It is difficult to envisage an abnormality in particular membrane exoenzymes. What do you think about this possibility?

Schmitz: I agree. Some of our electron microscopy on the tissue from this baby is reminiscent of the published work of Blok et al (1981) on culture of human intestine in the presence of colchicine.

Semenza: I would expect something to be wrong with the cytoskeleton. The microvilli presumably do not form and they become autophaged in some way.

Hauri: Have you seen any microtubules?

Schmitz: We have done better micrographs on another patient so we shall be able to look for that.

Hauri: Have you found any microvillus-like structures at the basolateral membrane, as with colchicine-treated animals?

Schmitz: We have seen some curious patterns, with normal microvilli next to apparently endocytosed microvilli. In some cases we have seen the basolateral membrane budding inside.

Alpers: But you don't know if it is budding in, or failing to get out.

Schmitz: I agree.

Bretscher: You seem to have vast numbers of disorganized intermediate filaments.

Semenza: Is the villin missing?

Booth: The defect cannot be generalized in the cytoskeleton because otherwise the placenta would not have functioned and the child would not have arrived in the world to start with.

Schmitz: Yes. We feel that the condition is due to an inherited defect localized to the intestine.

Matsudaira: Was the child breast-fed, and could the problem have derived from the mother?

Schmitz: The patient (C.Q.) was breast-fed for the first day of life and then she had to be perfused on the third day because of the profuse diarrhoea. The excessive quantity of mucus passed in the stools of this and similar patients was striking. Since localization of PAS staining was very abnormal we wondered whether there was some abnormality in the glycosylation processes. The mucus itself seemed to be abnormal, as studied by histochemical methods on a biopsy of the colon.

Rubino: Like Jacques Schmitz, I am more familiar with a very special type of mammal—the diseased child! When we see patients with chronic diarrhoea or malabsorption of unknown origin, we may ask ourselves if they have any as yet undescribed defect of a specific brush border enzyme or transport system. Taking into account the various peptidases that have been identified, and the transport system for dipeptides and tripeptides, I wonder how much these various components can overlap in substrate specificity and whether any one of them can be considered as a stronger candidate for causing protein malabsorption. Perhaps we should look for that specifically when we see a patient with protein malabsorption. If one peptidase in the brush border has a substrate specificity such that it cannot be substituted for by any other, then it could cause protein malabsorption.

Kenny: Perhaps the brush border endopeptidase might just qualify (Kenny et al 1981). Its specificity is for bonds involving the amino groups of hydrophobic amino acids. It readily attacks [125I]insulin-B chain or other peptides of similar length. In the case of insulin B chain the labelled residues are the tyrosines at 16 and 26. Pig microvilli in which the endopeptidase was inhibited by phosphoramidon released no radioactivity from this substrate. This implies that the exopeptidases cannot, even after prolonged incubation, make much progress towards the labelled residues. The endopeptidase might be a rate-limiting step for peptides of a size that cannot be readily degraded by exopeptidases.

Rubino: Could dipeptidyl peptidase be a candidate?

Kenny: This enzyme is special in that it requires alanine or, better, a proline in the second position before the susceptible bond. In some peptides its absence might be rate-limiting, but I think the endopeptidase might be generally relevant.

Sjöström: I would suggest dipeptidyl peptide IV. Proline is a frequent amino acid in the diet. However, amino acyl–proline binding differs from other peptide bonds, in that it lacks a hydrogen. Only a negligible or low activity in the microvillus membrane is capable of splitting this bond N-terminally. Dipeptidyl peptidase IV is probably a key enzyme for this digestion, liberating an amino acyl–proline dipeptide which can be absorbed as such, and hydrolysed intracellularly by prolidase. On this basis one would expect symptoms when this enzyme is lacking.

Rubino: To obtain more information about the splitting of the SI complex one could study samples from the intestinal mucosa of patients with pancreatic insufficiency. It is relatively easy to obtain intestinal mucosa from newborns operated on because of meconium ileus. These patients should have pancreatic insufficiency and one could measure their pro-SI levels.

Sjöström: Hanne Skovbjerg (1982) in our group has demonstrated the presence of a high M_r pro-sucrase–isomaltase in human fetal small intestine.

REFERENCES

Blok J, Ginsel LA, Mulder-Stapel AA, Onderwater JJM, Daems WT 1981 The effect of colchicine on the intracellular transport of ^{3}H-fucose-labelled glycoproteins in the absorptive cells of cultured human small-intestinal tissue. Cell Tissue Res 215: 1-12

Davidson GP, Cutz E, Hamilton JR, Gall DG 1978 **Familial enteropathy:** a syndrome of protracted diarrhea from birth, failure to thrive, and hypoplastic villus atrophy. Gastroenterology 75: 783-790

Goutet JM et al 1982 Familial protracted diarrhoea with hypoplastic villus atrophy: a report of two cases. XV Annual Meeting of the ESPGAN, Madrid.

Kenny AJ, Fulcher IS, Ridgwell K, Ingram J 1981 Microvillar membrane neutral endopeptidases. Acta Biol Med Ger 40: 1465-1471

Lindquist B, Meeuwisse GW, Melin K 1962 Glucose–galactose malabsorption. Lancet 2: 666

Skovbjerg H 1982 High-molecular weight pro-sucrase–isomaltase in human fetal intestine. Pediatr Res, in press

Conformational changes in the α-subunit, and cation transport by Na⁺, K⁺-ATPase

PETER L. JØRGENSEN

Institute of Physiology, Aarhus University, DK-8000 Aarhus C, Denmark

Abstract The relationship has been studied of structural changes in the α-subunit ($M_r \approx 100\,000$) of Na⁺,K⁺-ATPase to the binding and translocation of Rb⁺ and Na⁺. Two conformations, E_1 and E_2, are distinguished by controlled proteolysis of the α-subunit and fluorescence techniques. The de-phospho forms, E_1Na and E_2K, are stabilized by binding of Na⁺ and K⁺ or Rb⁺ to cytoplasmic sites on pure Na⁺,K⁺-ATPase in membrane fragments. In phospholipid vesicles reconstituted with pure Na⁺,K⁺-ATPase, the transitions between E_1Na and E_2K are coupled to translocation of cation in ouabain- or vanadate-sensitive passive fluxes along gradients for K⁺ and Na⁺. The direction of these fluxes is opposite to that of the active Na⁺-K⁺ transport. Coupling of transitions between the phospho forms, E_1P and E_2P, and the cation translocation was studied after selective proteolysis of the α-subunit. Cleavage with trypsin at the carboxyl-terminal side (bond 1) of the aspartyl phosphate residue or with chymotrypsin at the amino-terminal side (bond 3) blocks Na⁺, K⁺-ATPase and Na⁺–K⁺ transport, but the two splits have widely different effects on partial reactions. Cleavage of bond 3 blocks transition from E_1P to E_2P and abolishes both (ADP + ATP)–Na⁺/Na⁺ exchange and (ATP + Pᵢ)–Rb⁺/Rb⁺ exchange reactions. Cleavage of bond 1 interferes neither with the transitions nor with the exchange reactions. Thus, both the cation-induced transitions between E_1Na and E_2K and the transitions between the phospho forms, E_1P and E_2P, of the α-subunit are coupled to flipping of cation sites between the inside-exposed state (E_1) and the outside-exposed state (E_2).

1983 Brush border membranes. Pitman Books Ltd, London (Ciba Foundation symposium 95) p 253-272

In enterocytes and kidney tubule cells the prime function of the Na⁺–K⁺ pump is to maintain electrochemical gradients for Na⁺ across the cell membrane. The Na⁺ conductance of the cell membrane *per se* is low and the entry of Na⁺ along the gradient is coupled to secondary active transport of nutrients and ions across the brush border membrane (for refs see Schultz 1978, Jørgensen 1980). The ATP-independent carrier proteins in the brush border membrane and the pumps coupling ATP hydrolysis to osmotic work must be characterized and localized within each cell type to allow a satisfactory understanding of these integrated transport processes.

The present work on the pure Na^+–K^+ pump from kidney is part of our attempts to solve the reaction mechanism of the Na^+–K^+ pump in terms of interaction of molecular components. The nature of the Na^+–K^+ transport reaction leads one to assume that the translocation process involves motion of protein components in the pump; but it has been a problem to obtain direct evidence for coupling of conformational changes in the protein to ion translocation. Two principal conformations of the α-subunit of Na^+,K^+-ATPase (EC 3.6.1.3), E_1 and E_2, are defined by two patterns of tryptic cleavage and inactivation of enzymic activity (Jørgensen 1975, 1977) and by their different levels of tryptophan fluorescence intensity (Karlish & Yates 1978). Even in the absence of a detailed structural model of Na^+,K^+-ATPase, the transitions can be described in terms of differences between spatial arrangements of amino acid residues in states of the pump with different ligand affinities. The transitions between E_1 and E_2 forms of the α-subunit involve a significant number of side chains. In addition to the trypsin-sensitive bonds and the tryptophan residues there is evidence for involvement of sulphydryl groups, ionizable groups and intramembrane segments. The two forms have different affinities for nucleotides and phosphate and for the specific inhibitors, ouabain and vanadate (for refs see Jørgensen 1982). Explanations of the relationship of these transitions to ATP hydrolysis and ion translocation will be essential for understanding the transport process.

In terms of protein structure the cation-induced transitions between the de-phospho forms of the α-subunit, E_1Na and E_2K, are very similar to the transitions between the phospho forms, E_1P and E_2P, and the conformations are interconvertible through the action of ATP (Jørgensen 1975, Jørgensen & Karlish 1980). Passive Na^+/Rb^+ fluxes have been observed in the absence of nucleotides and inorganic phosphate (Karlish & Stein 1982a,b, Karlish et al 1982). The important problem is therefore to determine whether transitions between E_1 and E_2 forms of the α-subunit are always accompanied by conduction of cations across the membrane or whether input of chemical energy in the form of ATP is required for transitions between states with inside-exposed and outside-exposed cation-binding sites.

To examine this question, the experiments in the first section of this paper deal with the binding of cations, the cation-induced transitions and the translocation of cation in the absence of ligands other than Na^+, K^+ or Rb^+. This approach opens the possibility for dissecting the transport mechanism so that structural changes related to cation binding, translocation and release can be examined in the absence of energy-transducing reactions involving the nucleotides, inorganic phosphate and Mg^{2+}. The second part deals with experiments designed to examine the coupling of the conformational transitions between E_1P and E_2P to the cation exchange processes.

Pure membrane-bound Na$^+$,K$^+$-ATPase

The experiments are done with pure membrane-bound Na$^+$,K$^+$-ATPase from the outer renal medulla of mammalian kidney. During the purification procedure, the proteins of Na$^+$,K$^+$-ATPase are kept embedded in the bilayer while extraneous proteins are selectively extracted with sodium dodecyl sulphate (SDS) in the presence of ATP. The preparation consists of disc-shaped membrane fragments, densely packed with particles consisting of two proteins in a molar ratio of 1:1. The α-subunit, with M_r close to 100 000, forms 65–72% of the total protein. The β-subunit is a sialoglycoprotein with M_r about 38 000, plus about 17 000 for the carbohydrate moiety (Jørgensen 1974, 1982). The proteins have been crystallized in the membrane (Skriver et al 1981). Electron microscopy shows that the asymmetry of the Na$^+$–K$^+$ pump is retained in the pure enzyme since the sidedness of distribution of intramembrane particles on the fracture faces is similar to that in the native basolateral cell membrane (Deguchi et al 1977). Native lipoprotein associations are thus preserved in this preparation, which is therefore very suitable for studying protein structure and ligand interactions of the Na$^+$–K$^+$ pump.

Cation binding at equilibrium

Until recently the existence and properties of cation sites have been inferred from kinetic studies, but cation binding can now be measured at equilibrium. In the experiment in Fig. 1 separation of bound and free ^{86}Rb$^+$ was achieved by centrifugation. The data for ^{86}Rb$^+$ binding at equilibrium to native Na$^+$,K$^+$-ATPase fell on a straight line with maximum capacity 12.3 ± 0.4 nmol/mg protein and a dissociation constant (K_d) of $7.5\,\mu$M at 25 mM-Tris-Cl and pH 7.5. This corresponds to high-affinity binding of about two Rb$^+$ ions per α-subunit. The fluorescein enzyme contained 5–6 nmol fluorescein per mg protein, corresponding to about one fluorescein molecule per α-subunit. The maximum capacity for Rb$^+$ binding to the fluorescein enzyme was 12.8 ± 0.4 nmol/mg protein, close to that of native Na$^+$,K$^+$-ATPase, but the K_d ($29.2\,\mu$M) was much higher than that for native Na$^+$,K$^+$-ATPase ($K_d = 7.5$ μM). This reduction in apparent affinity for Rb$^+$ is in agreement with the notion that fluorescein is bound to an amino group in the ATP-binding area. The covalent attachment of the probe e.g. to a lysine residue, may exert an ATP-like effect on the affinity for Rb$^+$ and K$^+$.

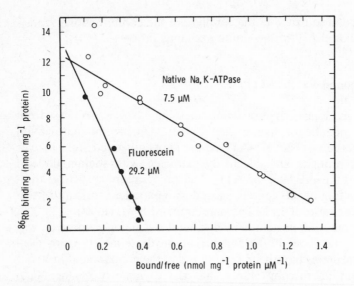

FIG. 1. Binding of [86]Rb+ at equilibrium to native Na+,K+-ATPase (open circles) and fluorescein enzyme (solid circles). 50–70 μg enzyme protein were mixed in centrifuge tubes with 0.1 μCi [86]Rb+ in 1 ml 25 mM-Tris-Cl, 0.1 mM-EDTA, pH 7.5 and RbCl in concentrations between 2 μM and 100 μM. Free and bound [86]Rb+ were measured after centrifugation for 90 min at 40 000 r.p.m. (Jørgensen & Petersen 1982).

For the native Na+,K+-ATPase, the binding capacity is higher and the K_d is lower than in previous reports on [86]Rb+ binding or [42]K+ binding. In other binding studies, the maximum capacities are 5–10 nmol/mg protein for K+ or Rb+ and 8 nmol/mg protein for Na+, corresponding to a maximum of about two ions per α-subunit. There is evidence for hybrid occupancy of up to two sites per α-subunit but not for the existence of separate sites for binding of Na+ or K+ or Rb+ (Hastings & Skou 1980, Yamaguchi & Tonomura 1980).

Cation binding and conformational transitions in the α-subunit

Tryptic and chymotryptic digestion

In a linear map of the α-subunit, the bonds exposed to primary tryptic cleavage at the cytoplasmic membrane surface are unique and well defined points of reference (Jørgensen 1975, 1977, Giotta 1975, Castro & Farley 1979). At any one time only one or two bonds are exposed to cleavage. Fig. 2 shows that the biphasic pattern for tryptic inactivation of Na+,K+-ATPase in

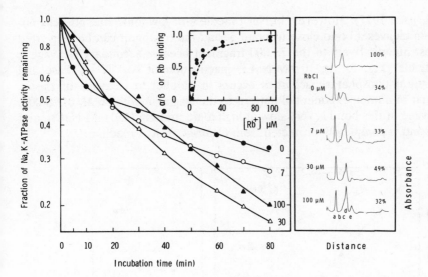

FIG. 2. Effect of Rb⁺ ions on tryptic inactivation of Na⁺,K⁺-ATPase (left) or the pattern of distribution of peptides remaining in the membrane (right). Digestion with $0.2\mu g$ Tos-Phe-CH₂Cl (TPCK) trypsin per $100\mu g$ protein was stopped by mixing with trypsin inhibitor and samples were transferred for assay of Na⁺,K⁺-ATPase. Curves are drawn as calculated for the equation $EA = A \cdot e^{-\alpha t} + B \cdot e^{-\beta t}$. The ratio of the rate constants $\alpha : \beta$ (solid circles) is compared with the curve of ⁸⁶Rb⁺ binding (dotted line) from Fig. 1. Distribution of peptides after 30–60 min of digestion was determined by electrophoresis and scanning after Coomassie blue staining; a, α-subunit; b, 78 000 fragment; c, β-subunit; d, 58 000 fragment; e, 46 000 fragment.

the presence of Tris-Cl was similar to that seen in the presence of NaCl (Jørgensen 1975). It was adequately described by two exponentials with a ratio of the rate constants $(\alpha : \beta)$ of 37 $(\alpha = -0.27 \, min^{-1}; \beta = -0.0074 \, min^{-1})$. The rate constant α corresponds to cleavage of bond 2 near the N-terminus of the α-subunit and the rate constant β to cleavage of bond 3, about 250 residues away from the N-terminus. The increase in Rb⁺ concentration gradually altered the biphasic pattern of digestion in 25 mM-Tris-Cl until it approached a single exponential pattern at $100\mu M$-RbCl. The inset in Fig. 2 shows that $K_{\frac{1}{2}}$ for this change in $\alpha : \beta$ ratio was 5–6μM and that it was closely related to saturation of cation-binding sites as measured in Fig. 1 by ⁸⁶Rb⁺ binding to the native Na⁺,K⁺-ATPase at equilibrium. The monoexponential loss of Na⁺,K⁺-ATPase activity in E_2K is related to cleavage of bond 1 near the middle of the α-subunit.

Bond 3 is cleaved slowly by trypsin when the protein is stabilized in the E_1 form. The products of this split remain in the membrane, but the relative amount of the 78 000 fragment remains low due to secondary cleavage

(Jørgensen 1977). However, in NaCl medium of low ionic strength, chymotrypsin cleaves a bond close to bond 3, and the α-subunit can be converted almost quantitatively to the 78 000 fragment because secondary cleavage is negligible (Fig. 3). In 10 mM-NaCl, inactivation of Na$^+$,K$^+$-ATPase and potassium phosphatase activities occurs in parallel to cleavage of the α-subunit in a monoexponential pattern to the fragment with an M_r of 78 000. Cleavage of this bond is very slow at high ionic strength (150 mM-NaCl), and the bond is completely protected from cleavage in KCl medium.

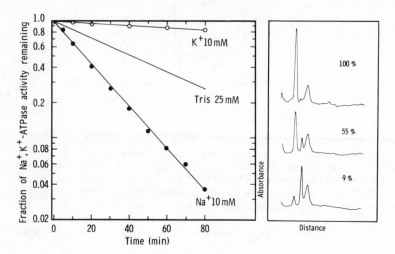

FIG. 3. Chymotryptic inactivation of pure membrane-bound Na$^+$,K$^+$-ATPase (left) and cleavage of α-subunit (right). Digestion at 37 °C was started by adding 5 μg α-chymotrypsin per 100 μg Na$^+$,K$^+$-ATPase in a volume of 1 ml, 15 mM-Tris, pH 7.5 and 10 mM-NaCl or 10 mM-KCl. At the times indicated, aliquots containing 2 μg protein were transferred for assay of Na$^+$,K$^+$-ATPase. To the right, the distribution after electrophoresis in SDS is shown for peptides and fragments remaining in the membrane in untreated enzyme (100% activity) or after digestion to 55% or to 9% Na$^+$,K$^+$-ATPase activity remaining.

Transition from E_1Na to E_2K thus involves protection of bond 3 and exposure of bond 1 to trypsin near the middle of the α-subunit, while the position of bond 2 near the N-terminus is altered so that cleavage of bond 2 becomes secondary to cleavage of bond 1 within the same α-subunit. The trypsin-sensitive bonds in the α-subunit are separated by intramembrane segments (Karlish et al 1977, Jørgensen 1982) and the bonds may be located in loosely structured loops in domains that protrude at the cytoplasmic surface. The changes in structure can be due to altered positions of side chains within the loops or to rearrangement of the cytoplasmic domains relative to each other.

Fluorescence of Na$^+$- and K$^+$-bound forms

The intensity of intrinsic tryptophan fluorescence of the E_2K form is 2–3% higher than that of the E_1Na form. This small but significant change in fluorescence can be due to changes in position of one or two tryptophan residues from a relatively hydrophilic microenvironment in E_1Na to a more hydrophobic state in E_2K (Karlish & Yates 1978). The levels of tryptophan fluorescence alter in parallel to saturation of two sites per α-subunit for high-affinity binding of ^{86}Rb$^+$ ($K_d = 7.5\,\mu M$) and to the changes in tryptic cleavage in these conditions (Jørgensen & Petersen 1982). Also, in the range of physiological ionic strength the structural changes detected with trypsin correlate with the changes in intensity of tryptophan fluorescence in titrations with both KCl versus choline chloride and KCl versus NaCl. At high pH, fluorescein–isothiocyanate (FITC) attaches covalently to an amino group in the 58 000 M_r segment in the vicinity of the ATP-binding area. With one fluorescein molecule per α-subunit, the transition from E_1Na to E_2K is accompanied by 20–25% quenching of fluorescence (Karlish 1980). At the lower level of affinity for Rb$^+$, saturation of the binding sites is also correlated with quenching of emission from fluorescein bound to the α-subunit (Jørgensen & Petersen 1982).

Monitoring the state of the nucleotide-binding area with fluorescent probes

Conformations in which the ATP-binding region is adapted for tight (E_1Na) or weak (E_2K) binding of nucleotide can be distinguished with radioactive ATP and ADP or with the fluorescent formycin analogues FTP or FDP (Nørby & Jensen 1971, Karlish et al 1978). Trinitrophenyl (TNP)–ATP (Moczydlowsky & Fortes 1981) and eosin (tetrabromo-fluorescein; Skou & Esmann 1981) are potent inhibitors of Na$^+$,K$^+$-ATPase, and they bind with high affinity ($K_d = 0.2$–$0.7\,\mu M$) to the ATP-binding site of E_1. Transfer of TNP–ATP or eosin from water to solvents of low polarity increases their fluorescence dramatically. The emission maximum and fluorescence intensity of the complexes with Na$^+$,K$^+$-ATPase suggest that the ATP-binding area in E_1 has a polarity close to that of ethanol. It is proposed that the conformational change induced by binding of Na$^+$ creates a hydrophobic pocket for nucleotide binding, while binding of K$^+$ either closes this pocket or transforms it into an open hydrated structure.

Assuming that the steps for binding or release of nucleotides and cations are relatively fast, the change in fluorescence of the probes is a convenient but indirect tool for monitoring the rate of the conformational transitions in the protein.

Sidedness of cation effects on protein structure

Titrations under strictly identical conditions show that the structural transitions between E_1Na and E_2K involve a number of different residues in the α-subunit. The changes are correlated to binding of Na^+ with relatively low affinity ($K_{\frac{1}{2}} = 0.5$–1 mM), or to binding of Rb^+ or K^+ with high affinity ($K_d = 7.5\,\mu M$) at low ionic strength or ($K_d = 40$–$60\,\mu M$) at physiological ionic strength (Jørgensen & Petersen 1982). The sidedness of these cation sites can be determined in experiments with tryptic or chymotryptic digestion after reconstitution of Na^+,K^+-ATPase in phospholipid vesicles. This system is ideal for these studies since only Na^+–K^+ pumps with their cytoplasmic aspect facing outward can be utilized for transport. In vesicles reconstituted with pure Na^+,K^+-ATPase, the linear pattern of decay of active Na^+–K^+ transport by tryptic digestion in KCl medium, or the biphasic pattern of inactivation in NaCl medium, can be demonstrated (Karlish & Pick 1981). Control of the cation composition at the two membrane surfaces shows that the binding of Na^+ and K^+ or Rb^+ at the cytoplasmic surface stabilizes the alternative patterns of tryptic or chymotryptic digestion of the α-subunit that are characteristic for the E_1Na or E_2K conformations.

These results therefore show that K^+ or Rb^+ bind with rather high apparent affinity to sites at the cytoplasmic surface of the Na^+–K^+ pump. The relatively high apparent affinity of K^+ binding has been explained by weak binding of K^+ to the E_1 form in a coupling with the conformational equilibrium between E_1K and E_2K, which is poised in the direction of E_2K (Karlish et al 1978). However, recent experiments show that it is necessary to assume that the E_1 form of the enzyme exposes sites for tight binding of K^+ or Rb^+ at the cytoplasmic surface. First, it is possible to abolish the transitions to E_2K, with thimerosal or chymotryptic cleavage of bond 3, without affecting the affinity or the capacity of $^{86}Rb^+$ binding. Secondly, Jensen & Ottolenghi (1982) showed that Rb^+ can bind to Na^+,K^+-ATPase with relatively high affinity ($K_d = 60$–$70\,\mu M$) in the presence of 2 mM-ATP. At this concentration ATP stabilizes the E_1 conformation, even at high concentrations of K^+ (Jørgensen 1975). The release of K^+ or Rb^+ from the binding sites at the cytoplasmic surface may therefore require the combined presence of ATP and Na^+. In physiological conditions, with the high concentration of K^+ in the cytosol, these cytoplasmic cation sites may control the rate of the reaction, and the slow rate of release of K+ from the cytoplasmic sites may be rate limiting for the overall Na+–K+ transport reaction.

Cation-induced transitions and ion translocation

It is important to determine if these cytoplasmic sites for binding of K+ or Rb+ are transport sites. We therefore measured the cation fluxes with ^{22}Na+ or ^{86}Rb+ in vesicles reconstituted with pure Na+,K+-ATPase and with gradients of Na+,K+ or Rb+ across the vesicular membrane. The permeability of the pure lipid vesicle to cations is very low. Even at very low protein : lipid ratios, leading to a density of one pump per vesicle (Skriver et al 1980), the insertion of Na+–K+-pump molecules into the vesicle membrane caused significant increases in permeability to ^{22}Na+ or ^{86}Rb+. A minor part of this leak is unspecific and due to the insertion of the protein in the membrane, but the majority of the fluxes are specific since they are blocked by vanadate or ouabain, as demonstrated by Karlish & Stein (1982a,b) and Karlish et al (1982).

The experiment in Fig. 4 was designed to determine the direction and apparent cation affinities for these fluxes through the protein. Vesicles were reconstituted with the amount of pure Na+,K+-ATPase required for one pump per vesicle. The vesicle interior was filled with either Na+ or K+ and the concentration dependence of the uptake of ^{22}Na+ or ^{86}Rb+ was measured. As shown in the lower part of Fig. 4, ouabain-sensitive uptake of ^{22}Na+ was observed in vesicles containing both K+ and pumps with their extracellular aspects facing outward to allow for inhibition by ouabain in the outside medium. The apparent affinity for Na+ ($K_{\frac{1}{2}}$ about 8 mM) was relatively low.

Ouabain-sensitive uptake of Rb+ was observed in vesicles containing Na+. This uptake of Rb+ had a much higher apparent affinity ($K_{\frac{1}{2}} = 100$–$200\,\mu$M) at an ionic strength of about 140 mM. The Rb+ ions must have been bound to cytoplasmic sites and released after translocation from extracellular sites, because inhibition of the Rb+ flux by ouabain required addition of the ouabain during vesicle formation, while ouabain added to the outside medium after formation of the vesicles had little effect. The specific inhibition shows that the flux involves specific binding and translocation of the cation through the protein of Na+,K+-ATPase, since ouabain and vanadate interfere with the cation-induced conformational changes. The direction for the passive ouabain-sensitive Na+/Rb+ exchange was opposite to that for the active ATP-dependent Na+/K+ exchange. The asymmetry of the Na+–K+ pump can therefore be demonstrated in the absence of nucleotides or

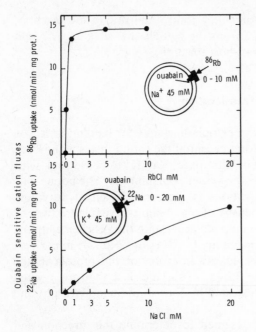

FIG. 4. Ouabain-sensitive passive flux of ^{86}Rb$^+$ or ^{22}Na$^+$ into vesicles reconstituted with pure renal Na$^+$,K$^+$-ATPase with 45 mM-NaCl or 45 mM-KCl inside and with RbCl or NaCl varying between 0 and 20 mM in the outside medium. Constant ionic strength was maintained at 140 mM with Tris-Cl. Reconstitution and exchange of media was done as described by Karlish & Pick (1981), with ouabain (10^{-4} M) inside or outside the vesicles.

inorganic phosphate (P$_i$), and it can be ascribed to the preference of the cytoplasmic cation sites for Rb$^+$ over Na$^+$.

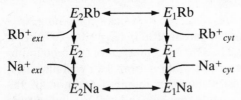

The scheme above illustrates the relationship of the binding and dissociation reactions at the membrane surfaces to the translocation steps, which are assumed to be identical to the transitions between E_1 and E_2 forms of the protein. The rate of the translocation in one direction (E_1Rb$\rightarrow E_2$Rb) is expected to be faster than the rate of translocation in the other direction (E_2Na$\rightarrow E_1$Na), while the rate of transition of the unliganded protein ($E_1 \rightleftharpoons E_2$) will be very low in the conditions of the experiments in Fig. 4. In this system one can expect 'trans' effects where the unidirectional fluxes are affected by the solute concentration in the compartment towards which they are directed as well as in the compartment from which they originate. Even if the rates of the binding and dissociation reactions at the surfaces are fast relative to the rate of translocation through the membrane, the constants obtained from the curves in Fig. 4 will reflect both the constants for binding at the two surfaces and the translocation rates.

Protein conformations of the phosphoenzymes

Phosphorylation of the α-subunit is a necessary condition for hydrolysis of ATP by Na$^+$,K$^+$-ATPase both in the presence of Na$^+$ alone and with Na$^+$ plus K$^+$ in the medium (Hobbs et al 1980). The relationships between the protein conformations and the reaction states identified in kinetic studies are illustrated in the scheme below:

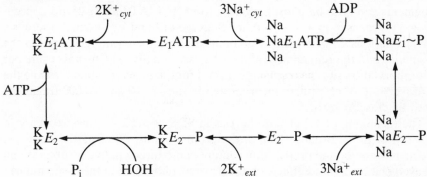

The E_1 conformation of the protein is phosphorylated from ATP in the presence of Mg^{2+} and Na$^+$. E_1P is a high-energy intermediate that can react with ADP to form ATP. E_2P is a low-energy form that reacts with water in the presence of K$^+$. The different qualities of E_1P and E_2P are a matter of different conformations rather than of basic differences in chemical states.

Tryptic digestion and fluorescence experiments suggest that the major change in structure of the α-subunit occurs when E_1P is transformed into E_2P, and not when phosphate is transferred from ATP to the protein. In experiments on tryptic digestion the effects of individual ligands have been resolved in some detail. Binding of Na$^+$ to MgE_1·ATP causes removal of bond 2 and 3 from the membrane surface while bond 1 becomes exposed at the same time as formation of a phosphoenzyme. The increase in tryptophan fluorescence intensity which accompanies the phosphorylation from ATP in the presence of K$^+$ reflects the formation of E_2P which has the same fluorescence intensity as E_2K. Conversely, the fluorescence intensity of E_1P is similar to that of the E_1 de-phospho forms. The tryptophan fluorescence technique thus provides a simple and rapid assay of the steady-state proportions of E_1P and E_2P (Jørgensen & Karlish 1980).

Phosphorylation and dephosphorylation after cleavage of the α-subunit at bond 1 and bond 3

The portion containing the aspartyl phosphate residue between bond 1 and bond 3 is potentially the most interesting part of the α-subunit. The locations of bond 1 and 3 at either side of the aspartyl phosphate suggest that selective cleavage of bond 1 with trypsin in KCl medium, or of bond 3 with chymotrypsin in NaCl medium, could be powerful tools in examination of the function of this protein segment. Cleavage of either bond 1 or bond 3 blocks Na^+,K^+-ATPase and Na^+/K^+ exchange, but the resulting 78 000 and 46 000 fragments can both be phosphorylated from $[\gamma^{32}P]$ATP at $20-25\,\mu M$ concentration (Jørgensen et al 1982). After cleavage of bond 1 or bond 3, there is a linear relationship between the amount of phosphoenzyme recovered in the α-subunit and the remaining Na^+,K^+-ATPase activity. The turnover rate per phosphorylation site thus remains constant for the intact α-subunits, while the turnover rate of phosphate incorporated in the 78 000 and 46 000 fragments must be close to zero.

The technique of gel electrophoresis in SDS at pH 2.4 allows recovery of 60–80% of the phosphoprotein in the protein bands. After partial cleavage, the membrane-bound preparation contains a mixture of native α-subunits and cleaved chains. Ligand effects on the aspartyl phosphate in the α-subunit can therefore be compared directly with effects on the aspartyl phosphate in the 78 000 and 46 000 fragments.

The experiment in Fig. 5 shows that the aspartyl phosphate of the 78 000 fragment is much less sensitive to K^+ than that of the intact α-subunit or that of the 46 000 fragment. In contrast, the aspartyl phosphate of the 78 000 fragment dephosphorylates rapidly after addition of ADP, like the α-subunit, while the 46 000 fragment dephosphorylates slowly after ADP addition. These observations suggest either that splitting of bond 3 interferes with binding of K^+ or that the aspartyl phosphate of the 78 000 fragment is unable to undergo the transition to the E_2P form. The first possibility is unlikely since $^{86}Rb^+$ binding, with K_d close to $7\,\mu M$, is unaffected after cleavage of bond 3. $[^{48}V]$vanadate-binding experiments support the notion that the 78 000 fragment has lost the ability to undergo the transition to E_2P, since vanadate binding is reduced in proportion to cleavage of bond 3 while it is unaffected by cleavage of bond 1. This latter cleavage, on the other hand, interferes

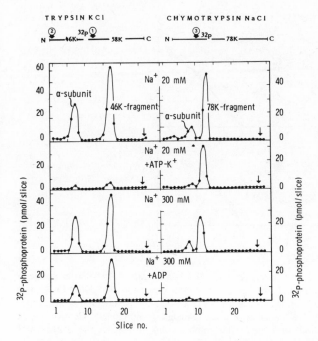

FIG. 5. Effect of KCl or ADP on dephosphorylation of α-subunit or its 46 000 and 78 000 fragments. Phosphorylation with 25 μM-[γ³²P]ATP in 25 mM-Tris-Cl, pH 7.5, 20 mM-NaCl (first panel) or 300 mM-NaCl (third panel). After 6 s either 1 mM-ATP plus 1 mM-KCl (second panel) or 2.5 mM-ADP (fourth panel) were added. At 2 s or 6 s later, perchloric acid was added. After precipitation and wash in 4% perchloric acid the phosphoproteins were dissolved in SDS and fractionated by electrophoresis at pH 2.4. The gels were sliced (3 mm) and counted.

neither with phosphorylation from ATP nor with transition to E_2P and K+-stimulated dephosphorylation. The 46 000 fragment can be phosphorylated from ATP and splitting of bond 1 does not prevent the structural changes accompanying transition from E_1P to E_2P.

Effect of cleavage of bond 1 and 3 on Na+/Na+ and Rb+/Rb+ exchange in reconstituted vesicles

Since cleavage at either the N-terminal side (bond 3) or at the C-terminal side (bond 1) of the aspartyl phosphate have different effects on the behaviour of the phosphoenzyme, we examined the effect of these splits on the cation exchange reactions. Tryptic or chymotryptic inactivation of Na+,K+-ATPase is accompanied by a parallel reduction in the rate of Na+–K+ transport, but

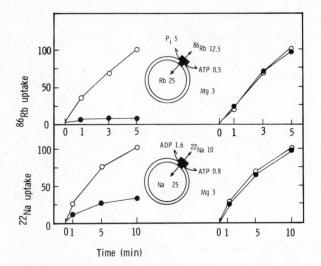

Time (min)

FIG. 6. Effect of cleavage of bond 1 (right) or bond 3 (left) on the rate of Rb$^+$/Rb$^+$ exchange or Na$^+$/Na$^+$ exchange in reconstituted vesicles. Pure membrane-bound Na$^+$,K$^+$-ATPase was inactivated with trypsin in KCl, until 29% Na$^+$,K$^+$-ATPase activity remained, or with chymotrypsin in NaCl until 23% Na$^+$,K$^+$-ATPase activity remained (solid circles). Controls (open circles) were incubated without protease. After solubilization in cholate, the enzyme was reconstituted into phospholipid vesicles by the freeze–thaw technique, with composition of intravesicular media as indicated. Exchange of external media was done by passage of vesicles over Sephadex G-50 (Karlish & Pick 1981). Na$^+$/Na$^+$ exchange at 24 °C was initiated by adding ^{22}Na$^+$, ADP and ATP. Intravesicular ^{22}Na$^+$ was measured after passage over an ion-exchange column and Na$^+$/Na$^+$ exchange was calculated as the difference in rate with and without nucleotides in the medium. Rb$^+$/Rb$^+$ exchange was calculated as the difference in rate of ^{86}Rb$^+$ accumulation with and without 1 mM-vanadate in the external medium.

the effects on Na$^+$/Na$^+$ and Rb$^+$/Rb$^+$ exchange depend on the location of the splits. Fig. 6 shows that cleavage of bond 3 inhibits Rb$^+$/Rb$^+$ exchange more than Na$^+$,K$^+$-ATPase activity, while Na$^+$/Na$^+$ exchange is inhibited in proportion to the reduction of enzyme activity. In contrast, cleavage of bond 1 causes only moderate changes in Na$^+$/Na$^+$ exchange or Rb$^+$/Rb$^+$ exchange.

Both ADP and ATP are required for the 1 : 1 isotope exchange of Na$^+_{cyt}$ for Na$^+_{ext}$ without net hydrolysis of ATP (for refs see Karlish et al 1978). The alternate exposure of Na$^+$-binding sites at the cytoplasmic and extracellular surfaces is believed to be coupled to transition between E_1P and E_2P as illustrated in the scheme:

$$Na^+_{cyt} + E_1ATP \leftrightarrows NaE_1ATP \leftrightarrows ADP + NaE_1P \leftrightarrows NaE_2P \leftrightarrows E_2P + Na^+_{ext}$$

The rate of Na$^+$/Na$^+$ exchange is linearly related to the ADP concentration. ADP could increase the reaction rate by promoting dephosphorylation of

E_1P. Alternatively, ADP could be required as an accelerator of the conversion from E_2PNa to E_1PNa because binding of ATP is prevented by the phosphoryl group already on the enzyme. These possibilities are discussed by Karlish et al (1978). Our data point to the latter possibility, since dephosphorylation of the 46 000 fragment by ADP is impaired while Na+/Na+ exchange is unaffected after cleavage of bond 1.

Rb+/Rb+ exchange requires both ATP and P_i (Simons 1974). Also, in this reaction, the transitions between RbE_1ATP and RbE_2P are proposed to be accompanied by alternate exposure of cation sites at the two surfaces:

$$Rb^+_{cyt} + E_1ATP \leftrightharpoons RbE_1ATP \leftrightharpoons ATP + RbE_2 \leftrightharpoons RbE_2P \leftrightharpoons E_2P + Rb^+_{ext}$$

Our data show that transitions between E_1P and E_2P are possible after cleavage of bond 1, and this split does not interfere with either of the exchange reactions. In contrast, cleavage of bond 3 blocks the transition from E_1P to E_2P and uncouples phosphoryl transfer from cation exchange. The data thus support the notion that the cation exchange reactions are tightly coupled to transitions between E_1P and E_2P.

Coupling of conformational changes in α-subunit to cation transport

The transitions between E_1 and E_2 forms of the α-subunit of the Na+–K+ pump involve the area for nucleotide binding and phosphorylation and the cation-binding sites. The data provide evidence that both the transitions between cation-stabilized forms, E_1Na and E_2K, and the transitions between the phospho forms, E_1P and E_2P, are coupled to translocation steps for cations across the membrane.

In the absence of ligands other than the monovalent cations, the Na+–K+ pump is capable of binding Rb+ with relatively high affinity at the cytoplasmic surface, conveying the cation across the membrane and releasing it on the extracellular surface in exchange for Na+ ions. In these experiments the pump is operating as a carrier that mediates passive ouabain-sensitive fluxes in a direction opposite to that of the ATP-dependent active Na+–K+ transport. The passive fluxes are slow ($0.1\,s^{-1}$ per α-subunit), as compared to the rate of the active Na+–K+ transport at 24 °C (30–40 s^{-1} per α-subunit), but they demonstrate that the cation-induced transitions are accompanied by movement of cation sites from one membrane surface to the other. These experiments show that the internal asymmetry of the Na+–K+ pump protein reflects the selectivity of the cation-binding sites and is independent of coupling to ATP hydrolysis.

The study of the partial reactions after selective cleavage with trypsin or chymotrypsin shows also that the transitions between the phosphoenzyme forms of the α-subunit constitute cation-transport steps: Na^+ movements involving the $E_1P \rightleftharpoons E_2P$ transitions and K^+ movements involving the E_2K to E_1ATP transition. Our previous studies demonstrate that the phosphoryl transfer reactions are accompanied by only minor changes in structure of the α-subunit. These phosphoryl transfer reactions are assumed to be coupled to the association and dissociation of cations to sites at the cytoplasmic and extracellular surface as illustrated in the scheme discussed here.

Acknowledgements

I thank Lene Jacobsen and Janne Petersen for excellent technical assistance. The study was supported by the Danish Medical Research Council.

REFERENCES

Castro J, Farley RA 1979 Proteolytic fragmentation of the catalytic subunit of the sodium and potassium adenosine triphosphatase. J Biol Chem 254:2221-2228

Deguchi N, Jørgensen PL, Maunsbach AB 1977 Ultrastucture of the sodium pump. Comparison of thin sectioning, negative staining and freeze fracture of purified, membrane-bound Na^+,K^+-ATPase. J Cell Biol 75:619-634

Giotta GJ 1975 Native $(Na^+ + K^+)$-dependent adenosine triphosphatase has two trypsin-sensitive sites. J Biol Chem 250:5159-5164

Hastings D, Skou JC 1980 Potassium binding to the $(Na^+ + K^+)$-ATPase. Biochim Biophys Acta 601:380-385

Hobbs AS, Albers RW, Froehlich JP 1980 Potassium-induced changes in phosphorylation and dephosphorylation of $(Na^+ + K^+)$-ATPase observed in the transient state. J Biol Chem 255:3395-3402

Hegyvary C, Jørgensen PL 1981 Conformational changes of renal sodium plus potassium ion-transport adenosine triphosphatase labeled with fluorescein. J Biol Chem 256:6296-6303

Jensen J, Ottolenghi P 1982 Binding of Rb^+ and ADP to a potassium-like form of Na^+,K^+-ATPase. In: Hoffmann JF, Forbush B (eds) Na, K-ATPase. Academic Press, New York, in press

Jørgensen PL 1974 Purification and characterization of $(Na^+ + K^+)$-ATPase. IV: Estimation of the purity and of the molecular weight and polypeptide content per enzyme unit in preparations from the outer medulla of rabbit kidney. Biochim Biophys Acta 356:53-67

Jørgensen PL 1975 Purification and characterization of $(Na^+ + K^+)$-ATPase. V: Conformational changes in the enzyme. Transitions between the Na-form and the K-form studied with tryptic digestion as a tool. Biochim Biophys Acta 401:399-415

Jørgensen PL 1977 Purification and characterization of $(Na^+ + K^+)$-ATPase. VI: Differential tryptic modification of catalytic functions of the purified enzyme in presence of NaCl and KCl. Biochim Biophys Acta 466:97-108

Jørgensen PL 1980 Sodium and potassium pump in kidney tubules. Physiol Rev 60:864-917

Jørgensen PL 1982 Mechanism of the Na,K-pump. Protein structure and conformations of the pure Na,K-ATPase. Biochim Biophys Acta 694:27-68

Jørgensen PL, Karlish SJD 1980 Defective conformational response in a selectively trypsinized

($Na^+ + K^+$)-ATPase studied with tryptophan fluorescence. Biochim Biophys Acta 597:305-317

Jørgensen PL, Petersen J 1982 High-affinity ^{86}Rb binding and structural changes in the α-subunit of Na$^+$,K$^+$-ATPase as detected by tryptic digestion and fluorescence analysis. Biochim Biophys Acta 705:38-47

Jørgensen PL, Skriver E, Hebert H, Maunsbach AB 1982 Structure of the Na,K-pump: crystallization of pure membrane-bound Na,K-ATPase and identification of functional domains of the α-subunit. Ann NY Acad Sci (USA), in press

Karlish SJD 1980 Characterization of conformational changes in Na,K-ATPase labelled with fluorescein at the active site. J Bioenerg Biomembr 12:11-136

Karlish SJD, Yates DW 1978 Tryptophan fluorescence of Na,K-ATPase as a tool for study of the enzyme mechanism. Biochim Biophys Acta 527:115-130

Karlish SJD, Pick U 1981 Sidedness of the effects of sodium and potassium ions on the conformational state of the sodium-potassium pump. J Physiol (Lond) 312:505-529

Karlish SJD, Stein WD 1982a Passive rubidium fluxes mediated by Na–K-ATPase reconstituted into phospholipid vesicles when ATP- and phosphate-free. J Physiol (Lond) 328:295-316

Karlish SJD, Stein WD 1982b Effects of ATP or phosphate on passive rubidium fluxes mediated by Na–K-ATPase reconstituted into phospholipid vesicles. J Physiol (Lond) 328:317-331

Karlish SJD, Jørgensen PL, Gitler C 1977 Identification of a membrane-embedded segment of the large polypeptide chain of (Na$^+$, K$^+$)ATPase. Nature (Lond) 269:715-717

Karlish SJD, Yates DW, Glynn IM 1978 Conformational transitions between Na-bound and K-bound forms of Na,K-ATPase, studied with formycin nucleotides. Biochim Biophys Acta 525:252-264

Karlish SJD, Lieb WR, Stein WD 1982 Combined effects of ATP and phosphate on rubidium exchange mediated by Na–K-ATPase reconstituted into phospholipid vesicles. J Physiol (Lond) 328:333-350

Moczydlowsky E, Fortes PAG 1981 Characterization of 2',3'-o-(2,4,6-trinitrocyclohexadienyl-idine) adenosine-5'-triphosphate as a fluorescent probe of the ATP site of sodium and potassium transport adenosine triphosphatase. J Biol Chem 256:2346-2356

Nørby JG, Jensen J 1971 Binding of ATP to Na,K-ATPase. Biochim Biophys Acta 233:104-116

Schultz SG 1978 Ion-coupled transport across biological membranes. In: Andreoli TE et al (eds) Physiology of membrane disorders. Plenum, New York, p 273-286

Simons TJB 1974 Potassium: potassium exchange catalysed by the sodium pump in human red cells. J Physiol (Lond) 237:123-155

Skou JC, Esmann M 1981 Eosin, a fluorescent probe of ATP binding to Na,K-ATPase. Biochim Biophys Acta 647:232-240

Skriver E, Maunsbach AB, Jørgensen PL 1980 Ultrastructure of Na,K-transport vesicles reconstituted with purified renal Na,K-ATPase. J Cell Biol 86:746-754

Skriver E, Maunsbach AB, Jørgensen PL 1981 Formation of two-dimensional crystals in pure membrane-bound Na$^+$,K$^+$-ATPase. FEBS (Fed Eur Biochem Soc) Lett 131:219-222

Yamaguchi M, Tonomura Y 1980 Cation binding to Na$^+$,K$^+$-ATPase. J Biochem (Tokyo) 88:1365-1375

DISCUSSION

Rodewald: Were you using the α β complex in all these experiments?

Jørgensen: The reconstitution experiments involve solubilization and incorporation of the pure Na$^+$,K$^+$-ATPase in vesicles after detergent removal.

After solubilization by non-ionic detergents the $\alpha\beta$ complex is the minimum active unit of Na$^+$,K$^+$-ATPase (Brotherus et al 1981). Chemical labelling and cross-linking experiments also suggest that the α- and β-subunits are close to one another in the membrane. In all the systems I have described the α- and β-subunits remain closely associated.

Louvard: With respect to this β-subunit, how do you determine the relative molecular masses of the protein and carbohydrate moieties?

Jørgensen: The information that I gave earlier (p 157) about the glycoprotein was obtained in Dr D.D. Sabatini's laboratory. The unglycosylated β-subunit is detected as a chain with an M_r of 38 000 in cells treated with tunicamycin. In the presence of monensin, glycosylation in the Golgi is blocked and one sees formation of a 45 000 M_r protein. The monensin-sensitive secondary-stage glycosylation in the Golgi increases the M_r to 38 000, plus 17 000 for carbohydrate.

Louvard: I would not have thought you could find out the M_r of the carbohydrate moiety by subtraction in the SDS method. The SDS relationship is true only for polypeptides.

Jørgensen: That is true. This is a complex issue, as the glycoprotein β-subunit shows anomalous behaviour in the SDS-PAGE system. In the normal range of acrylamide concentrations, the β-subunit migrates as a protein with an apparent M_r between 50 000 and 60 000. This means that the carbohydrate adds to the length of the chain in SDS solution. Analytical ultracentrifugation in detergent also gives an M_r of 37 000 for the unglycosylated β-subunit.

Louvard: What is your opinion about a proteolipid component that is believed to be part of the structure of the ATPase?

Jørgensen: This can be called the γ-subunit. It is assumed to be a proteolipid with an M_r of around 10 000. An operational definition of the γ-subunit is that it is covalently labelled by ouabain from the extracellular surface when the labels are attached to the sugar moiety of the cardiac glycosides (Forbush et al 1978). It is not well defined as a protein. The γ-peptides are not particularly hydrophobic with respect to amino acid composition, and extraction with chloroform/methanol is not always quantitative. That is why I prefer the term 'γ-subunit' to 'proteolipid'.

Sjöström: As I suggested earlier (p 153) it may be a general phenomenon that membrane proteins having their N-terminals on the cytoplasmic side are synthesized without a cleaved signal. How good is the evidence that Na$^+$,K$^+$-ATPase and Ca^{2+}-ATPase have their N-terminal amino acids on the cytoplasmic side?

Jørgensen: For Na$^+$,K$^+$-ATPase the evidence is indirect but good. Tryptic cleavage of bond 2 close to the N-terminus gives a fast inactivation of half the Na$^+$,K$^+$-ATPase activity. This split releases from the chain a peptide of M_r about 2000 and reveals a new N-terminal alanine instead of glycine. This can also be demonstrated in vesicles reconstituted with pure Na$^+$,K$^+$-ATPase to measure Na$^+$,K$^+$-transport rather than Na$^+$,K$^+$-ATPase activity. In the vesicles one can work only with the pumps that have their cytoplasmic aspects facing outward. These experiments show that bond 2 is cleaved from the cytoplasmic surface. Since a peptide is released, it follows that the N-terminus must be located at that membrane surface. Allen et al (1980) found that the N-terminus of Ca^{2+}-ATPase of sarcoplasmic reticulum is located at the cytoplasmic surface. Recent studies show that this enzyme is synthesized by cotranslational insertion without a signal sequence (Mostov et al 1981).

Sjöström: This means that up to now three proteins have been described (band 3 protein of erythrocytes, Na$^+$,K$^+$-ATPase and Ca^{2+}-ATPase) with their N-terminal amino acids on the cytoplasmic side, and having a non-cleaved signal. Aminopeptidase N is a further candidate for this group. Furthermore, I do not know of any membrane protein having its N-terminal amino acid on the cytoplasmic side and a cleaved signal.

Alpers: If you are making unilamellar liposomes or lipid particles you may have an aqueous milieu inside as well, and the complex could be facing either way or both ways in the group. So how do you know that the ouabain-insensitive transport is not simply due to a population of vesicles in which the complex is placed the opposite way, with its outside out and its cytoplasmic end in?

Jørgensen: That is true. Most of the ouabain-insensitive flux is due to the insertion of the protein into the vesicle. The pure phospholipid vesicle has a very low permeability, which is increased by the insertion of the protein. The ouabain-insensitive flux can be due to unspecific leaks produced by insertion of protein into the bilayer or it can be due to dissipative fluxes through proteins organized in such a way that ouabain cannot block the flux.

Alpers: It may not be important for the protein itself, but may simply be a methodological problem.

Jørgensen: On the other hand this does not interfere with the conclusion that we have demonstrated ouabain-sensitive fluxes through proteins that were inserted into the vesicles with their ouabain binding sites facing outwards.

Semenza: Several proteins are inserted without the pre-piece being cleaved—e.g. epoxide hydrolase of the endoplasmic reticulum. So we must be prepared to face the fact that 'pre-pieces' need not *really be* 'pre-pieces', but could simply be a natural part of the final protein which is not cleaved off, and which is highly hydrophobic.

Hauri: I have a question concerning the structural topology of the α-subunit. Your model indicates that the α-subunit is a transmembrane protein, but that it is not glycosylated, which would be an extremely important finding. How good is the evidence for the α-subunit not being glycosylated?

Jørgensen: Carbohydrate has been demonstrated in α-subunits from different sources by Churchill et al (1979) and by Peters et al (1981).

Hauri: Could you speculate on the function of the β-subunit?

Jørgensen: The reactions discussed here—the ATP-driven cation exchange and the phosphorylation and dephosphorylation—appear to be mediated exclusively by the α-subunit. Evidence relating catalytic functions to the β-subunit is not available.

Hauri: Would it be possible to separate both subunits to elucidate their individual functions?

Jørgensen: Nobody has been able to separate the α-subunit from the β-subunit, except in SDS, of course. A functional system consisting only of α-subunits has not been isolated. This is a paradox because in other systems, e.g. the Ca^{2+}-ATPase from sarcoplasmic reticulum and the H^+-ATPase from gastric mucosa or Neurospora, one can see a functioning pump with only one chain having an M_r close to 100 000, like the α-subunit. These proteins are also phosphorylated, and they exist in equilibrium between E_1 and E_2 conformations, but they function without the presence of other peptides while the α-subunit can catalyse Na^+– K^+-transport only in the presence of the β-subunit.

REFERENCES

Allen G, Trinnaman BJ, Green NM 1980 The primary structure of the calcium ion-transporting adenosine triphosphatase protein of rabbit skeletal sarcoplasmic reticulum. Biochem J 187: 591-616

Brotherus JR, Møller JV, Jørgensen PL 1981 Soluble and active renal Na,K-ATPase with maximum protein molecular mass 170,000 ± 9,000 daltons; formation of larger units by secondary aggregation. Biochem Biophys Res Commun 100: 146-154

Churchill L, Peterson GL, Hokin LE 1979 The large subunit of (sodium + potassium)-activated adenosine triphosphatase from the electroplax of *Electrophorus electricus* is a glycoprotein. Biochem Biophys Res Commun 90: 488-490

Forbush B III, Kaplan JH, Hoffman JF 1978 Characterization of a new photoaffinity derivative of ouabain: labeling of the large polypeptide and of a proteolipid component of the Na,K-ATPase. Biochemistry 17: 3667-3676

Mostov KE, Defoor P, Fleischer S, Blobel G 1981 Co-translational membrane integration of calcium-pump protein without signal sequence cleavage. Nature (Lond) 292: 87-88

Peters WHM, Depont JJHH, Koppers A, Bonting SL 1981 Studies on $(Na^+ + K^+)$-activated ATPase. Chemical composition, molecular-weight and molar ratio of the subunits of the enzyme from rabbit kidney outer medulla. Biochim Biophys Acta 641: 55-70

Properties of immunoglobulin G–Fc receptors from neonatal rat intestinal brush borders

NEIL SIMISTER and ANTHONY R. REES

Laboratory of Molecular Biophysics, Department of Zoology, University of Oxford, South Parks Road, Oxford OX1 3PS, UK

Abstract Newborn rats acquire immunity passively by receptor-mediated uptake of maternal immunoglobulin G (IgG) from the first milk. Specific IgG binding to brush borders and IgG transport across the gut increase concomitantly for 10–12 days after birth and then fall until closure at about 21 days. Cortisol acetate administration accelerates this decline. Two classes of binding site are resolved by their affinities ($K_A1 = 1.3 \times 10^8$M; $K_A2 = 5.15 \times 10^6$M). Persistence of the low-affinity site after closure precludes a transport role (see Rodewald et al, this volume). Target size analysis gives a preliminary M_r for the high-affinity site of 90 000–100 000. IgG recognition involves a small number of positively charged residues in the Fc region. An Fc binding activity is solubilized from intestinal brush borders by lithium 3,5-diiodosalicylate.

1983 Brush border membranes. Pitman Books Ltd, London (Ciba Foundation symposium 95) p 273-286, and 297-299

The work of F. W. Rogers Brambell in the late 1950s and 1960s on the transport of immunoglobulin G (IgG) across brush border barriers led him to propose a receptor model which explained his observations on the specificity and saturability of the transport process (Brambell 1970). The essential features of this model were: (1) endocytosis of IgG at the luminal surface of distal enterocytes; (2) binding of IgG to specific intracellular receptors within the endocytic vesicles; (3) fusion of these vesicles with lysosomes during which non-bound protein only is degraded; and (4) exocytosis of vesicles at the abluminal surface and release of receptor-bound IgG into the serosal plasma. While the major features of this model have remained intact it has become clear from the work of R. Rodewald and others on the neonatal rat intestine that the selection takes place on the luminal surface *prior* to internalization and involves specific membrane receptors associated with

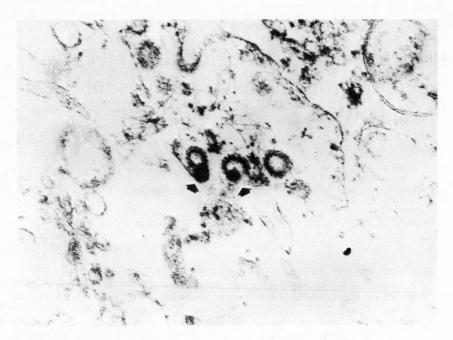

FIG. 1. Autoradiographic electron microscopic section of a coated vesicle preparation after perfusion of human placenta with human [^{125}I]IgG (A. R. Rees & C. D. Ockleford, unpublished observations).

coated pits (Rodewald 1970). In the most recent modification to the original model, Rodewald (1981) has suggested that receptor-bound IgG is endocytosed into coated tubular vesicles along with other non-bound luminal proteins by a constitutive endocytic process (see also Rodewald et al, this volume). These tubular vesicles then become subject to a sorting process, mediated by lysosomes, which results in the degradation of non-receptor-bound protein and the transfer of receptor-bound IgG to a second class of coated vesicle, which moves to the basolateral membrane where fusion and exocytosis take place. How these coated vesicles are generated is not known but there is strong evidence that only the protein that is initially membrane-bound finds its way to the abluminal surface, and that the protein is usually observed to be in coated vesicles.

In contrast to this model, Wild (1975, 1976) has proposed that endocytosis takes place *directly* into coated vesicles that form at the luminal surface. These vesicles are prevented from fusing with lysosomes by the coat structure and thus are involved in ferrying IgG directly from luminal to abluminal membrane. This mechanism is contradicted by the sorting hypothesis and, while IgG has been observed in coated vesicles from neonatal rat (Rodewald 1976), human placenta (Pearse 1982, A. R. Rees, unpublished observations: see Fig. 1) and rabbit yolk-sac endoderm (Wild 1976), there remains uncertainty about the precise role of this class of endocytic vesicle. The uncertainty may be resolved when the molecular events immediately following receptor binding are dissected in detail. The first step must be the isolation and characterization of the receptor itself, an objective towards which we have made some progress.

Localization of IgG binding sites

While F. W. R. Brambell and co-workers were convinced that the distal region of the small intestine was the site of specific IgG transport it was later shown by Rodewald (1976) that the major transporting cells reside in the proximal jejunum and duodenum, with a gradual decrease in specific transport as the jejunum gives way to the ileum. Rodewald investigated the

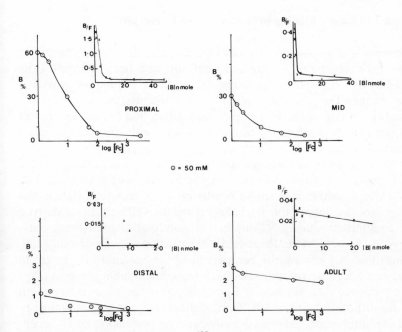

FIG. 2. Equilibrium binding (B) of ^{125}I-labelled Fc to brush border membranes from the proximal, mid- and distal small intestine of 11-day-old rats, and from the proximal small intestine of adult (23-day-old) rats. Bound : free ratios are also plotted against the concentrations of bound Fc.

specificity of this process by looking at the relative efficiency of transport of either Fab or Fc fragments conjugated to HRP or ferritin.

We have measured the Fc-binding activity in brush borders, prepared from small intestines of 10–14-day-old neonatal rats, by the methods of Wallace & Rees (1980). We have done this at various points along the intestine and can confirm that there is a sharp reduction in receptor number in the proximal-to-distal direction. (see Fig. 2).

This supports the view that proximal sites operate a selective sequestration of IgG from the luminal fluid in addition to, or as part of, a constitutive endocytic process (Rodewald 1981) whereas the ileum operates a non-selective absorption of protein that is ultimately destined for degradation. Thus, the type of vesicle in which the immunoglobulin is sequestered is likely to be dictated by the receptor-mediated events at the luminal membrane and may result directly from the interactions between receptor and coat protein. Indeed, IgG molecules are localized in regions of coated pits at the luminal surface (Rodewald 1976), although the existence of a receptor–clathrin interaction is at present only conjectural.

Equilibrium and kinetic binding properties of the Fc receptor

Prior to the work of Wallace & Rees in 1980 the specificity, saturability and ontogeny of Fc receptors in the neonatal rat had been inferred from morphological and transport data alone. While these techniques provide a qualitative picture they do not allow a quantitative assessment of (a) the affinity and specificity of the Fc-receptor interaction and (b) the number of receptors per cell, both of which can be measured with simple radioligand binding methods.

Fig. 3a shows equilibrium binding data for brush borders of the proximal jejunum. Using Scatchard analysis and computer fitting, we obtained the data shown in Table 1, which also shows results obtained from association and dissociation kinetics, where the K_A values compare well with those derived from the equilibrium studies. A number of points arise from these data, particularly in the light of R. Rodewald's observation (see Rodewald et al, this volume) that the low-affinity component of the Scatchard is present in 21-day-old rats where no receptor-mediated immunoglobulin transport takes place. We proposed (see Wallace & Rees 1980) that the biphasic Scatchard could be due either to the presence of two distinct receptor populations or to a cooperative interaction between a homogeneous population of Fc receptors. We favoured this latter interpretation on the basis of kinetic experiments in which the dissociation rate of [^{125}I]IgG bound to brush borders was increased when unlabelled IgG was present in the dilution buffer (Fig. 3b).

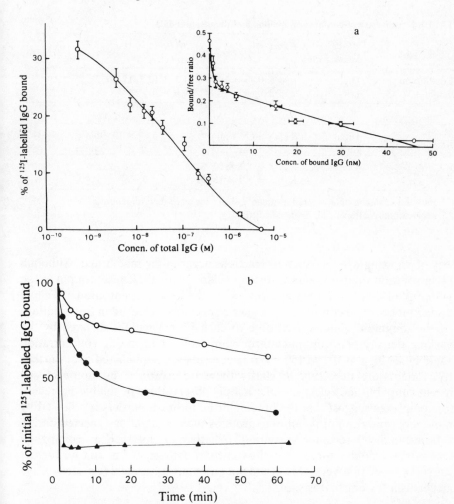

FIG. 3.(a) Equilibrium binding of [^{125}I]IgG to brush border membranes from the proximal small intestine of 10–12-day-old rats, showing a direct displacement curve and a computer-fitted Scatchard curve. (b) Time course of dissociation of [^{125}I]IgG from brush border membranes: without (open circles) unlabelled IgG; with (solid circles) unlabelled IgG at 2×10^{-8}M; solid triangles show non-specifically bound [^{125}I]IgG (from Wallace & Rees 1980.)

(This phenomenon has been observed with a number of receptor systems; see De Meyts 1976.) We have repeated these experiments, using ^{125}I-labelled Fc, and have observed the same phenomenon.

A second interpretation of these results is that Fc–Fc interactions at high receptor occupancy decrease the affinity of Fc for its receptor. We have no

TABLE 1. Summary of equilibrium binding and dissociation data

	Affinity of binding site	$K_A{}^a$	nRT	R^b
Equilibrium binding, 37 °C	High	$1.30 \pm 0.43 \times 10^8 M^{-1}$	$1.7 \times 10^{-9} M$	0.99
	Low	$5.15 \pm 0.69 \times 10^6 M^{-1}$	$4.6 \times 10^{-8} M$	0.97
		K_{on}	K_{off}	
Kinetics at 37 °C	High	$8.25 \times 10^5 M^{-1} min^{-1}$	$6.50 \times 10^{-3} min^{-1}$	
	Low	$8.25 \times 10^5 M^{-1} min^{-1}$	$2.25 \times 10^{-1} min^{-1}$	
$K_A = \dfrac{K_{on}}{K_{off}}$	Therefore,	$K_A{}^{high} = 1.2 \times 10^8 \ M^{-1}$ $K_A{}^{low} = 5.0 \times 10^6 \ M^{-1}$		

[a] Equilibrium binding data is given as mean $\pm$ 1 SD for > 20 determinations.
[b] R, correlation coefficient for Scatchard fitting.

way of knowing whether such interactions occur in the membrane. Although Fc in solution does not aggregate appreciably over the concentration range 1–10 mg ml^{-1} (see Augener & Grey 1970), the local concentration of Fc in a coated pit could be considerably higher than can be achieved in free solution. (If the minimum volume accessible to each Fc molecule is dictated by the packing density of receptor–clathrin complexes, then the Fc concentration could be as high as 0.5 M (50 g ml^{-1}) in a close-packed coated pit.) Further experiments are necessary to clarify these observations, but some of our recent (unpublished) electron microscopic observations of soluble Fc–receptor complexes suggest that the binding of Fc to brush borders is followed by rapid reorganization of membrane proteins such as might be expected during a ligand-induced receptor clustering. Whether or not such a 'capping' of receptors is an obligatory step in the transport pathway is a matter for further study but, even if it were, this would not automatically preclude a constitutive mechanism for endocytosis.

Effect of pH and ionic strength

The pH-dependence of trans-placental transport of IgG was discovered by Jones & Waldmann (1972), and a similar dependence was observed by Rodewald (1976) for the neonatal brush border. We have studied quantitatively the effects of pH and ionic strength on the rat system, and the results are summarized in Fig. 4. The pH optimum of 5.8–6.4 corresponds to the ambient pH of the proximal jejunum during the transport period and suggests an obvious mechanism for the vectorial transfer of IgG, because the serosal pH is about 7.4, at which no IgG will bind. As the neonate ages the luminal

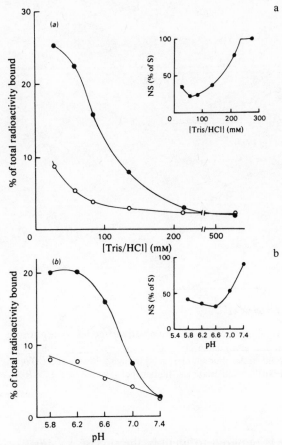

FIG. 4. Dependence of IgG binding on (a) ionic strength and (b) pH. (a) solid circles, specific binding of [^{125}I]IgG (5×10^{-10}M); open circles, non-specific binding of [^{125}I]IgG in the presence of unlabelled IgG at 3×10^{-6}M. Insets: non-specific binding (NS) expressed as a percentage of specific bindings (S). The pH for all the determinations was 6.75. (From Wallace & Rees 1980.)

pH decreases until at 21 days or so it is outside the range in which IgG would bind. However, no receptors are present then, and the loss of transport is therefore not simply a pH effect. The hormonally controlled switch in gene expression as the enterocyte takes on adult status is clearly linked to a similar switch in the cells that secrete acid, although the agents responsible for these changes are unknown.

The dependence on ionic strength, though curious, may be explained by a disproportionate effect of salt on high- and low-affinity sites such that the low-affinity sites are abolished under isotonic conditions (see Rodewald et al,

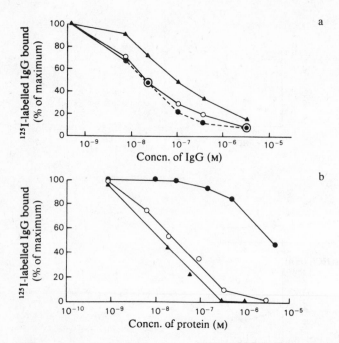

FIG. 5. Comparisons of the relative abilities of (a) IgG from various species to displace rat [^{125}I]IgG, and of (b) rat F(ab)′$_2$, rat IgG and human Fc to displace human [^{125}I]Fc from brush borders. (a) open circles, rat IgG; solid circles, human IgG; solid triangles, bovine IgG (b) open circles, rat IgG; solid circles, rat F(ab)′$_2$; solid triangles, human Fc. (From Wallace & Rees, 1980.)

this volume). Further study is required to identify the precise locations of these apparently independent binding sites.

Specificity of the Fc interaction

Various workers have previously shown that while Fc antagonizes the transport of [^{125}I]IgG in the neonatal rat intestine, Fab or other non-immunoglobulin proteins do not (for a review, see Rees & Wallace 1980). We have compared the ability of IgGs from various species and IgG fragments to inhibit the binding of rat [^{125}I]IgG to brush borders, and the data are shown in Fig. 5. Human Fc seems to have a slightly higher affinity for the receptor than rat IgG although neither rat F(ab)′$_2$ nor human F(ab)′$_2$ (data not shown) is capable of displacing the labelled IgG. Bovine IgG is somewhat less inhibitory although it is known to be efficiently transported. These data lead to the

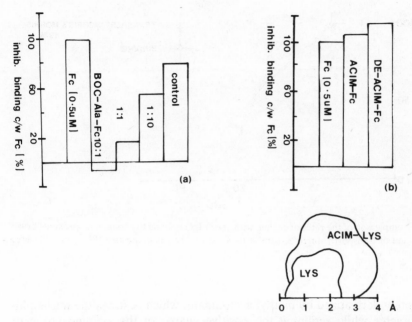

FIG. 6. Comparison of the inhibition of [^{125}I]Fc binding to neonatal rat brush border membranes by Fc and various amino-substituted derivatives. (*a*) *t*-butyloxycarbonylalanine (BOC-Ala) was coupled to Fc at the molar excess over Fc amino groups indicated. Amino acid analysis showed no substitution at 1:10, 10% substitution (4–5 amino groups) at 1:1, and 100% substitution (38 amino groups) at 10:1. The control is non-derivatized Fc recovered from the reaction solvents. (*b*) Fully acetimidylated Fc (ACIM-Fc) was prepared by reaction of Fc with methyl acetimidate. Fc is regenerated by deprotection at pH 11.3 (DE-ACIM Fc). *Inset*: Relative sizes of the substituents on the ε carbon atoms of the normal and acetimidylated lysine side chains (from Wofsy & Singer 1963).

conclusion that the receptor recognizes the Fc fragment of IgG. Recent results from the laboratory of Schlamowitz (Johanson et al 1981) suggest that in the rabbit yolk-sac the binding site is located in the C_H2 region of Fc. This conclusion is based on the inhibitory strength of various rabbit IgG fragments to bind to the rabbit yolk-sac membrane: whereas neither the F(ab)$'_2$ nor the isolated C_H3 domain can inhibit IgG binding, the Facb fragment of rabbit IgG (which contains only the C_H2 domain of Fc) is an efficient inhibitor.

We have chemically modified human Fc in various ways and have preliminary evidence that the Fc–receptor interaction involves a positively charged surface provided by one or more of the groups of arginine and lysine side-chains distributed around the Fc molecule. Fig. 6 shows that when Fc is

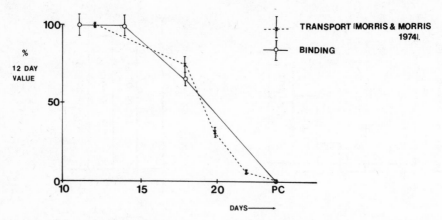

FIG. 7. Comparison of the rates of decline with age of IgG binding to neonatal rat proximal brush borders and of transport (Morris & Morris 1974) across the small intestine. PC = post closure.

completely derivatized by methyl acetimidate, which destroys the nucleophilic character while retaining the positive charge of the ε-amino group of lysine, no loss of binding capacity is seen. However, when a substituent that destroys this charge is used (*t*-butyloxycarbonyl alanine) the capacity of Fc to bind to its receptor is lost when less than five lysine amino groups have been masked. Further experiments are in progress to define the receptor binding site in more detail.

Ontogeny of the transport process

In 1974 Morris & Morris demonstrated a time-dependent change in the rate of transport of IgG across the neonatal rat small intestine. They used [^{125}I]IgG as a marker, and the appearance of labelled IgG in the circulation as an index of transport. Their results showed that the maximum rate of transport was achieved at about 10–12 days and thereafter it fell sharply until at 20–25 days transport was more or less abolished. We have measured the Fc receptor concentrations over the same time period and found that receptor levels changed *pari passu* with transport (see Fig. 7). Furthermore, when cortisol acetate is administered to 10-day-old rats, by 12 days their receptor numbers have fallen in parallel with a decrease in the rate of transport, supporting the view that receptors for and transport of IgG decline together during maturation of the neonatal rat (R. S. Moore and A. R. Rees, unpublished observations).

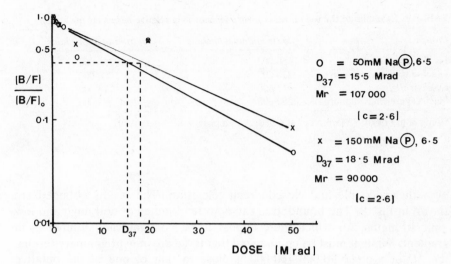

FIG. 8. Dependence on radiation dose of the loss of Fc-binding to neonatal rat proximal brush borders. Activity was measured by equilibrium binding of [^{125}I]Fc and is expressed as the ratio of bound (B) to free (F) ligand for various radiation doses as a function of the ratio at zero dose [(B/F)$_0$]. M_r = relative molecular mass. C = temperature correction factor (see text).

Molecular studies of the Fc receptor

(i) Target size analysis of the Fc receptor

Dose-dependence of inactivation of proteins by ionizing radiation may be used to estimate relative molecular mass. M_r is related to the dose (D_{37}) at which 37% of the initial activity remains by:

$$M_r = \frac{6.4 \times 10^{11}}{D_{37}}$$

(see Kepner & Macey 1963). While this empirical equation was obtained for irradiation at 30 °C, the target volume at −100 °C is apparently smaller by a factor of about 2.6 (Kempner & Schlegel 1979).

This method has been used to determine the M_r of a number of membrane proteins (see Table 2), and we have used it to investigate the functional size of the Fc receptor in the neonatal rat intestine. We irradiated brush border membranes at −100 °C, using the 4 Mev van der Graaf accelerator at the Gray Laboratories (Mount Vernon Hospital, Middlesex, UK). We used a liquid nitrogen spray to maintain the low temperature, which was monitored

TABLE 2. Examples of the use of target theory for assessing relative molecular mass (M_r)

Protein	M_r from target analysis	M_r from other methods
Insulin receptor[a]	350 000, 90 000	300 000–350 000
Glucose transport protein[b]	220 000	200 000
Lysozyme[c]	15 000	14 600
Mg^{24}ATPase (mitochondrial)[c]	280 000	284 000

[a] Jung et al (1980); [b] Harmon et al (1980); [c] Kempner & Schlegel (1979).

by a thermocouple and closed-circuit television. The results obtained are shown in Fig. 8. The bound:free ratios were obtained at both high and low ionic strengths, for which there appear to be no significant differences in gradient. While it must be emphasized that these are only preliminary results, the M_r of around 90 000–100 000 is close to that of one of the putative Fc–receptor glycoproteins extracted by Niezgódka et al (1981) from human placenta (see below). We are currently repeating these experiments, using both neonatal rat brush borders and human placental microvillar membranes. By using the wide variety of enzyme and hormone receptor markers in these membranes we expect to obtain further information about the Fc receptor structures in these transporting tissues.

(ii) Solubilization studies on Fc receptor

Receptor–ligand complexes have been extracted from Fc-saturated brush borders using sodium deoxycholate (Wallace 1980). This material chromatographed with an M_r in excess of 1×10^6, suggesting extensive aggregation. Similarly, Cobbs et al (1980) obtained a receptor–IgG complex, by Nonidet P40 extraction from fetal rabbit yolk-sac membranes, with an $M_r > 1.5 \times 10^6$.

Uncomplexed Fc receptor from human placenta has been partially purified by Niezgódka et al (1981), and glycoprotein solubilization by lithium 3,5-diiodosalicylate (LIS) gave an extract which inhibited the binding of [^{125}I]IgG to placental membranes. Polyacrylamide gel electrophoresis with sodium dodecyl sulphate revealed at least five components, the two major species having M_r values of 74 000 and 104 000.

We have made the preliminary observation of an inhibition of [^{125}I]Fc binding to brush borders by an LIS extract from neonatal rat intestine. Work is in progress to characterize this material and to achieve further purification by using affinity techniques.

Conclusions and prospects

Since F. W. R. Brambell's observations of IgG transport, the central role of the Fc receptor has become the major subject of enquiry. Systematic biochemical studies have described a receptor that is present in the rat proximal intestine for the first three weeks of life. Data on target inhibition suggest an M_r of about 100 000. The observed pH dependence of the IgG–receptor interaction supports the view that unidirectional transport results from the pH difference between the serosal fluid and the intestinal lumen in the neonate.

While the route of transcellular transport of IgG continues to emerge from R. Rodewald's electron micrographs, we still know little of the underlying molecular events. Further progress will depend on the availability of the receptor in a pure form for structural analysis and on the production of specific antibody markers. This objective is close to being realized, although to describe the process of Fc–receptor interaction and the subsequent internalization events at the molecular level, there will probably have to be a collaboration between workers involved with the biochemistry of the receptor, the membrane morphology and the cytoskeleton. We very much hope that this will happen.

Acknowledgements

We thank the MRC for a grant, Richard Maugham of the Gray Laboratory, (Middlesex, UK) for doing the radiation exposures, and Richard Rodewald for helpful discussions.

REFERENCES

Augener W, Grey HM 1970 Studies on the mechanism of heat aggregation of human IgG. J Immunol 105:1024-1030

Brambell FWR 1970 The transmission of passive immunity from mother to young. Front Biol 18

Cobbs CS, Shaw AR, Hillman K, Schlamowitz M 1980 Assay and partial characterisation of detergent-solubilised rabbit yolk-sac membrane Fc receptors. J Immunol 124:1648-1655

De Meyts P 1976 Cooperative properties of hormone receptors in cell membranes. J Supramol Struct 4:241-258

Harmon JT, Kahn CR, Kempner ES, Schlegel W 1980 Characterisation of the insulin receptor in its membrane environment by radiation inactivation. J Biol Chem 255:3412-3419

Johanson RA, Shaw AR, Schlamowitz M 1981 Evidence that the C_H2 domain of IgG contains the recognition unit for binding by the fetal rabbit yolk sac membrane receptor. J Immunol 126:194-199

Jones EA, Waldmann TA 1972 The mechanism of intestinal uptake and transcellular transport of IgG in the neonatal rat. J Clin Invest 51:2916-2927

Jung CY, Hsu TL, Jong SH, Cha C, Haas MN 1980 Glucose transport carrier of human erythrocytes. J Biol Chem 255:361-364

Kempner ES, Schlegel W 1979 Size determination of enzymes by radiation inactivation. Anal Biochem 92:2-10

Kepner GR, Macey RI 1968 Membrane enzyme systems: molecular size determination by radiation inactivation. Biochim Biophys Acta 163:188-203

Morris B, Morris R 1974 The absorption of ^{125}I-labelled immunoglobulin G by different regions of the gut in young rats. J Physiol (Lond) 240:761-770

Niezgódka M, Mikulska J, Ugorski M, Boratyński J, Lisowski J 1981 Human placental membrane receptor for IgG-I. Studies on properties and solubilisation of the receptor. Mol Immunol 18:163-172

Pearse BMF 1982 Coated vesicles from human placenta carry ferritin, transferrin and immunoglobulin G. Proc Natl Acad Sci USA 79:451-455

Rees AR, Wallace KH 1980 Coated vesicles and receptor biology. In: Ockleford CJ, Whyte A (eds) Coated vesicles. Cambridge University Press, London, p 219-242

Rodewald R 1970 Selective antibody transport in the proximal small intestine of the neonatal rat. J Cell Biol 45:635-640

Rodewald R 1976 Intestinal transport of peroxidase-conjugated IgG fragments in the neonatal rat. In: Hemmings WA (ed) Maternofoetal transmission of antibodies. Cambridge University Press, London, p 137-154

Rodewald R 1981 Evidence for the sorting of endocytic vesicle contents during the receptor-mediated transport of IgG across the newborn rat intestine. J Cell Biol 91:270-280

Wallace KH 1980 Studies on an immunoglobulin receptor. D Phil thesis, University of Oxford

Wallace KH, Rees AR 1980 Studies on the immunoglobulin-G Fc-fragment receptor from neonatal rat small intestine. Biochem J 188:9-16

Wild AE 1975 Role of the cell surface in selection during transport of proteins from mother to foetus and newly born. Philos Trans R Soc Lond B Biol Sci 271:395-407

Wild AE 1976 Mechanism of protein transport across the rabbit yolk-sac endoderm. In: Hemmings WA (ed) Maternofoetal transmission of immunoglobulins. Cambridge University Press, London, p 155-165

Wofsy L, Singer SJ 1963 Effects of the amidination reaction on antibody activity and on the physical properties of some proteins. Biochemistry 2:104-116

Immunoglobulin G receptors of intestinal brush borders from neonatal rats

RICHARD RODEWALD, DOROTHY MADDEN LEWIS and JEAN-PIERRE KRAEHENBUHL*

*Department of Biology, University of Virginia, Charlottesville, Virginia, USA and *Institute of Biochemistry, University of Lausanne, Epalinges, Switzerland*

Abstract Intestinal absorptive cells of the neonatal rat display on their brush border membranes receptors for immunoglobulin G (IgG) which function in selective transfer of maternal IgG. Our Scatchard analysis of [^{125}I]IgG binding to isolated brush borders has corroborated the presence of two classes of specific binding sites ($K_A1 = 2.4 \times 10^7$ M^{-1} and $K_A2 = 3.7 \times 10^5$ M^{-1}) and the increase in overall binding with decreased buffer concentration, as shown by Wallace & Rees 1980. However, our Scatchard analysis of binding at different buffer concentrations indicates that the only significant effect of lowered buffer concentration is to increase the number of low-affinity sites. Neither the number nor the affinity of the high-affinity sites is affected. Furthermore, brush borders from rats at 21 days have only the low-affinity sites and at this age the selective transfer of IgG has ceased. Morphological experiments with tracers for both light and electron microscopy suggest that the high-affinity sites correspond to the specific IgG receptors on the apical membrane. The majority of the low-affinity sites are found within the terminal web and are likely not to be involved in selective transport of IgG.

1983 Brush border membranes. Pitman Books Ltd, London (Ciba Foundation symposium 95) p 287-296, and 297-299

Intestinal transfer of maternally derived immunoglobulin G (IgG) in the neonatal rat is a highly selective transport process mediated by receptors on the brush border membranes of absorptive epithelial cells in the duodenum and jejunum. Our extensive morphological experiments (for reviews see Rodewald 1980, Rodewald & Abrahamson 1982) have led us to propose a model for transport in which IgG enters the luminal surface of the cell by receptor-mediated endocytosis within coated vesicles. After transfer to a second class of coated vesicles, the IgG is released from the cell by exocytosis at the basolateral surface. The detection of receptors with similar binding properties on both apical and basolateral membranes (Wild & Richardson 1979, Rodewald 1980) has suggested that IgG is transferred across the cell as receptor–ligand complexes on vesicle membranes. Consistent with this

287

hypothesis is the observation that binding of IgG to its receptor is extremely pH-dependent (Jones & Waldmann 1972, Rodewald 1980), such that ligand binds with high affinity to receptors on the apical membrane exposed to the luminal pH of 6.0–6.5, but is released from receptors at the basolateral surface which is in contact with serosal fluid near pH 7.4 (Waldmann & Jones 1973, Rodewald 1980).

The central function of the receptor in IgG transport has led us and others to characterize the receptors biochemically and to define carefully their binding properties. The initial studies have been greatly aided by the relative ease of isolation of brush border fragments, which retain a high binding capacity, from neonatal epithelial cells. The first extensive examination of the binding properties of neonatal brush borders was reported by Wallace & Rees (1980), who used a simple radioassay to measure the binding of [125I]IgG (see also Simister & Rees, this volume). In addition to demonstrating that binding was pH-dependent and specific for the Fc region of the IgG molecule, they made two unexpected and interesting observations. First, binding was greatly enhanced at low buffer concentrations. Second, under equilibrium conditions that gave maximal binding, they resolved two separate classes of binding site. They proposed, on the basis of dissociation experiments, that these two classes represented different forms of the same receptor whose binding exhibited negative cooperativity. They speculated that binding of IgG could cause aggregation of receptors on the brush border membrane, possibly within endocytic pits, with a concomitant decrease in affinity for IgG. They proposed, however, that overall binding would be enhanced in the intact tissue if the receptors resided in an environment of locally low ionic strength within the intestinal lumen.

Influence of buffer concentration on brush border binding

These novel findings and their implications for receptor behaviour during transport across intact cells have led us to examine in detail some of the characteristics of IgG binding to neonatal brush borders. Brush borders that we isolate by methods described previously (Rodewald et al 1976) appear as large fragments of apical membrane, of relatively uniform size. Each brush border consists of the entire microvillar surface of a single cell, a band of lateral membrane from the region of the disrupted junctional complex, and a large portion of the cytoskeletal and other elements of the terminal web (Fig. 1). We have studied IgG binding to these brush borders using an [125I]IgG radioassay (as described in Table 1) similar to the one used by Wallace & Rees (1980). Preliminary studies indicated that equilibrium binding in this assay was reached by 2–3 h, but for most experiments brush borders were

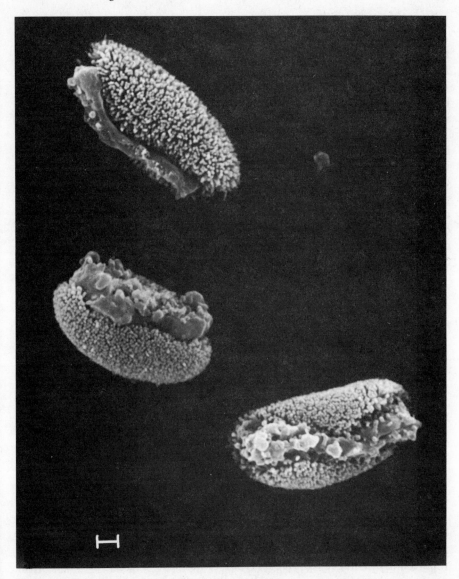

FIG. 1. Scanning electron micrograph of brush borders isolated from intestinal epithelial cells of the neonatal rat. The relatively smooth band of junctional membrane that borders the microvillar surface is evident in the uppermost two examples. Brush borders were fixed in buffered 2% glutaraldehyde, were critically point-dried, and were coated with gold. Bar indicates 1.0 μm.

incubated overnight. Binding was strongly pH-dependent: less than 4% of the radioactivity that bound specifically at pH 6.0 could be measured when the brush borders were incubated at pH 7.4 or 8.0. As reported by Wallace & Rees (1980), binding was also markedly influenced by buffer concentration. There was a sharp increase in specific binding below 0.1 M in phosphate buffer at pH 6.0. In 0.05 M buffer, the binding was over twice as great as that in 0.05 M buffer.

Since Wallace & Rees (1980) had shown that two classes of binding site could be detected in low ionic strength buffers, we investigated in detail the influence of buffer concentration on each of these two classes. Using brush borders from 12-day-old rats, we measured specific binding of [^{125}I]IgG in the presence of unlabelled ligand at concentrations up to 3.5 mg/ml in 0.05, 0.10 and 0.15 M phosphate buffer at pH 6.0. Data were then analysed with the aid of a Scatchard-fitting computer program (Munson & Rodbard 1980). The apparent affinities and the number of binding sites per brush border calculated from these experiments are summarized in Table 1. In 0.05 M

TABLE 1 Summary of [^{125}I]Immunoglobulin G binding to brush borders from the rat

Age (days)	Buffer (M)	K_A1 (M^{-1})	N1/BB	K_A2 (M^{-1})	N2/BB
12	0.05	$2.3(\pm 0.5) \times 10^7$	$3.4(\pm 0.9) \times 10^5$	$3.9(\pm 0.5) \times 10^5$	$1.6(\pm 0.1) \times 10^7$
12	0.10	$2.4(\pm 0.4) \times 10^7$	$3.2(\pm 0.6) \times 10^5$	$3.7(\pm 0.2) \times 10^5$	$3.4(\pm 1.8) \times 10^6$
12	0.15	$1.8(\pm 0.7) \times 10^7$	$3.3(\pm 1.9) \times 10^5$	$1.9(\pm 2.5) \times 10^6$	$5.5(\pm 2.1) \times 10^5$
21	0.05	n.d.	n.d.	$3.4(\pm 0.3) \times 10^5$	$1.6(\pm 0.1) \times 10^7$

Brush borders (1.5×10^6 per 0.3 ml assay volume), isolated from either 12- or 21-day-old rats, were incubated overnight at 4 °C with [^{125}I]IgG in the presence of 1% bovine serum albumin and 0–3.5 mg/ml of unlabelled IgG in pH 6.0 phosphate buffer at the molarities indicated. Washed brush borders were then centrifuged for 10 min at $1500 \times g$, and pellets were counted for radioactivity. Apparent affinities (K_A1, high; K_A2, low) and number (N) of binding sites, expressed as average per brush border (N/BB), were determined by computer analysis. Values are given ± standard error of the mean; n.d., not detectable.

buffer, both high- and low-affinity sites were evident, in the approximate ratio of 1 : 50. The affinities that we measured are somewhat lower than those reported by Wallace & Rees (1980), who used slightly different assay conditions, but otherwise our results at this buffer concentration are similar to theirs. When the concentration was raised to 0.10 and 0.15 M, the only significant detectable change in binding was a large decrease in the number of low-affinity sites. In 0.15 M phosphate these sites were barely detectable, and their number had fallen to less than 3% of those found at 0.05 M. In striking contrast, neither the affinity nor the number of the high-affinity sites changed significantly over this range of buffer concentrations.

These results indicate that the low- and high-affinity sites are unrelated to each other and do not represent a single population of receptors undergoing conversion between two different binding states. Furthermore, the weak affinity and extremely large number of low-affinity sites suggest that these sites are probably unrelated to the specific membrane receptors that bind IgG.

To test the functional significance of the low-affinity sites further, we also examined binding to brush borders from rats that were 21 days old, by which time selective transport of IgG has ceased and membrane receptors for IgG can no longer be detected on intact cells (Rodewald 1980). The results of a Scatchard analysis of binding in 0.05 M phosphate buffer at pH 6.0 (Table 1) demonstrate that the high-affinity sites are no longer present on brush borders at this age. In contrast, the low-affinity sites appear at the same density found in the brush borders from younger animals. These results provide strong evidence that only the high-affinity sites, whose numbers are not influenced by buffer concentration, represent the membrane receptors responsible for IgG transport (see also Simister & Rees, this volume).

Location of binding sites in brush borders

We next wished to determine the morphological distributions of the high- and low-affinity sites within the brush borders. In experiments for light microscopy we used, as specific ligand, rat IgG derivatized with biotinyl-N-hydroxysuccinimide (IgG–biotin) (Heitzmann & Richards 1974). Binding of this ligand was then detected by fluorescence microscopy of brush borders that were further treated with a lissamine conjugate of streptavidin, a fungal analogue of avidin, with which it shares an extremely high affinity for biotinylated proteins (Papermaster et al 1981). Fig. 2a,b illustrates IgG–biotin localization in brush borders incubated in 0.05 M phosphate buffer containing 1 mg/ml of IgG–biotin. Fluorescence was extremely strong and was apparent throughout the interior of the brush borders. Fluorescence was stronger within the terminal web than on or within the microvilli, and was most intense in a marginal band that probably corresponded to the area of the terminal web near the junctional complex. In 0.15 M phosphate (Fig. 2c,d) overall fluorescence was greatly reduced, and binding to the terminal web band was not usually seen. The remaining fluorescence had a slightly patchy, non-uniform appearance, although it was not possible to resolve any clear association with identifiable substructures. In control experiments, in which brush borders were incubated (1) with IgG–biotin in the presence of excess underivatized IgG at pH 6.0, (2) with IgG–biotin at pH 7.4 (see Fig. 2e,f) or pH 8.0, or (3) without IgG–biotin at pH 6.0, almost no fluorescence was seen at either high or low buffer concentration.

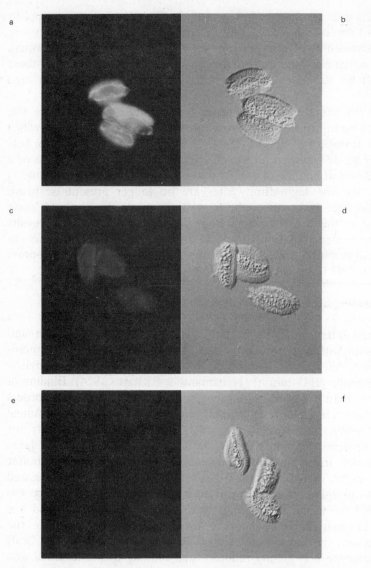

FIG. 2. Brush borders treated with IgG–biotin in phosphate buffer, at (a, b) 0.05 M, pH 6.0; (c, d) 0.15 M, pH 6.0; and (e, f) 0.05 M, pH 7.4 (controls). (a, c, e) Fluorescence light micrographs of brush borders stained with streptavidin–lissamine. In (a), a marginal band of relatively intense staining is apparent within the terminal web. (b, d, f) Nomarski light micrographs of the identical field shown in (a, c, e) respectively. Brush borders were incubated overnight at 4 °C with 1 mg/ml IgG–biotin in buffer that contained 1% bovine serum albumin (BSA). After washing in buffer with BSA alone, brush borders were treated sequentially with buffered solutions of 1% formaldehyde, 50 mM-NH$_4$Cl, and 0.1 mg/ml streptavidin–lissamine with 1% BSA before final washing. (× 1500)

These results provide evidence primarily for the distribution of the high-density, low-affinity sites whose binding is altered by buffer concentration, and they suggest that a majority of these sites reside within the terminal web. The limits in resolution and sensitivity of these experiments, however, did not allow us to identify unequivocally the location of the high-affinity sites.

To resolve the locations of both classes of site more precisely, we have also analysed by electron microscopy the binding to brush borders of a ferritin conjugate of rat IgG (IgG–Ft). For these experiments, brush borders were incubated for 2 h with IgG–Ft (Rodewald 1973) at 1 mg/ml (approximately 0.1 mg/ml with respect to IgG) in 0.05 or 0.15 M phosphate buffer at pH 6.0. After washing, brush borders were fixed and embedded by conventional means for electron microscopy. To control for non-specific binding due to the presence of the ferritin tracer, additional samples of brush borders were treated with unconjugated ferritin (1 mg/ml) at both high and low buffer concentrations. Photographic prints of randomly selected brush borders from each sample were then prepared, and the ferritin particles on the apical membrane and within the terminal web were counted. Mean counts from IgG–Ft experiments were corrected for non-specific ferritin binding and were expressed as particles bound per square micrometer of apical membrane area or per cubic micrometer of terminal web volume.

Fig. 3a,b illustrates the basic features of IgG–Ft binding. At both phosphate concentrations, particles were distributed over the entire microvillar membrane surface, either singly or in small clusters. Within the terminal web, the majority of the IgG–Ft was interspersed throughout the extensive filament network but was also occasionally associated with small membrane vesicles. The densities of binding varied widely from brush border to brush border. However, as apparent from the particle counts summarized in Table 2, binding within the terminal web was, on average, significantly greater ($P < 0.001$) at the lower buffer concentration (Fig. 3a). On the other hand, no significant difference ($P > 0.5$) was found between particle densities on the apical membrane at the two buffer concentrations.

TABLE 2. Ferritin–immunogobulin G binding to brush borders of the rat

Buffer (M)	Particles on luminal membrane (per μm²)	Particles in terminal web (per μm³)
0.05	65(± 15)	460(± 70)
0.15	53(± 10)	160(± 20)
	$P > 0.5$[a]	$P < 0.001$[a]

Measurements are expressed as mean counts ± standard error of the mean for 24 samples for each experiment. [a]Two-tailed t-tests.

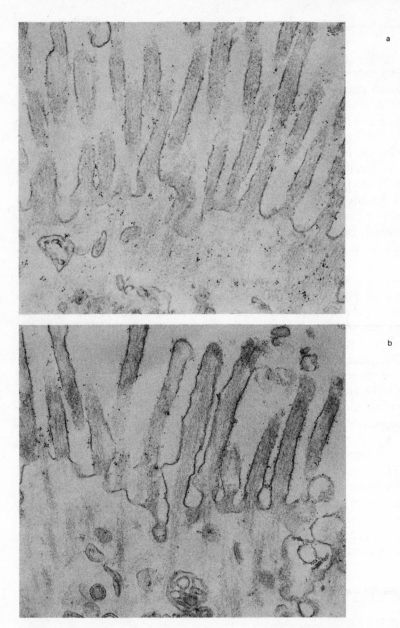

FIG. 3. Electron micrograph of apical regions of brush borders treated with IgG–Ft in (a) 0.05 M and (b) 0.15 M phosphate buffer, pH 6.0. Ferritin particles can be identified on the apical plasma membrane and within the terminal web. Brush borders were incubated for 2 h at 4 °C with 1 mg/ml IgG–Ft in buffer that contained 1% BSA. Cells were then washed in buffer with BSA alone and were fixed in 2% glutaraldehyde. Samples were further post-fixed in osmium tetroxide and were embedded in epoxy resin by conventional methods for thin sectioning. The section was stained for 1 min in lead citrate. (× 40 000)

In summary, these findings support our interpretation that the low-affinity sites reside within the terminal web and are not present on the brush border membrane. Furthermore, the binding sites that are detectable on the apical surface, and therefore likely to be specific transport receptors, correspond to high-affinity sites which are not influenced by buffer concentration.

It is interesting to speculate about which component of the terminal web might exhibit a weak, though specific, capacity to bind IgG. The very large number of low-affinity sites detected at low buffer concentration suggests that the sites may reside on a major component of the extensive microfilament network of the terminal web. This would agree with our morphological results which showed binding of IgG tracers within the terminal web areas that were rich in filaments. That actin may be responsible for this binding is supported by the work of Fechheimer et al (1979) who have provided compelling evidence for a direct, weak interaction between actin and IgG *in vitro*. Most interestingly, their results indicate that this is a specific, Fc-mediated interaction, which is enhanced by acid pH and low ionic strength. These characteristics are strikingly similar to those of the low-affinity sites that we detect in brush borders. The functional significance, if any, of an IgG interaction with actin is unclear. However, we do not believe that it would play any direct role in selective transport of IgG across intact intestinal cells.

REFERENCES

Fechheimer M, Daiss JL, Cebra JJ 1979 Interaction of immunoglobulin with actin. Mol Immunol 16:881-888

Heitzmann H, Richards FM 1974 Use of avidin–biotin complex for specific staining of biological membranes in electron microscopy. Proc Natl Acad Sci USA 71:3537-3541

Jones EA, Waldmann TA 1972 The mechanism of intestinal uptake and transcellular transport of IgG in the neonatal rat. J Clin Invest 51:2916-2927

Munson PJ, Rodbard D 1980 Ligand: a versatile computerized approach for characterization of ligand-binding systems. Anal Biochem 107:220-239

Papermaster DS, Lyman D, Schneider BG, Labienic L, Kraehenbuhl J-P 1981 Immunocytochemical localization of the catalytic subunit of (Na^+, K^+)ATPase in *Bufo marinus* kidney, bladder and retina with biotinyl–antibody and streptavidin–gold complexes. J Cell Biol 91:273a (abstr)

Rodewald R 1973 Intestinal transport of antibodies in the newborn rat. J Cell Biol 58:189-211

Rodewald R 1980 Distribution of immunoglobulin G receptors in the small intestine of the neonatal rat. J Cell Biol 85:18-32

Rodewald R, Abrahamson DR 1982 Receptor-mediated transport of immunoglobulin G across the intestinal epithelium of the neonatal rat. In: Membrane recycling. Pitman Books Ltd, London (Ciba Found Symp 92) p 209-232

Rodewald R, Newman SB, Karnovsky MJ 1976 Contraction of isolated brush borders from the intestinal epithelium. J Cell Biol 70:541-554

Waldmann TA, Jones EA 1973 The role of cell-surface receptors in the transport and catabolism of immunoglobulins. In: Protein turnover. Elsevier/North-Holland, Amsterdam (Ciba Found Symp 9) p 5-23

Wallace KH, Rees AR 1980 Studies on the immunoglobulin-G Fc-fragment receptor from neonatal rat small intestine. Biochem J 188:9-16

Wild AE, Richardson LJ 1979 Direct evidence for pH-dependent Fc receptors on proximal enterocytes of suckling rat gut. Experientia 35:838-848

Discussion after the preceding two papers

Quaroni: Does the glycocalyx influence how the immunoglobulin reaches the brush border membrane?

Rodewald: I don't know. The glycocalyx in the neonatal rat is sparse compared with that in other species. In addition, not as much mucus is secreted in the neonate as in the adult.

Rees: We found a lot of non-specific binding to brush borders that still had glycocalyx. We prepare our brush borders by treatment with hyaluronidase and also see non-specific binding with DNA contamination. If we treat them with DNase as well, that reduces non-specific binding.

Boyd: Is this a rather fancy co-transport system? You have talked about the importance of pH for immunoglobulin binding and there is evidence for a Na^+/H^+ exchange in this tissue. Has anyone looked at the effects on immunoglobulin transport of agents that might block this, such as amiloride? Secondly, is the pH in the luminal bulk phase the same as that in the glycocalyx, in view of the results by Blair et al (1975) on adult small intestine, where the microclimate has a substantially different pH from that in the bulk phase?

Rodewald: The influences of these inhibitors or drugs on IgG transport have not been studied, to my knowledge. I don't know what sorts of microenvironments there may be. Wallace & Rees (1980) suggested that there could be a microenvironment with a low ionic strength that would enhance binding (see Simister & Rees, this volume). One interesting thing is that the lumen of the intestine in the neonate is highly buffered by the cells. I once tried to do transport experiments with tracers in buffers of different pHs. When a pH of 7.4 was used, the intact tissue could quickly reduce this pH to 6.0–6.5 in a matter of minutes.

Smith: I am interested in the horseradish peroxidase (HRP) labelling of the Fc receptor, because there appeared to be heavier labelling towards the villus tip. Is this done in conditions where you measure only the high-affinity site?

Rodewald: Yes, and I presume these sites are freely accessible at the luminal surface.

Smith: This seems to be another example of a receptor that first appears in enterocytes that are old. You commented that the receptor seemed to be part of the structural apparatus of the microvillar membrane and yet the membrane is probably assembled long before the increase in receptor population takes place.

Rodewald: It is really a question of *when* the receptor is expressed on the membrane. Our work suggests that this occurs towards the second half of a cell's migration up the villus.

Louvard: Did you try to inhibit the transcellular pathway by using lysosomotropic agents such as ammonium chloride or chloroquine?

Rodewald: I am doing these experiments at present. The rationale is that the ligand must remain bound to the receptor during transfer through the cell. Transport within the cell might be blockable by increasing the pH in some of the compartments through which the ligand may pass. I have evidence that one of these compartments may be related to a lysosome. If this is so, it is possible that use of a lysosomotropic agent might increase the pH sufficiently within this compartment to cause the IgG to dissociate from its receptor and thus block the transfer of IgG across the cell.

Alpers: What is the timing of the sequences from binding to terminal web vesicle, to sorting, and to basolateral membrane?

Rodewald: Uptake is relatively slow compared to some of the other receptor-mediated endocytic systems that have been described. It takes 10–15 min to label with tracers most of the endocytic vesicles within the terminal web, and 30–60 min to observe release of tracer at the basolateral surface. However, since the tracers I use are conjugates of IgG with HRP or ferritin, free IgG may be transported much more quickly.

Hauri: Dr Rees said it takes two months to book the van der Graaf machine. In that time one could iodinate membrane vesicles to high specific radioactivity and, by affinity chromatography, isolate the receptor. What's wrong with this approach?

Rees: Dr Rodewald and I have each tried it! We have been looking for detergents that retain the binding activity in solution. Deoxycholate appears to destroy it. Triton is poor at extracting the receptor but, having got it out, one cannot measure soluble binding complexes. However, we have bound ^{125}I-labelled Fc to membranes and then extracted the complex and looked at that. When we take it out with deoxycholate and then reduce the concentration below the critical micelle concentration it aggregates ($M_r > 1\,000\,000$), so we abandoned that. We have since extracted with lithium diiodosalicylate, which retains activity in solution (N. Simister & A.R. Rees, unpublished results). We are currently trying to affinity-purify that.

Jørgensen: Lithium diiodosalicylate is particularly active with glycoproteins.

Schmitz: Do you have any information about this receptor other than its M_r?

Rodewald: I am currently using the approach suggested by Dr Hauri. We are using an IgG affinity resin and are taking advantage of the pH-dependency of binding, which I described, to elute the receptor. Our very preliminary analysis, by SDS-PAGE, of iodinated eluates suggests that the receptor has an M_r in the range 55 000–60 000.

REFERENCES

Blair JA, Lucas ML, Matty AJ 1975 Acidification in the rat proximal jejunum. J Physiol (Lond) 245: 333-350

Wallace KH, Rees AR 1980 Studies on the immunoglobulin-G Fc-fragment receptor from neonatal rat small intestine. Biochem J 188: 9-16

Cotransport systems in the brush border membrane of the human placenta

C. A. R. BOYD

Department of Human Anatomy, South Parks Road, Oxford, OX1 3QU, UK

Abstract The cotransport systems present in the brush border membrane of the human placental syncytiotrophoblast are reviewed. Attention is focused on the systems that are powered by the electrochemical gradient of Na^+ (for example, for neutral amino acids but not for glucose), and on recently described systems in which K^+ flux is coupled to Cl^- flux or to that for Na^+ and Cl^-. These systems are similar to those found in other tissues and may be significant for net trans-placental transport and its control, as well as for the regulation of placental trophoblast volume.

1983 Brush border membranes. Pitman Books Ltd, London (Ciba Foundation symposium 95) p 300-314

The unit of function of the human placenta is the chorionic villus, a structure that has the unusual distinction of being covered by trophoblast, which is the only tissue forming a true syncytium in the human body. The plasma membrane of the maternal surface of the syncytiotrophoblast is highly folded, forming a 'lawn' of microvilli which project into the maternal blood circulating through the intervillous space. The structure of this brush border is reviewed by Booth & Vanderpuye, in this volume. The other ('fetal-facing') plasma membrane of the trophoblast faces the connective tissue and interstitial fluid in the core of the villus, through which fetal blood circulates in capillaries. The syncytiotrophoblast is thus an epithelium that separates two body-fluid compartments, maternal plasma and fetal interstitial fluid: its position defines its importance as the structure primarily responsible for the multifarious roles carried out by the placenta—as the organ of fetal respiration, nutrition and excretion; as an important endocrine gland; and as a tissue with unusual metabolic and immunological properties. In this review I shall consider aspects of the placenta which relate only to its role as an organ of transport, and I shall focus on coupled solute movements at the maternal-facing brush border membrane. I shall deal with the methods by which such membrane transport may be studied, the results so far achieved and the possible significance of such systems for the control of placental function.

Although the brush border of the syncytiotrophoblast in the human chorionic villus is similar in many ways to brush borders that are better characterized in other epithelia (particularly in the small intestine and renal proximal tubule) it is worth remembering that there are some striking differences in function between these brush borders. The one in the placenta does not face the lumen of a viscus but, rather, its microvilli are in direct contact with maternal plasma: this means that receptors for endocrine (and paracrine) signals may be present in this membrane (see below); this would be unlikely to occur in, for example, the brush border of the kidney, bathed as it is by tubular fluid rather than plasma. In addition, the absence of a paracellular route across the epithelium means that the overall epithelial properties of the trophoblast will depend on the sum of the properties of the two separate plasma membranes, and there will be no electrical 'cross-talk' between the brush border and the basal membrane like that found in 'leaky' epithelia. Finally, endocytosis and membrane flow may be more important in the trophoblast brush border than in more 'orthodox' epithelia; by contrast, the surface digestive properties of the microvillous plasma membrane of the trophoblast are likely to be less important.

Results and discussion

Na+-coupled cotransport systems: studies using plasma membrane vesicles

Background. Recently both Smith (1981) and Bissonnette (1982) have reviewed work on membrane vesicles in placental brush border. These vesicles are easily prepared and have been valuable in elucidating the mechanisms involved in membrane transport across the brush border. Transport assays that use isolated membranes depend on the ability of the membrane effectively to separate two aqueous solutions. During isolation the continuity of the plasma membrane is necessarily disrupted and therefore such continuity must be re-established *in vitro*. This happens when membranes are converted to small vesicles where the membrane forms a permeability barrier between the intravesicular and the extravesicular solution (Hopfer 1978). For such membrane vesicles to be used in investigating epithelial transport, plasma membranes from the 'cis' and the 'trans' sides of the epithelium must be separated. Analysis of marker enzymes is required to monitor procedures that are used to achieve such a separation. After the isolation of the plasma membrane fraction, transport of solutes into the vesicles may be studied by using rapid filtration to separate the vesicles from the external medium: the flux of substrate can then be determined by measuring the amount of solute retained inside the vesicles. Such studies on membrane vesicles from the placental brush border have demonstrated, for both sugars and amino acids, that the measured uptake varies inversely with the osmolarity of the external medium, when the latter is adjusted by addition of an impermeant solute. Furthermore, extrapolation of these data to infinite osmolarity of the medium indicates zero uptake. These experiments have led to the conclusion that sugars and amino acids are not bound to the membrane vesicles and that transport into an internal volume is being measured.

Facilitated diffusion of glucose. The rate of D-glucose uptake into microvillous plasma membrane vesicles from human placental trophoblast is very much greater than that found for L-glucose. Furthermore, the rate of D-glucose uptake is an alinear function of the external glucose concentration, the process becoming saturated at high external concentrations of glucose. However, in contrast to the glucose transport system found in the brush border membrane of small intestine and renal tubule, glucose transport in the placenta is not coupled to sodium. This conclusion is matched by the finding that the pattern of inhibition of D-glucose transport (phloretin is a more effective inhibitor than phlorizin; cytochalasin B is a very effective competitive inhibitor of glucose transport at micromolar concentrations) is very similar to that seen in the erythrocyte membrane. The specificity of the D-glucose transporter also fits with this conclusion. D-glucose entry into the vesicles is not inhibited by α-methyl-D-glucoside while 2-deoxy-D-glucose and 3-O-methyl-D-glucose decrease the uptake of D glucose. Hexose transport by the D-glucose transporter is therefore very specific with respect to substitutions in the monosaccharide molecule, requiring the normal glucose configuration at carbon 1 but being able to tolerate substitutions at carbons 2 and 3. Both the response to specific inhibitors and the specificity of the carrier strongly suggest that glucose transport across the maternal brush border membrane of the trophoblast resembles the facilitated diffusion system found in, for example, the plasma membrane of the adipocyte, and that this glucose transport is different to the Na^+-coupled secondary active transport system found in the brush border membrane of the renal and intestinal tract.

Sodium-coupled amino acid transport. Boyd & Lund (1981) have shown that when a sodium gradient (outside concentration higher than inside) is present at the beginning of L-proline uptake, the amino acid reaches a concentration inside the vesicles which is 2–3 fold greater than that present at equilibrium. This transient accumulation of amino acid (or 'overshoot') indicates that the substrate may be moved against its concentration gradient for as long as the inwardly directed sodium gradient is maintained. In the intact trophoblast the inwardly directed sodium gradient is maintained by the sodium pump present in the basal plasma membrane: the vesicles, however, rapidly fill up with sodium and thus the observed accumulation of amino acid within the vesicles is only transient. Further studies have shown that this cotransport of neutral amino acid and sodium is electrogenic. For example, if a potassium gradient is set up (inside concentration higher than outside), with sodium in equal concentrations on both sides of the vesicles, then in the presence of valinomycin (an ionophore which increases membrane K^+ permeability) L-proline accumulates transiently within the vesicles. Thus, enhanced K^+ conductance leads to an electrical potential difference (inside negative) which drives the sodium influx, no L-proline overshoot being seen in the absence of valinomycin. This indicates that during proline transport, in the presence of sodium, a net positive charge is transferred in the same direction as the amino acid. The influence of an inside-negative membrane potential is also seen in studies where the anion is varied. L-Proline accumulation is seen very early with sodium thiocyanate but is not present with sodium sulphate; thiocyanate is very permeable across membranes while sulphate is not.

Such studies have shown that active transport of amino acids is specific for sodium and is not seen with other cations. The studies with amino acid transport point out a number of advantages of the membrane vesicle preparation; the experimental conditions can be arranged so that at the start of the experiment the precise ionic composition of solutions on each side of the membrane is known. Moreover, by the use of ionophores, the permeability of the membrane to various ions can be manipulated in order to test various models of membrane transport.

K^+-coupled cotransport systems in the human placental brush border membrane

Response to hypertonicity: evidence for a Na^+, K^+ and Cl^- contransport. Flux coupling between ions seems to occur also in the human placental brush border membrane. Experiments with membrane vesicles have shown that there is a coupled Na^+/Cl^- cotransport system, which is frusemide-sensitive and apparently dependent on the presence of K^+ in the external medium (Boyd et al 1980). Moreover, recent *in vitro* experiments using a new preparation (the intact, isolated placental chorionic villus; Boyd 1982) have allowed us to examine this process in the intact epithelium.

Fig. 1 shows the results of an experiment in which K^+ efflux from an isolated villus has been studied. [86]Rb was used as a substitute for K^+ because of its more convenient half-life. The tissue initially was loaded, after dissection from a full-term normal placenta immediately following delivery,

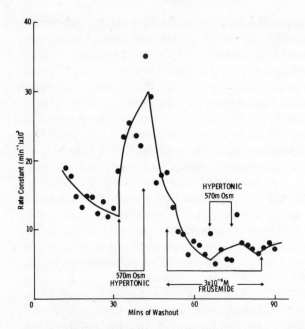

FIG. 1. Influence of hypertonicity on K⁺ permeability in the brush border membrane of an isolated chorionic villus from a human full-term placenta. The villus was loaded with isotope for 1 h before the start of the experiment and, during the subsequent washout (in isotope-free solution), the Krebs–Ringer solution was made hypertonic, where indicated, by the addition of sucrose. Note the dramatic rise in K⁺ permeability associated with this perturbation and the subsequent fall in K⁺ efflux on exposure to frusemide (3×10^{-5} M). In the presence of frusemide the effect of hypertonicity is inhibited.

by incubation for 1 h in an appropriately gassed Krebs–Ringer bicarbonate solution containing 5 mM glucose. The efflux of isotope was then studied and was expressed as a wash-out rate constant (that is, the fraction of the total K⁺ present that leaves the tissue across the brush border membrane per unit time). The rate constant slowly settled to a steady value (about 0.011 min⁻¹ in this instance). The tissue was then exposed to a Ringer solution made hypertonic by the addition of sucrose and having roughly double the osmolarity of the control solution. This produced an immediate and dramatic increase in isotopic efflux, which was reversed on return to an isotonic extracellular medium. A significant increase in K⁺ permeability was seen to follow very much smaller increases in osmolarity; indeed, a significant change was found on increasing the osmolarity by as little as 10 mOsm. The response of the tissue to hypertonicity was markedly reduced after exposure to frusemide (3×10^{-5} M). Frusemide (furosemide) is a diuretic drug that inhibits Cl⁻-coupled cotransport systems in a number of epithelia (see Ellory 1982). The addition of frusemide itself markedly inhibited the K^+ efflux rate constant, reducing it to about 50% of control values with a K_i of approximately 3×10^{-6} M.

Fig. 2 shows the result of an experiment using a similar technique, in which the effects were studied of chloride removal (SO_4^{2-} substitution, with mannitol being used to maintain isotonicity) on K^+ efflux. On removal of chloride from the external medium, there was a small, reversible decrease in permeability. The usual response to hypertonicity was not much altered by removal of chloride, and chloride removal did not abolish the inhibitory effect of frusemide upon K^+ efflux.

Removal of both Na^+ and Cl^- (by Tris substitution) did, however, alter both responses (Fig. 3). Thus, on removal of both ions K^+ efflux fell sharply; and the response of the tissue to hypertonicity was nearly completely abolished. Moreover, in the absence of both Na^+ and Cl^- from the external medium, frusemide no longer had any effect on the wash-out rate constant. These findings are consistent with the presence in the brush border membrane of a system regulating permeability to K^+ in response to increases in extracellular fluid osmolarity. It is important to note that in these experiments only unidirectional efflux of K^+ has been measured. Nevertheless it is quite clear that the responses are dependent on Na^+ and Cl^- and are inhibited by frusemide.

The most likely explanation is that the underlying membrane transport system behaves similarly to that seen in other (non-epithelial) cells (for example in the nucleated erythrocyte of the duck), which appears to be involved in a 'volume regulatory increase' in response to cellular shrinkage. Such systems (reviewed by Kregenow 1981, Palfrey & Greengard 1981) are frusemide-sensitive, appear to be activated by hypertonic solutions and involve a coupled $Na^+/K^+/Cl^-$ transport system in which there is additional net movement of Na^+, K^+ and Cl^- into the cell. The entry into the cell of this additional salt increases cell water content and hence cell volume. The system appears to require that the bathing medium must contain all three transported electrolytes. The cation fluxes in these systems are not those of a simple diffusion system; thus, for example, after exposure to hypertonicity at a low external K^+ concentration rapid bidirectional Na^+ and K^+ fluxes, resembling exchange diffusion, continue indefinitely; however, these fluxes appear to reflect bidirectional movements of NaCl and KCl, and they are probably most easily explained on the basis of interactions between the Na^+ and K^+ electrochemical gradients, and with the net movement through the system responding to the sum of these two potentials. Thus, Na^+ entering the cell can drag K^+ into the cell against its electrochemical gradient; similarly, K^+ leaving the cell can drag Na^+ out of the cell against its gradient. In nucleated

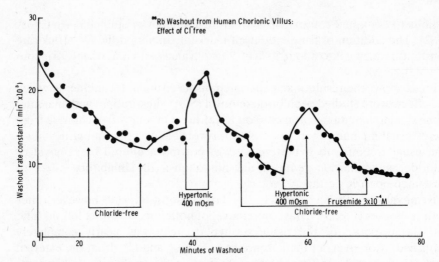

FIG. 2. Influence of chloride removal on the K$^+$ permeability of the brush border membrane of the human placental chorionic villus. Note the modest, reversible and repeatable fall in permeability on removal of external chloride (with sulphate substitution). Note also that the increase in K$^+$ efflux after exposure to hypertonic medium is not abolished in chloride-free medium and that frusemide still inhibits in the absence of external chloride.

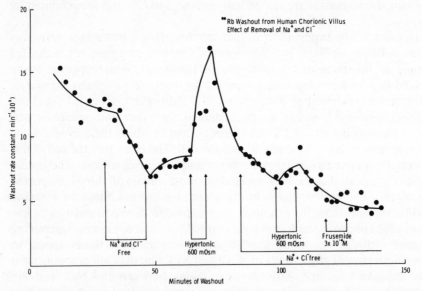

FIG. 3. Effect of removal of Na$^+$ and Cl$^-$ (by Tris sulphate substitution) on the K$^+$ permeability of the brush border membrane of the human chorionic villus. Note the large fall in K$^+$ efflux following removal of Na$^+$ and Cl$^-$ and that both the stimulatory effect of hypertonicity and the inhibitory effect of frusemide are much reduced in the absence of both Na$^+$ and Cl$^-$.

erythrocytes when external K+ concentration is reduced to 2.5 mM the sum of the electrochemical potential for Na+ and K+ is zero, and there is no net cation flux since there is no net force. Raising the external potassium concentration causes the sum of the electrochemical gradient for sodium and potassium to become negative, and provides a driving force for the uptake of cation, including the uphill movement of K+. However, it is not clear how this system is activated when the cell shrinks.

Response to hypotonicity: evidence for a KCl cotransport in human placenta. Fig. 4 shows the result of an experiment in which the effect was studied of

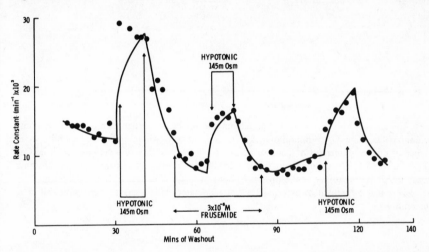

FIG. 4. Influence of hypotonicity on K+ permeability of the brush border membrane of the isolated human chorionic villus. Note that exposure to hypotonic medium (half-strength Krebs–Ringer bicarbonate solution) increases the K+ permeability. Frusemide (3 × 10^{-5} M) does not inhibit this effect.

exposure to hypotonicity on unidirectional K+ efflux from the trophoblast across the brush border membrane. Clearly, there is a large reversible increase in the efflux rate constant associated with this manoeuvre. This increase seems to be insensitive to inhibition by frusemide (in contrast to the response to hypertonicity). This system in the placenta appears similar to that seen during volume regulatory decrease in other cells, in which net KCl egress follows cell swelling (Kregenow 1981).

Other K+ channels in the brush border of human placenta.
   (1) Ca^{2+}–activated. In attempts to elucidate the overall pathways by which

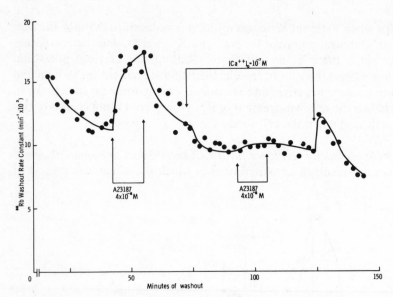

FIG. 5. Evidence for a Ca^{2+}-activated K^+ channel in the brush border membrane of the human chorionic villus. The Ca^{2+} ionophore A23187 was added, where indicated, initially in the presence of normal external Ca^{2+} and subsequently in the presence of a very low external Ca^{2+} (EGTA-buffered Ca^{2+} concentration of 10^{-7} M). Note that the ionophore causes a substantial increase in K^+ permeability in the presence, but not in the absence, of normal external Ca^{2+}. Note also that the removal of external Ca^{2+} is associated with a modest reversible fall in K^+ permeability.

K^+ may cross the brush border membrane it is of interest to know if there is a Ca^{2+}-gated K^+ channel (Gardos channel) in the trophoblast brush border. Fig. 5 produces evidence strongly suggesting that such a channel exists. It appears to be activated by an increase in the cytoplasmic Ca^{2+} concentration. Thus, in the presence of a normal external Ca^{2+} concentration, K^+ permeability is increased on addition of the calcium ionophore A23187. Such an increase is not seen when the external Ca^{2+} is reduced to 10^{-7} M. Note that in Fig. 5 there is a fall in K^+ efflux on reduction of external Ca^{2+} and a rise on its return. This K^+ channel in the placental brush border appears to be supplementary to, and separate from, that involved in the 'volume regulatory increase', since frusemide sensitivity is retained even in the presence of A23187.

(2) α-adrenergic-activated K^+ channels. The placenta is known, from biochemical studies, to have β-adrenoreceptors in its basal (fetal-facing) plasma membrane (Boyd et al 1979). Are there, in addition, α-receptors in the brush border membrane? Activation of such receptors might be expected

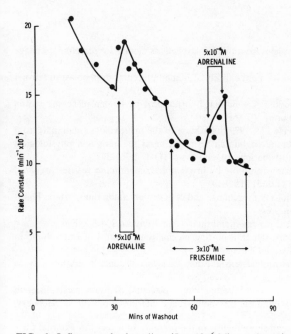

FIG. 6. Influence of adrenaline (5×10^{-6} M) on the K^+ permeability of the brush border membrane of the human chorionic villus. Note the modest increase in K^+ permeability on exposure to adrenaline, and that this stimulation is not lost in the presence of frusemide, suggesting that the diuretic-sensitive ion cotransport is not involved in the hormone-evoked change of ion permeability.

to increase cytoplasmic Ca^{2+} concentration and hence to activate the K^+ channels in the brush border membrane. Fig. 6 provides evidence that such receptors do exist in the membrane. A small but consistent increase in the rate constant for K^+ efflux is seen on exposure to adrenaline: this effect is inhibited by the α-blocker phenoxybenzamine. Like the Gardos effect, α-adrenergic stimulation of K^+ efflux from the trophoblast across the brush border membrane appears to be independent of the Na^+, K^+, Cl^- cotransport involved in the response to cell shrinkage since it also is retained in the presence of frusemide.

Acknowledgements

I would like to thank Miss Karen Webb for technical assistance with some of the experimental findings reported here.

REFERENCES

Bissonnette JM 1982 Membrane vesicles from trophoblast cells as models for placental exchange studies. Placenta 3:99-106

Boyd CAR 1982 The regulation of K^+ permeability of human placental trophoblast in vitro. J Physiol (Lond) 325:64P

Boyd CAR, Chipperfield AR, Lund EK 1980 NaCl cotransport by human placental plasma membrane vesicles. J Physiol (Lond) 307:86P

Boyd CAR, Chipperfield AR, Steele LW 1979 Separation of the microvillous (maternal) from the basal (fetal) plasma membrane of human term placenta: methods and physiological significance of marker enzyme distribution. J Dev Physiol (Oxf) 1:361-377

Boyd CAR, Lund EK 1981 L-proline transport by brush border membrane vesicles prepared from human placenta. J Physiol (Lond) 315:9-19

Ellory JC 1982 Introduction to various net, exchange and co-transport anion transporters. Philos Trans R Soc Lond B Biol Sci, in press

Hopfer U 1978 Transport in isolated plasma membranes. Am J Physiol 234:F89-F96

Kregenow FM 1981 Osmoregulatory salt transporting mechanisms: control of cell volume in anisotonic media. Annu Rev Physiol 43:493-505

Palfrey HC, Greengard P 1981 Hormone-sensitive ion transport systems in erythrocytes as models for epithelial ion pathways. Ann NY Acad Sci 372:291-307

Smith CH 1981 Incubation techniques and investigation of placental transport mechanisms in vitro. In: Young M et al (eds) Placental transfer methods and interpretations. W. B. Saunders, Philadelphia, p 163-178

DISCUSSION

Semenza: How large are these vesicles or, rather, how large is the osmotic space per mg protein? In both kidney and small intestinal vesicles this space is about 1 μl/mg protein.

Boyd: In our hands the values for the placenta are much the same. However, Ruzycki et al (1978) have also studied amino acid transport in placental vesicles and found much larger vesicles. The osmotic space in their experiments was about 4 μl/mg protein.

Semenza: The proline transport seems to be clearly electrogenic, from your experiments. Have you compared the efficiencies of transport of different anions, e.g. thiocyanate, nitrate, perchlorate, chloride, sulphate, isothiocyanate, and so on?

Boyd: We have studied thiocyanate, chloride and sulphate. With thiocyanate, proline transport goes so fast that it is difficult to detect the peak of the very rapid overshoot.

Semenza: We have looked at ascorbate transport in renal vesicles, which is electrogenic in the presence of minute amounts of azide, for reasons unknown. It is inhibited by thiocyanate, again by an unknown mechanism. This results in a totally distorted sequence of anion stimulation (Toggenburger et al 1982).

Boyd: I have met thiocyanate as a rather specific inhibitor in the context of placental iodide transport.

Semenza: We are now working with iodide transport in the intestine, and also find inhibition by thiocyanate. Are you studying the same in the placenta?

Boyd: No. R.D.H. Boyd et al (1981) are studying that.

Matsudaira: How tightly coupled is transport with the ionic composition of the fetal blood?

Boyd: The composition of the fetal extracellular fluid is normally kept constant. In basal membrane vesicles amino acid transport appears to be independent of the sodium gradient, since experiments on proline using a preparation of basal membranes produced no evidence of a transient overshoot (C.A.R. Boyd, unpublished work). One could explain polarity of amino acid transport across the whole epithelium if there were powered Na^+-dependent entry, and transport systems for exit that are not ion-coupled.

Rubino: Have you done kinetics on various substrate concentrations and do you have any evidence for the number of binding sites? In the intestine there are apparently two transport systems for proline.

Boyd: We find 'saturation kinetics' with a K_m of about 1 mM, but we cannot exclude there being more than one system.

Smith: How do you interpret the rapid overshoot that you found with thiocyanate?

Boyd: Thiocyanate is known to be very permeable across plasma membranes, so this suggests that our electrogenic system is perhaps driven by the thiocyanate diffusion potential.

Smith: Is the thiocyanate transport blocked by frusemide?

Boyd: I have not looked at that.

Smith: This happens in fish intestine (Katz et al 1982). Loop diuretics inhibit the transport not only of chloride but also of thiocyanate on the same transport system.

Boyd: There is evidence that frusemide may affect amino acid transport in erythrocytes (Chipperfield & Perring 1981) so that might be worth looking at in the placenta.

Mooseker: When you were describing oscillations in membrane potential, you mentioned possible oscillations in intracellular calcium concentration. Could you expand on that?

Boyd: Indirect evidence suggests oscillations in intracellular calcium. The measured membrane potential oscillates at 2–4 times/min. Ion channels open during hyperpolarization because the membrane resistance has fallen. It is probably a K^+ permeability channel that is opening. A Ca^{2+}-activated K^+ channel is suggested here, as in many other tissues. But the cytoplasmic measurement of free intracellular Ca^{2+} would be a very useful technique to provide direct evidence (see p 244).

Jørgensen: You have shown that the placental membrane has relatively few proteins as compared to the brush border membrane of the kidney or intestine in mammals, and it has no peptidases. It would therefore be a good subject for attempts at solubilizing and reconstituting the carrier transport proteins. Has this been attempted?

Boyd: Bissonnette et al (1981) have tried to solubilize the glucose transporter from the maternal surface of the human placenta. It is unlike the sodium-coupled system in intestine and kidney but similar to that of the erythrocyte. Thus, glucose transfer is via a facilitated diffusion system which is inhibited by phloretin. They have not isolated the transporter or tried to characterize it chemically, but that would be possible, and probably easier to do with the placenta than with erythrocytes. Nobody to my knowledge has attempted to do this for the sodium-coupled amino acid transport systems from the placenta.

Smith: I have a general comment about the syncytiotrophoblast. You are emphasizing that it does not have tight junctions. But in terms of protein synthesis, and the way that it grows, it is also an extremely interesting tissue, with binucleate cells migrating from the fetal side and fusing. This tissue presumably obtains its precursors for growth as a mixture of cellular constituents from the fetus and transported nutrients from the mother. This unusual situation may be useful when studying brush border synthesis.

Boyd: Recently Hoshina et al (1982) have localized the mRNAs for certain placental hormones in the trophoblast. They have tried to find out whether the messenger is exclusively in the syncytium throughout gestation or whether it is preformed in the cytotrophoblast and then subsequently inserted into the syncytiotrophoblast. The same techniques applied to membrane proteins would be extremely interesting.

Norén: How many different amino acid transport systems are present in the placenta?

Boyd: It is too early to say yet, as it probably is still for the intestine!

Schmitz: Have you looked for dipeptide transport?

Boyd: Yes; and there may be some, but we have not yet done enough work on this.

Inoue: Can we expect the same extent of metabolic change in the maternal kidney and in the placenta when the mother is treated with frusemide?

Boyd: It is extraordinary that frusemide is so widely used clinically and is so non-toxic, given that *in vitro* it has effects on ion transport in many different tissues. This must reflect its renal handling: secretion into the tubules ensures that high concentrations are found in the thick ascending limb of the loop of Henle.

Inoue: Do you know the K_i value of frusemide? Since frusemide is an organic anion, its transtubular secretion into urine might significantly increase the luminal level of frusemide as compared with its placental concentration. The *in vivo* effect of frusemide may be different in the two tissues.

Boyd: It hasn't, to my knowledge, been looked at.

Semenza: Na^+ and Cl^- transport were believed to be tightly coupled on the same carrier (Frizzell et al 1979a,b). This has now been questioned and the coupling may be indirect: in Liedtke & Hopfer's view (1981a,b) there is a Cl^-/OH^- exchange and a H^+/Na^+ exchange. Do you have any relevant evidence?

Boyd: This is very important but I do not have much useful information on it. The crucial experiments would be to voltage-clamp the vesicles with an ionophore and then to observe whether coupled transport takes place. Such experiments, however, are difficult to interpret because of the stoichiometry. If for every Na^+ and K^+ there are 2 Cl^- then it is fine, but any other stoichiometry produces ambiguous results. In the placenta there seems to be a Na^+/H^+ exchange, and probably also a Cl^-/HCO_3^- one too, so indirect coupling would be possible.

Alpers: The experiments you described were on full term placentas but is there any information about less-than-term placentas having a reduced capacity for transport?

Boyd: I don't know, but we shall be addressing that problem in the next year, and particularly whether, towards term, any of these systems is switched 'on'.

Alpers: Synthesis *is* switched 'on' for other proteins and, as for the human placenta, about 10% of the translatable mRNA at term is human placental lactogen, and mRNAs for the other proteins are much less abundant.

Rees: You mentioned that the placental syncytiotrophoblast contains receptors for many hormones. Is it actually known whether receptors for insulin and epidermal growth factor (EGF) exist in the intestine? Insulin could perhaps stimulate transport processes. In its normal action, EGF is a potent mitogen, and any stimulation of division in a continuous cytoplasm such as the placental syncytium might be difficult to imagine. But have people looked for mitogenic hormonal effects of EGF in small intestinal cells?

Smith: Yes. This is being developed for the treatment of peptic ulcers (Konturek et al 1981). References to work on the stomach and small intestine can be obtained from the paper of Malo & Ménard (1982). The assay method for EGF is a stimulation of mitosis in a population of crypt cells so that the receptors must be there at that stage of development.

Mooseker: Is there any fluid-phase endocytosis across the placental surface, as opposed to receptor-mediated endocytosis?

Boyd: The question is: how important is placental fluid transport quantitatively? The whole syncytium is full of vesicles. I don't know how one could determine the importance of pinocytosis there.

Rodewald: Let me add that in the human syncytiotrophoblast there is a selective and rapid transport of maternal IgG that is receptor-mediated (Gitlin et al 1964a,b, McNabb et al 1975).

Booth: The canalicular structures that can be seen in the yolk sac are certainly not apparent in the human placenta, in my experience!

REFERENCES

Bissonnette JM, Black JA, Wickham WK, Acott KM 1981 Glucose uptake into plasma membrane vesicles from the maternal surface of human placenta. J Membr Biol 58: 75-80

Boyd RDH, Canning JF, Stacey TE, Ward RHT 1981 Iodide transfer across the near term sheep placenta. J Physiol (Lond) 312: 23P

Chipperfield AR, Perring VS 1981 Frusemide-sensitive glycine transport in human erythrocytes. J Physiol (Lond) 310: 21P

Frizzell RA, Field M, Schultz SG 1979a Sodium-coupled chloride transport by epithelial tissues. Am J Physiol 236: F1-F8

Frizzell RA, Smith PL, Vosburgh E, Field M 1979b Coupled sodium-chloride influx across brush border of flounder intestine. J Membr Biol 46: 27-40

Gitlin D, Kumate J, Urrusti J, Morales C 1964a The selectivity of the human placenta in the transfer of plasma proteins from mother to fetus. J Clin Invest 43: 1938-1951

Gitlin D, Kumate J, Urrusti J, Morales C 1964b Selective and directional transfer of 7S gamma-globulin across the human placenta. Nature (Lond) 203: 86

Hoshina M, Boothby M, Boime I 1982 Cytological localization of chorionic gonadotropin α and placental lactogen mRNAs during development of the human placenta. J Cell Biol 93: 190-198

Katz U, Lau KR, Ramos MMP, Ellory JC 1982 Thiocyanate transport across fish intestine (*Pleuronectes platessa*). J Membr Biol 66: 9-14

Konturek SJ, Radecki TB, Piastucki I et al 1981 Gastric cytoprotection by epidermal growth factor. Gastroenterology 81: 438-443

Liedtke CM, Hopfer U 1981a Mechanism of Cl$^-$ translocation across the small intestinal brush-border membrane. I: Absence of Na$^+$– Cl$^-$ co-transport. Am J Physiol 242: G263-G271

Liedtke CM, Hopfer U 1981b Mechanism of Cl$^-$ translocation across the small intestinal brush-border membrane. II: Demonstration of Cl$^-$/OH$^-$ exchange and Cl$^-$ conductance. Am J Physiol 242: G272-G280

Malo C, Ménard D 1982 Influence of epidermal growth factor on the development of suckling mouse intestinal mucosa. Gastroenterology 83: 28-35

McNabb T, Kuh TY, Dorrington KJ, Painter RH 1975 Structure and function of immunoglobulin domains. V: Binding of immunoglobulin G and fragments to placental membrane preparations. J Immunol 117: 882-888

Ruzycki SM, Kelley LK, Smith CH 1978 Placental aminoacid uptake. IV: Transport by microvillous membrane vesicles. Am J Physiol 234: C27-C35

Toggenburger G, Kessler M, Semenza G 1982 Phlorizin as a probe of the small intestinal Na$^+$, D-glucose cotransporter. A model. Biochim Biophys Acta 688: 557-571

General Discussion III

Cytoskeleton and membrane–cytoskeleton interactions

Smith: I have recently become interested in finding out more about the relationship between brush border membrane assembly and the expression of both hydrolytic and absorptive functions in the rabbit ileal enterocyte.

For absorptive function, quantitative autoradiography has been used to measure the ability of individual enterocytes to transport amino acids across their brush border membranes (King et al 1981). Tritiated amino acid taken up by the enterocyte is cross-linked to cellular protein with glutaraldehyde before the autoradiography is done, silver grain density being determined subsequently along the villus in 5 μm spots, by means of a Vickers microdensitometer. Hydrolytic function was assessed from histochemical analysis (by Mr I.S. King) of aminopeptidase N activity, by using L-alanine-4-methoxy-β-naphthylamide as substrate (see Lojda et al 1976). The density of the reaction product in the brush border membrane was measured, along the villus, using microdensitometry. Microvillus length was measured (by Mr M.A. Peacock) from photographs of sections of distal ileum taken on a Philips 400 electron microscope. The technique used to select areas for measurement is illustrated, for a single villus, in Fig. 1.

Arrows indicate the points at which high magnification showed the microvilli to be sectioned longitudinally. Graphs plotting microvillus length against distance from the crypt–villus junction were constructed, and from these were derived estimates of microvillus length at 50 μm intervals from crypt to tip of the villus. We related all measurements of amino acid transport, aminopeptidase N activity and microvillus length to enterocyte age by using thymidine labelling data obtained in a parallel series of experiments (Cremaschi et al 1982). The results are summarized in Fig. 2.

Microvillus assembly takes place at a constant rate of 0.03 μm/h during the first 50 h of an enterocyte's life (identical rates of microvillus assembly have also been found in rat, hamster and guinea-pig small intestine). Assembly then virtually ceases for the remaining 45 h after which the enterocyte is extruded from the villus tip. Aminopeptidase N activity in the brush border membrane increases from the crypt–villus junction with a time-course more or less identical to that seen for brush border membrane assembly. The ability of the brush border membrane to transport alanine, however, is not expressed until both

315

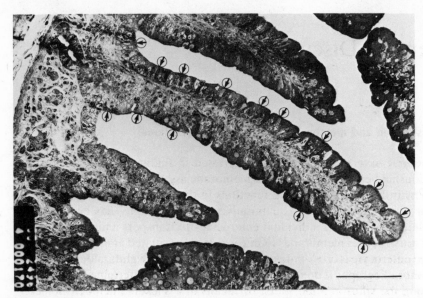

FIG. 1. (*Smith*) Longitudinal section of glutaraldehyde-fixed, osmium-treated villi, taken from the rabbit distal ileum. Arrows show the points where microvillus length was measured. Scale bar: 100 μm.

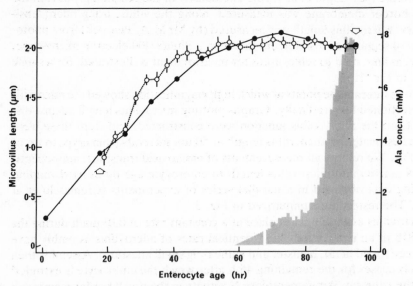

FIG. 2. (*Smith*) Developing structure and function in the rabbit ileal enterocyte. Measurements of microvillus length (solid circles), aminopeptidase N activity (open circles) and alanine transport capacity (shaded area) were made by using methods described in the text. Arrows ↑ and ↓ show the location of the crypt–villus junction and villus tip respectively. Error bars show SEM of 15 estimates (5 rabbits).

microvillus assembly and the expression of aminopeptidase N activity are completed. Minimal transport activity is located in the enterocyte 60 h after birth. Carrier function then shows a slow and a fast rate of appearance (60–80 and 80–95 h after birth, respectively). A similar distribution of both sugar and amino acid uptake into hamster enterocytes was reported originally by Kinter & Wilson (1965).

The conclusion to be drawn from this work is that both microvillus structure and digestive function develop with the same time-course during enterocyte differentiation, and that absorptive function is finally expressed after completion of these earlier aspects of enterocyte development. By studying these three factors together during different developmental and adaptational circumstances we should now be able to find out more about how the enterocyte differentiates.

Kenny: How do you know that the alanine uptake is at the luminal and not at the basolateral side?

Smith: We expose the intestinal surface in a microbath for 45 s and put isotope in contact only with the luminal surface. Control experiments show that the distribution of alanine is not artifactual. In other words, it is not time-dependent or dependent on the speed at which the solution bathing the mucosal surface is stirred (King et al 1981, Paterson & Smith 1982).

Hauri: You showed that alanine transport is highest in the extrusion zone; could this be an artifact?

Smith: No, it is sodium-dependent. The extrusion zone is only at the very tip but sodium-dependent alanine uptake extends at least 120 μm from the villus tip.

Hauri: How did you measure transport? Did you prepare membrane vesicles from isolated enterocytes?

Smith: The tritiated isotope is presented to the intact tissue from the luminal surface for a period of a few seconds and the amino acid is then cross-linked to cellular proteins by washing with glutaraldehyde. The amino acid is therefore inside the cell, which can then be sectioned for autoradiography and quantitative measurements. The concentration within enterocytes at the villus tip is about 8 mM after 45 s when the concentration outside is 1 mM. So it is a concentrative event, which is sodium-dependent and not due to dead-cell artifacts.

Alpers: Are the villi still next to each other?

Smith: Yes, but stirring does not affect location of uptake.

Alpers: How do you know if you have equal availability of luminal alanine at the base of the villi compared to the tips?

Smith: I don't, but we can change the rate of entry of amino acid without changing the number of enterocytes taking up alanine by varying the time of incubation from 5 to 180 s.

Rodewald: Strictly speaking, you are looking at the accumulation of the amino acid in the cell and, of course, what is important is the transport across the cell. So although you don't see accumulation in a certain region of the villus, there nevertheless may be a rapid transport across the cell in that region.

Smith: Our work is *in vitro* and one can see where the counts are going, with time. There are no counts in the bottom half of the villus. The counts in the top half of the villus move out from the cell, and one can use this technique to study the kinetics of the amino acid efflux across the basolateral membrane (Paterson et al 1982).

Semenza: You are measuring an approach to the steady state, which depends on the velocities of each of the two transport steps. McDougal et al (1960) showed that this is not a 'pull' system but a 'push' system. That is, the velocity of entry from the lumen into the cell is much faster than the velocity of exit from the basolateral membrane. One would get a transient accumulation contrary, for example, to the transport of calcium, which is a 'pull' system and in which the velocity of exit tends to be fast compared to the velocity of entry, which results in a low intracellular concentration of calcium. Does that answer Dr Rodewald's question?

Rodewald: The question is: what is happening at the basolateral surface? If transport across the basolateral membrane is slowing down, there could be accumulation within the cell.

Semenza: Accumulation occurs even in isolated cells (e.g. Kimmich 1970).

Schmitz: Are you implying that only the apical cells are able to absorb amino acids and that, during a lifetime of 100 h, it is only during the last 24 h or so that the enterocyte is able to absorb?

Smith: In saying that, I would only be confirming the work of Kinter & Wilson (1965). But I have also tried to say something more—that the enterocyte can distinguish the time at which it can do certain things. It expresses its hydrolytic function before it decides to absorb material, and the mechanism whereby that is organized is what I find interesting.

Boyd: It might be a rather efficient way of putting together the whole structure if the hydrolysis were occurring predominantly lower down the villus and the escape products were not allowed to enter the bulk phase of the lumen because they pass the high entry zone on their way out. The two things together may produce an efficient system.

Schmitz: To my knowledge it would be the first evidence that those two functions would not be highly correlated.

Boyd: It is a question of cellular correlation versus villus correlation. Rather few techniques are available for analysing transport at the level of the individual cell.

Smith: It is probably the first time anybody has tried to integrate these separate events at the cellular level.

Alpers: Has anyone isolated cells from halfway down the villus at various times and looked at amino acid transport?

Smith: Yes, Garvey et al (1975) did this and found more transport in the cells at the tip.

Alpers: But transport is surely not zero in the middle of the villus?

Smith: I believe amino acids could always enter from the blood side but not from the lumen in the middle of the villus.

Quaroni: The cells are much more leaky when isolated. Also, different incubation times are needed to isolate cells at different levels of the villi, and this may influence their leakiness.

The importance of structure for understanding the biosynthetic process

Norén: For a more detailed insight into the biosynthesis of microvillar membrane proteins, future structural studies should aim to provide information on biosynthetic events. Table 1 (p 157) showed the M_r of several enzymes at different stages of their 'life-cycle' but detailed structural information in terms of partial sequences has appeared only for sucrase–isomaltase, aminopeptidase N and dipeptidyl peptidase IV in their final forms. Speakers at this symposium have placed the N-terminal amino acid (located in the anchor) alternately on the cytosolic or the non-cytosolic side. Determination of the sidedness of the N-termini of different enzymes would help in postulating the existence of cleaved or non-cleaved signals. Furthermore, from the loop hypothesis we must consider whether the microvillar enzymes during some period of their life-cycles are C-terminally inserted. Some studies suggest that C-terminal anchors are unlikely in the final forms of the enzymes, but this does not exclude their existence during the intracellular phase of these enzymes. Another important question concerns what determines the transport of microvillar enzymes from the site of translation to the microvillar membrane and not, say, to the mitochondria or to the lysosomes. The mechanisms behind sorting are unsolved.

Sjöström: In connection with the sorting problem, the homology between glycophorin and sucrase–isomaltase is very interesting. Our paper (this volume) suggests that a protein in the endoplasmic reticulum with a recognition site on the inside may pick up proteins destined for the plasma membrane via the homologous segments. Such a protein may span the membrane and have an interacting site for further transport on the outside. The hydrolases of the microvillus membrane are a good model system for looking for such homologies in the sequence as we can now prepare three or four enzymes in reasonably large amounts for N-terminal sequencing.

Kenny: The possibility that structural details in the glycosylation of the precursor forms of membrane proteins might provide the key to the intriguing question of sorting has not received any experimental support.

Alpers: There is no firm evidence either way.

Kenny: Such experiments that have been reported have suggested that glycosylation is not the key.

Alpers: Yes, but perhaps the correct part of the molecule has not been examined.

Quaroni: The work done on MDCK cells is fairly comprehensive and seems to demonstrate that the glycosidic chains do not play any role in determining the destination of the newly synthesized membrane glycoproteins (Green et al 1981).

Alpers: But what about tunicamycin?

Quaroni: They have used various techniques which seem to prove that changes in the structure of the glycosidic chains have no obvious effects.

Alpers: Yes. So *some* proteins reach the membrane without their carbohydrate chains being put on.

Norén: I believe that the importance of the sequence in the anchors of viral membrane proteins has been studied at EMBL (in Heidelberg) to find out the importance of this part of the molecule for sorting.

Future advances in study of brush border cytoskeleton

Mooseker: We still know little about the function of the structural proteins in the brush border. Many of us use the brush border as a model system to help define the molecular basis of the widespread interactions of actin with its binding proteins and with membranes. The next couple of years should see us clarify how actin associates with membranes in different types of cell. But is there a physical (i.e. mechanical) attachment between the membrane and the cytoskeleton? Dr Matsudaira has shown that the connecting ligands along the length of the core are ATP-dissociable, and that this dissociation can be done at low concentrations of free ATP. Our experiments have shown that actin can be polymerized from the membrane at the tip of the microvillus, and yet, by ultrastructural criteria, it remains 'attached'. So what is the function of this close proximity between cytoskeleton and membrane in all cells? We must try to relate rearrangements of the cytoskeleton with gut physiology e.g. ion movements. We must also look at the growth differentiation of the intestinal epithelial cells from the crypt to the tip. We know that cytoskeletal proteins contain information 'stored' in their structure, in that they self-assemble with one another. Perhaps some correlations may be revealed between structure, biochemistry and molecular biology of intestinal epithelial cells that arise from the crypts.

Kenny: Do the experiments of Tilney & Cardell (1970) on the disappearance and reappearance of microvilli *in vitro* relate to microvillus development *in vivo*? They found that the microvilli disappeared at high pressures and then reappeared when the pressure was reduced.

Mooseker: Tilney & Cardell (1970) used a hydrostatic pressure bomb to raise the pressure to those high levels, and they interpreted their results to suggest that the whole brush border solated (or disappeared) under pressure, and the membrane ballooned out. When they restored normal pressure, the microvilli grew out from the apical membrane by what looked like nucleated polymerization of core filaments. The experiments have not so far been repeated, but we hope to try that. If the model of Tilney & Cardell (1970) is correct, then actin assembly is very important in the making of the microvillus. The work of Chambers & Grey (1979) on microvillus assembly during embryogenesis in the chick suggests, however, that the membrane buds out to form a microvillus-like protrusion and then the filaments fit together inside the protrusion. So the two available pieces of evidence on how the microvillus is built are diametrically opposed.

Smith: Is it likely that microvillus differentiation in culture will be successfully achieved in the next few years?

Alpers: Chick embryo intestine will differentiate in culture (Black & Moog 1978) into mature intestine, but I do not know if there is enough material available for the approach you have suggested. It may be more valuable to start looking at mammalian gut cytoskeleton.

Matsudaira: Electron microscopic correlations during formation of microvilli have been done mostly on the chick (Chambers & Grey 1979, Overton & Shoup 1964) and the mouse (Overton 1965). The intermediate stages of microvillar growth are always elusive to electron microscopy, and we do not yet know their speed of assembly. Study of live cells may provide a better approach.

Mooseker: A good culture system for the study of crypt-to-tip development might reveal what key synthetic events take place in the terminal web.

Quaroni: I doubt that culture systems for kidney or intestinal cells are at present capable of answering these questions. Until recently, most cell-culture conditions have been selected for the culture of fibroblasts and not epithelial cells. Futhermore, differentiaton *in vivo* is likely to be the result of a complex set of stimuli rather than a single one, and may be influenced by mesenchymal factors and the basement membrane. We may have to wait many years before culture systems can be made as sophisticated as would be necessary.

Louvard: A. Zweibaum and his colleagues in Paris use a well established line of the colonic cancer cell HT-29, which is unlike an enterocyte because it doesn't have tight junctions, is not polarized and does not express enterocyte enzyme and cytoskeleton markers. When the cell-line is grown in a medium where glucose has been replaced by galactose it will differentiate into something we can call an enterocyte because cytoskeletal proteins and several intestinal enzymes are made and a brush border develops (M. Pinto et al, unpublished data). This cell-line may therefore be useful since it is possible to modulate the expression of membrane proteins as well as cytoskeletal proteins typical of differentiated enterocytes.

Quaroni: I believe that the HT-29 cells express low activities of those enzymes even in the *absence* of the selective conditions. I do not think that true differentiation is happening there, but rather the modulation of expression of specific, already present, differentiated functions. *In vivo* when one studies intestinal cell differentiation in the crypts, one is really examining the *induction* of cell differentiation, which is a completely different phenomenon.

Louvard: I disagree. With sucrase–isomaltase, the increase in activity in galactose-containing medium is over 100-fold. Secondly, the dramatic morphological changes and the formation of brush border and tight junctions do suggest a differentiation.

Quaroni: This is more than a matter of definition. The same cell-line has been studied by Y. Kim, who has detected their sucrase–isomaltase activity under normal cell-culture conditions. So if the sucrase–isomaltase is *already* present, one cannot attribute the 100-fold increase to *differentiation*. It may simply be a matter of translational regulation.

Louvard: So how do you define differentiation?

Quaroni: It could be gene activation or rearrangement. In undifferentiated crypt cells one cannot detect any sucrase–isomaltase activity.

Louvard: Aminopeptidase is found all over the body, with about 1% of the specific activity being in the intestine. It also exists in fibroblasts. Regulation of the assembly of an organized structure such as the brush border is surely a criterion for differentiation, and polarity is another aspect.

Quaroni: For intestinal aminopeptidase one must consider which of the different enzymes one is talking about, so it is a bad example. If we use a variety of monoclonal antibodies against aminopeptidase all we label is the epithelial cells. The aminopeptidase enzyme activity, as present in fibroblasts, may be a completely different protein from what you observe in epithelial cells.

Louvard: I am not talking about the activity, but also about aminopeptidase N being recognized by specific antibodies.

Photo-affinity labelling to identify components of the neutral amino acid carrier in the intestinal microvillar membrane

Norén: We are aiming to identify the neutral amino acid carrier of the small intestinal microvillar membrane by using the photo-label azido-phenylalanine, in non-radioactive and radioactive form, synthesized according to Schwyzer &

Caviezel (1971) and Fischli et al (1976), respectively. The transport characteristics of azido-phenylalanine have been studied on isolated microvillar vesicles by the filtration assay technique (Hopfer et al 1973). Our results show that this compound is specifically transported by the neutral amino acid transporter: (1) the transport of azido-phenylalanine is stimulated four-fold by 100 mM-Na^+ in relation to a potassium-containing control; (2) the uptake is concentrative, as an 'overshoot' is seen; (3) the uptake is inhibited by L-alanine and L-phenylalanine but not by glucose and L-lysine; and (4) preloading of the microvillar vesicles with L-alanine stimulates the uptake of radioactive azido-phenylalanine (i.e. trans-stimulation). Microvillar vesicles, treated with azido-phenylalanine in combination with photoactivation, irreversibly abolished the sodium-dependent alanine-transporting activity. That did not happen when photoactivation was omitted and the azido-phenylalanine was removed by dialysis. Thus, there should be a basis for labelling of the carrier by using [^{3}H]azido-phenylalanine. Such experiments done with 0.1 mM-[^{3}H]azido-phenylalanine in the presence of 100 μM-Na^+ showed incorporation in six peptides belonging to the cytoskeletal fraction obtained after Triton X-100 demembranation (Bretscher & Weber 1978). None of the peptides in the soluble fraction was found labelled. The M_r values of the labelled cytoskeletal proteins, as determined by polyacrylamide gel electrophoresis (PAGE), were 42 000, 33 000 and 17 000. In addition, three bands were seen close to the electrophoretic front. The two largest peptides are thus similar in size to actin and tropomyosin. The other peptides are unidentified. Omission of sodium from the reaction mixture or addition of alanine results in evenly diminished intensity of the labelled bands. Thus, we have no firm indication yet about which of the microvillar components is part of the neutral amino acid transporter.

Semenza: We had similar results using nitrene generators synthesized from phlorizin, and we ran into similar problems. We could inactivate the sodium-dependent glucose carrier specifically but encountered great difficulties when we wanted to identify a specific band in the general unspecific labelling (Hosang et al 1981a,b). The Na^+,D-glucose cotransporter is present in very minute amounts (about 14 pmol mg $^{-1}$ protein; Toggenburger et al 1978).

Alpers: The intrinsic factor–cobalamin receptor that we have purified to homogeneity is purified over 65 000-fold. If the receptors you have described are comparable it will be impossible to see the specific bands, given the small amounts of material available, unless the label is exquisitely specific.

Schmitz: But one would imagine that there are more carriers for phenylalanine, for example, than for cobalamin.

Alpers: Not necessarily, depending on the efficiency of the transport mechanism.

Semenza: Phlorizin binding has shown us that the glucose carrier that is present is about 0.1% of the membrane protein (Toggenburger et al 1978). The turnover number of the sodium-dependent sugar transporter in the small intestine is similar to that reported for the kidney—about 20/s, assuming a 1:1 stoichiometry of phlorizin binding (Toggenburger et al 1978).

Jørgensen: In the fractionation experiment you said that the label remains in the pellet, after Triton X-100 treatment, with some of the cytoskeletal components. Is there any way to remove the cytoskeletal components first, leaving a membrane residue on which the detergent can work?

Norén: We have also looked specifically for azido-phenylalanine-labelled peptides in the chloroform phase after chloroform/methanol extraction, but we found no labelled peptides in this phase.

Inoue: This affinity-labelling reagent is rather hydrophobic. Have you measured uptake into the osmotically reactive intravesicular space and calculated the free and membrane-bound ligand after its translocation into the vesicles?

Norén: The uptake of azido-phenylalanine is osmotic-dependent like that of L-alanine. Extrapolation to infinite osmolarity showed significant uptake for both compounds. In relation to the hydrophobicity of azido-phenylalanine this compound does not label the anchors of the stalked hydrolases, as tested by immunoelectrophoresis followed by autoradiography.

Inoue: Affinity labelling of the transport carrier protein(s) would occur specifically. However, a hydrophobic ligand sometimes binds to the inner surface of membrane vesicles after being transported into the intravesicular space. We found significant intravesicular redistribution of transported taurocholic acid in vesicles from isolated sinusoidal plasma membranes from rat liver (Inoue et al 1982). Photo-affinity labelling of intestinal brush border vesicles with bile acid analogues revealed that at least four protein bands, including actin, were labelled (Burckhardt et al 1982). Since interaction of a solute with the carrier protein(s) might occur even at low temperature, photolysis should be done for short periods at low temperatures to minimize the intravesicular redistribution of transported affinity-labelling reagent which might increase the non-specific labelling from within the vesicles.

Smith: We should not be too pessimistic about Dr Semenza's figure of 0.1%. If the top few cells are taken from a villus, that should provide a 20 to 40-fold increase in concentration if the carrier appears towards the end of the enterocyte's life. Vesicles are not made from all the mucosa but only from a selected number of cells.

Jørgensen: To return to the *cytoskeleton* present in these membrane preparations, does that 0.1% include actin filaments?

Semenza: Yes.

Jørgensen: So how much would the cytoskeleton represent in terms of protein in the membrane?

Semenza: If we extract these membranes by deoxycholate, thereby removing the cytoskeleton and some intrinsic membrane, we reach a concentration of 1–4%. So we can purify it by a factor of 10–40 (Klip et al 1979).

Jørgensen: So is it not possible to remove this cytoskeleton from the membrane material?

Quaroni: If, instead of calcium precipitation, one uses the technique of Hopfer et al (1973), one can obtain vesicles with little or no cytoskeleton inside.

REFERENCES

Black BL, Moog F 1978 Alkaline phosphatase and maltose activity in the embryonic chick intestine in culture. Dev Biol 66: 232-246

Bretscher A, Weber K 1978 Purification of microvilli and an analysis of the protein components of the microfilament core bundle. Exp Cell Res 116: 397-407

Burckhardt G, Kramer W, Kurz G, Wilson FA 1982 Uptake and binding of photolabile bile acid derivatives in intestinal brush border membrane vesicles. Fed Proc 41:1683

Chambers C, Grey RD 1979 Development of the structural components of the brush border in absorptive cells of the chick intestine. Cell Tissue Res 204: 387-405

Cremaschi D, James PS, Meyer G, Peacock MA, Smith MW 1982 Membrane potentials of differentiating enterocytes. Biochim Biophys Acta 688: 271-274

Fischli W, Caviezel M, Eberle A, Escher E, Schwyzer R 1976 Synthese von 4'-azido-3',5'-ditritio-L-phenylalanin-peptiden als 'photo-affinitätsproben' für ligand-receptor-wechselwirkungen. Helv Chim Acta 59: 878-879

Garvey TQ, Hyman PE, Isselbacher KJ 1975 γ-Glutamyl transpeptidase of rat intestine: localization and possible role in amino acid transport. Gastroenterology 71: 778-785

Green RF, Meiss HK, Rodriguez-Boulan E 1981 Glycosylation does not determine segregation of viral envelope proteins in the plasma membrane of epithelial cells. J Cell Biol 89: 230-239

Hopfer U, Nelson K, Perrotto J, Isselbacher KJ 1973 Glucose transport in isolated brush border membrane from rat small intestine. J Biol Chem 248: 25-32

Hosang M, Vasella A, Semenza G 1981a Specific photoaffinity inactivation of the D-glucose transporter in small intestinal brush border membrane using new phlorizin analogues. Biochemistry 20: 5844-5854

Hosang M, Gibbs EM, Diedrich DF, Semenza G 1981b Photoaffinity labeling and identification of (a component of) the small intestinal Na$^+$,D-glucose transporter using 4-azidophlorizin. FEBS (Fed Eur Biochem Soc) Lett 130: 244-248

Inoue M, Kinne R, Tran T, Arias IM 1982 Taurocholate transport by rat liver sinusoidal membrane vesicles. Evidence for Na$^+$-cotransport. Hepatology 2:572-579

Kimmich GA 1970 Active sugar accumulation by isolated intestinal epithelial cells. A new model for sodium-dependent metabolite transport. Biochemistry 9: 3669-3677

King IS, Sepúlveda FV, Smith MW 1981 Cellular distribution of neutral and basic amino acid transport systems in rabbit ileal mucosa. J Physiol (Lond) 319: 355-368

Kinter WB, Wilson TH 1965 Autoradiographic study of sugar and amino acid uptake by everted sacs of hamster intestine. J Cell Biol 25: 19-39

Klip A, Grinstein S, Semenza G 1979 Partial purification of the sugar carrier of intestinal brush border membranes. Enrichment of the phlorizin binding component by selective extractions. J Membr Biol 51: 47-73

Lojda Z, Gossram R, Schriebter TH 1976 Enzymhistochemische Methoden. Springer, Berlin

McDougal DB Jr, Little KD, Crane RK 1960 Studies on the mechanism of intestinal absorption of sugars. IV: Localization of galactose concentrations within the intestinal wall during active transport in vitro. Biochim Biophys Acta 45: 483-489

Overton J 1965 Fine structure of the free cell surface in developing mouse intestinal mucosa. J Exp Zool 159: 195-202

Overton J, Shoup J 1964 Fine structure of cell surface specializations in the maturing duodenal mucosa of the chick. J Cell Biol 21: 75-85

Paterson JYF, Smith MW 1982 Testing the hypothesis that substrate availability determines the cellular distribution of amino acid uptake by rabbit ileal mucosa. J Physiol (Lond) 327: 96P-97P

Paterson JYF, Sepúlveda FV, Smith MW 1982 Amino acid efflux from rabbit ileal enterocytes. J Physiol (Lond) 331:537-546

Schwyzer R, Caviezel M 1971 p-Azido-L-phenylalanine: a photoaffinity `probe` related to tyrosine. Helv Chim Acta 54: 1395-1400

Tilney LG, Cardell RR Jr 1970 Factors controlling the reassembly of the microvillous border of the small intestine of the salamander. J Cell Biol 47: 408-422

Toggenburger G, Kessler M, Rothstein A, Semenza G, Tannenbaum C 1978 Similarity in effects of Na^+ gradients and membrane potentials on D-glucose transport by and phlorizin binding to vesicles derived from brush borders of rabbit intestinal mucosal cells. J Membr Biol 40: 269-290

Chairman's closing remarks

A. J. KENNY

Department of Biochemistry, University of Leeds, Leeds LS2 9JT, UK

At the start of this symposium I suggested that our subject had reached a stage where a good deal of the structure and function of brush borders could be usefully described in molecular terms. That we have succeeded so well is a testimony to the volume of research that has been lavished on this membrane, and we who earn our living from research in this field should be grateful to the brush border for its marvellous variety of function as well as its beauty of form. What membrane, other than the erythrocyte ghost, could deserve and sustain so much study from such a diverse group of scientists? Enzymologists and transport physiologists have been interested in brush borders for many years. Other specialists have joined in more recently, and I regard it as a special bonus that many of those who work on the cytoskeleton should have found the brush border such a useful model. In this, and other respects, we all owe a lot to the pioneers who, many years ago, worked out reliable methods for preparing brush border fractions.

I shall not attempt to précis all that is presented in this book but shall try to look briefly into the future and to speculate on what new information will interest a symposium on the same subject in three or four years time.

No-one here has presented DNA sequences for any brush border protein, but there can be little doubt that we shall see this development sooner rather than later. Perhaps the main benefit from this will be a clearer understanding of the mode of assembly and processing of these proteins. I suspect, too, that we shall be profitably addressing questions about the sorting of membrane proteins and the way in which polarity is established in the brush border-bearing epithelial cells. We may also be near to using the techniques of image analysis to tell us something of the three-dimensional structure of the membrane hydrolases. Moreover, the elegant work on the ultra- and molecular structure of the cytoskeleton of the brush border and terminal web will surely lead on to explanations, in dynamic terms, of the genesis of microvilli and the processes of endocytosis and membrane recycling. Lastly, and very importantly, I expect that major progress will ultimately be achieved in the isolation and molecular characterization of some of the carrier proteins of the brush border. At present the technical difficulties seem formidable but this last goal cannot be long delayed.

Index of contributors

Indexes compiled by John Rivers

Subject index